BASIC MATHEMATICS

A Custom Edition
Prepared Exclusively for
the Skyline College
Mathematics Department

Selected content from
Mathematics in Action: An Introduction to Algebraic, Graphical and Numerical Problem Solving by the Consortium for Foundation Mathematics
and

Basic College Mathematics, Fifth Edition by Margaret Lial, Stanley Salzman, Diana Hestwood and Charles Miller

Material prepared by Soodi Zamani and Pat Deamer for use in Mathematics 811

Pearson
Custom
Publishing

Cover image of Skyline College courtesy of Mario Zelaya.

Excerpts taken from:

Basic College Mathematics, Fifth Edition,
by Margaret L. Lial, Stanley A. Salzman, Diana L. Hestwood and Charles D. Miller
Copyright © 1998 by Addison Wesley Longman, Inc.
A Pearson Education Company
Boston, Massachusetts 02116

Mathematics in Action: An Introduction to Algebraic, Graphical, and Numerical Problem Solving,
by The Consortium for Foundation Mathematics
Copyright © 2001 by Addison Wesley Longman, Inc.

This special edition published in cooperation with Pearson Custom Publishing

Printed in the United States of America

10 9 8 7 6 5 4 3 2 1

Please visit our web site at www.pearsoncustom.com

ISBN 0–536–63488-2

BA 993321

PEARSON CUSTOM PUBLISHING
75 Arlington Street, Suite 300, Boston, MA 02116
A Pearson Education Company

Contents

Chapter 1

Number Sense

Your goal in this chapter is to use the numerical mathematical skills you already have —and those you will learn or relearn—to solve problems. Chapter activities are based on practical, real-world situations that you may encounter in your daily life and work.

Before you begin the activities in Chapter 1, we ask you to think about your previous encounters with mathematics and choose one word to describe those experiences.

Enjoy solving the problems of Chapter 1!

Using Number Sense to Solve Problems

ACTIVITY 1-1

The Bookstore
Topic: *Problem Solving*

By 11:00 A.M., a line has formed outside the crowded bookstore. You ask the guard at the gate how long you can expect to wait. She provides you with the following information: She is permitted to let 6 people into the bookstore only after 6 people have left; students are leaving at the rate of 2 students per minute; she has just let 6 new students in. Also, each student spends an average of 15 minutes gathering books and supplies and 10 minutes waiting in line to check out.

Currently 38 people are ahead of you in line. You know that it is a ten-minute walk to your noon class. Can you buy your books and still expect to make it to your noon class on time?

1. What was your initial reaction after reading the problem?

2. Have you ever worked a problem such as this before?

3. Organizing the information will help you solve the problem.

   a. How many students must leave the bookstore before the guard allows more to enter?

   b. How many students per minute leave the bookstore?

   c. How many minutes are there between groups of students entering the bookstore?

   d. How long will you stand in line outside the bookstore?

   e. Now finish solving the problem and answer the question: How early or late for class will you be?

4. Write, in complete sentences, what you did to solve this problem. Then, explain your solution to a classmate.

E X E R C I S E S

1. Think about the various approaches you and your classmates used to solve Activity 1.1, The Bookstore. Choose the approach that is best for you, and describe it in complete sentences.

2. What mathematical operations and skills did you use?

Time Management
Topics: *Problem Solving, Estimating, Tables, Bar Graphs, Using Fractions*

Your friend is a first-semester freshman carrying a full course load of 15 credit hours. Because Biology lab lasts for three hours, not one, her schedule actually consists of 17 classroom hours. Two hours of study are expected for each hour spent in the classroom or laboratory. She is also working 18 hours per week and has two children at home.

Your friend commutes to campus 1 hour each way every day that she has class, Monday through Friday. Child care and household chores consume 25 hours per week. Each day these chores consume a minimum of 1 hour before school and 2 hours after school. She averages 7 hours of sleep per night, never less than 5 hours or more than 10 hours. She tries to reserve 2 hours per day for leisure and exercise activities and 3 hours per day for personal time.

1. List each activity and the number of hours spent per week on each activity.

2. Is this schedule possible? Explain.

3. What suggestions would you make to your friend for a more workable schedule?

4. Use the information from Problems 1 and 3 to fill in the following grid with a workable schedule:

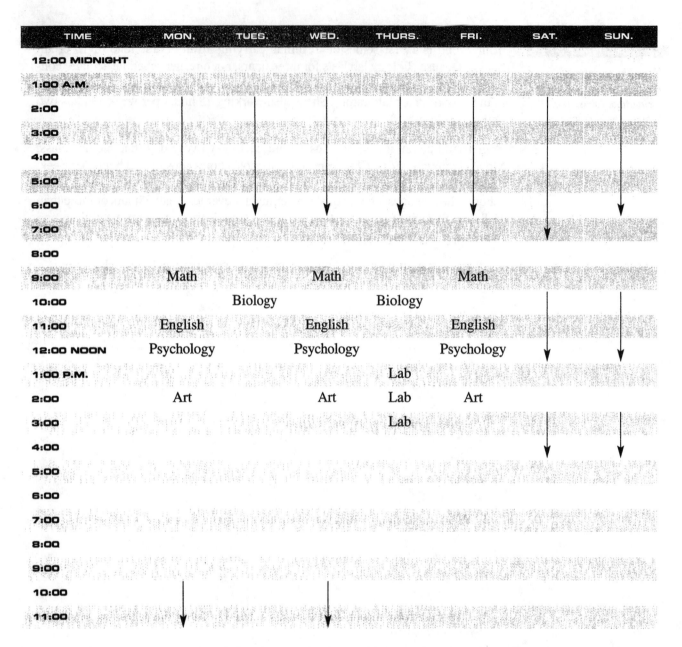

TIME	MON.	TUES.	WED.	THURS.	FRI.	SAT.	SUN.
12:00 MIDNIGHT							
1:00 A.M.							
2:00							
3:00							
4:00							
5:00							
6:00							
7:00							
8:00							
9:00	Math		Math		Math		
10:00		Biology		Biology			
11:00	English		English		English		
12:00 NOON	Psychology		Psychology		Psychology		
1:00 P.M.				Lab			
2:00	Art		Art	Lab	Art		
3:00				Lab			
4:00							
5:00							
6:00							
7:00							
8:00							
9:00							
10:00							
11:00							

5. Make a bar graph of your friend's schedule from Problem 4. Put the activities (chores, classes, etc.) on the horizontal axis and the number of hours per week on the vertical axis.

6. **a.** What activity does the highest bar on the graph represent? What part of the week's total of 168 hours does your friend spend doing that activity?

b. As an estimate, is this activity closest to $\frac{1}{2}$, $\frac{1}{3}$, or $\frac{1}{4}$ of the total week? Explain.

c. What advice would you give your friend about the time she spends doing this activity?

7. Your friend spends 17 hours per week in class, out of the week's total of 168 hours. That means she spends $\frac{17}{168}$ of the week in class. As an estimate, is the time spent in class closer to $\frac{1}{5}$ or $\frac{1}{10}$ of the total week?

8. Which activities consume at least $\frac{1}{4}$ of your friend's week? Explain.

9. **a.** Choose another activity and determine the fractional part of the total week your friend spends doing that activity.

b. What simple fraction would be a suitable estimate for your answer to part a?

EXERCISES

1. List the time commitments in your life by category as you did in Problem 1 for your friend.

2. Use the following grid to create your weekly schedule.

TIME	MON.	TUES.	WED.	THURS.	FRI.	SAT.	SUN.
12:00 MIDNIGHT							
1:00 A.M.							
2:00							
3:00							
4:00							
5:00							
6:00							
7:00							
8:00							
9:00							
10:00							
11:00							
12:00 NOON							
1:00 P.M.							
2:00							
3:00							
4:00							
5:00							
6:00							
7:00							
8:00							
9:00							
10:00							
11:00							

3. a. What part of your total weekly schedule do you spend studying outside of class?

b. What part of your total time do you spend working at a paid job?

c. What part of your total time do you spend on household chores and/or child care?

4. Make a bar graph depicting your schedule.

5. Use your bar graph to think about your schedule. Are there any changes that you could make in your schedule to help you use your time more efficiently and effectively as you pursue your educational goals? Use complete sentences to write down your thoughts.

ACTIVITY 1.3

Course Grades and Your GPA

Topics: *Problem Solving, Using Percents, Simple Averages, Weighted Averages*

Throughout your college years, different instructors may use different methods to determine your grade.

> The most common method of determining your course grade is to average exam scores that are all based on 100 points. You add all your scores and divide the sum by the number of exams. An average calculated this way is called a **simple average.** Note that a simple average is also called a **mean.**

You are a college freshman and the end of the semester is approaching. You are concerned about keeping a B– (80) average in your English literature class, where your instructor uses the simple-average method to determine averages. Your grade will be determined by averaging your exam scores. So far, you have scores of 82, 75, 85, and 93 on four exams. Each exam is based on 100 points.

1. What is your current average for the four exams?

2. What is the lowest score you could achieve on the fifth exam to maintain an 80 average?

3. Describe, in complete sentences, the procedure that you used to answer Problem 2.

4. Is it possible to achieve an A– average (90) in the course? Explain why or why not.

In some grading systems, certain graded work is counted more heavily than other work in determining your course grade. In such systems, the average is known as a **weighted average.** In one method for determining a weighted average, your instructor would assign different percent weights to different components of the course (for example, quizzes, 20%; exams, 50%; and projects, 30%). Note that the weights (given here in percent) will always sum to 100% or 1.0.

> Here is how to determine the weighted average of several components:
> 1. Calculate the simple average (based on 100) of each component.
> 2. Multiply each component's simple average by the weight assigned to that component.
> 3. Sum these weighted component averages to obtain the final weighted average.

For example, in mathematics class, your grade is determined by averaging quizzes, group activities, projects, and exams. The instructor uses the following set of weights: quizzes are worth 15% of the grade; group activities, 30%; projects, 10%; and exams, 45%. The following table categorizes your grades. Your instructor drops your lowest quiz grade when determining your quiz average. Each score is based on 100 points.

QUIZZES	GROUP ACTIVITIES	PROJECTS	EXAMS
70	95	100	81
85	90	95	85
40	75		72
90	60		
75			

5. Determine the simple average for each of the categories and list it in the given table. Also list the weight of each component.

COMPONENT	SIMPLE AVERAGE	WEIGHT
QUIZZES		0.15
GROUP ACTIVITIES		
PROJECTS		
EXAMS		

6. Multiply the simple average for each category (from Problem 5) by the weight assigned to that category. Then sum these weighted values to determine your weighted average in mathematics class.

7. Suppose that the grading scale used at your college is as given in the following chart. What letter grade would you earn in mathematics class? Note that "90 to 93" means to include 90 but not 93.

CLASS AVERAGE	93 to 100	90 to 93	87 to 90	83 to 87	80 to 83	77 to 80	73 to 77	70 to 73	67 to 70	63 to 67	60 to 63	below 60
LETTER GRADES	A	A–	B+	B	B–	C+	C	C–	D+	D	D–	F

Your college grade point average (GPA) is another example of a weighted average.

The weight of a course is the fractional portion of your total credit load that the course represents. It is determined by dividing the number of credit hours of the course by your total credit hours for the semester. Therefore, the larger the number of credits carried by the course, the more strongly it will be weighted in your GPA.

For example, in a 12-credit load, a 3-credit course would have a weight of $\frac{3}{12} = 0.250$ and a 2-credit course would have a weight of $\frac{2}{12} = 0.167$.

8. This semester, your friend is taking two 3-credit courses, one in English and the other in Spanish, a 4-credit course in mathematics, and a 5-credit chemistry course. What is the weight of each course?

COURSE	English	Spanish	Mathematics	Chemistry
WEIGHT				

Your letter grade for a course is translated to a numerical equivalent by the following table:

LETTER GRADES	A	A–	B+	B	B–	C+	C	C–	D+	D	D–	F
NUMERICAL EQUIVALENTS	4.00	3.67	3.33	3.00	2.67	2.33	2.00	1.67	1.33	1.00	0.67	0.00

Suppose you took 17 credit hours this past semester, your third semester in college. You earned an A– in psychology (3 hours); a C+ in economics (3 hours); a B+ in chemistry (4 hours); a B in English (3 hours), and a B– in mathematics (4 hours).

9. Your semester GPA is the weighted average of the numerical equivalents of your course grades. Use the following procedure to complete the table and calculate your semester GPA. (Use a spreadsheet program if you have access to a computer.)

   a. Use the first four columns to record the information regarding the courses you took. As a guide, the information for your psychology course has been recorded for you.

1 COURSE	2 LETTER GRADE	3 NUMERICAL EQUIVALENT	4 CREDIT HOURS	5 WEIGHT	6 CONTRIBUTION TO GPA
Psychology	A–	3.67	3	3/17 = 0.176	0.176 · 3.67 = 0.646

   b. Calculate the weight for each course and enter it in column 5.

c. For each course, multiply the course's weight (column 5) by your numerical grade (column 3). Round to three decimal places and enter this product in column 6, the course's contribution to your GPA. You can now calculate your semester GPA by summing the contributions of all your courses. What is your semester GPA?

EXERCISES

1. A grade of W is given if you withdraw from a course before a certain date. The W appears on your transcript but is not included in your grade point average. Suppose that instead of a C+ in economics, you receive a W. Recalculate your GPA.

2. Now suppose that you earn an F in economics. The F is included in your grade point average. Recalculate your GPA.

3. In your first semester in college, you took 13 credit hours and earned a GPA of 2.13. The following semester your GPA of 2.34 was based on 12 credit hours. You calculated this past semester's GPA in Problem 9.

   a. Explain why the calculation of your overall GPA for the three semesters requires a weighted average.

   b. Calculate your overall GPA for the three semesters.

Exercise numbers appearing in color are answered in the Selected Answers section of this book.

4. You are concerned about passing your economics class with a C– (70) average. Your grade is determined by averaging your exam scores. So far, you have scores of 78, 66, 87, and 59 on four exams. Each exam is based on 100 points. Your economics instructor uses the simple-average method to determine your average.

   a. What is your current average for the four exams?

   b. What is the lowest score you could achieve on the fifth exam to have at least a 70 average?

5. In chemistry class, your grade is determined by calculating the weighted average of your quiz, lab, and exam grades. The instructor uses the following set of weights: quizzes are worth 20% of the grade; labs, 30%; and exams, 50%. The following table categorizes your grades. Your instructor drops your lowest quiz grade when determining your quiz average. Each score is based on 100 points. Calculate your average for chemistry.

QUIZZES	LABS	EXAMS
78	90	81
85	80	85
55	85	93
90	95	
80	75	
	80	

6. Suppose you took 15 credit hours last semester. You earned an A— in English (3 hours); a B in mathematics (4 hours); a C+ in chemistry (3 hours); a B+ in health (2 hours); and a B— in history (3 hours). Calculate your GPA for the semester.

7. Suppose your history professor discovers an error in his calculation of your grade from last semester. Your newly computed history grade is a B+. Use this new grade and the information in Exercise 6 to recalculate your GPA.

8. Have you encountered any other grading systems used by your instructors? Describe them. How do they work? Give an example.

The Electric Bill

Topics: *Problem Solving, Estimating, Percents, Bar Graphs*

Suppose you receive the following electric bill.

Electric Service

Niagara Mohawk buys low-cost energy that includes hydroelectric power purchased from the New York Power Authority. These hydroelectric purchases have a savings value of $8.88.

This meter reading, Feb. 24, 00 (actual)............	18052
Last meter reading, Dec. 23, 99 (actual)............	−17307
Amount of electricity used.........................kWh	745

Current charges for 63 days—residential service (Rate 1)

Basic service charge (not including usage).........	$14.66
Charge for 745 kWh @ 10.1530¢ each kWh...	+ 75.64
Electric adjustments...	+ 3.64
Sales tax (2.000%)...	+ 1.88
Total cost for electric service............................	$95.82

Your energy use and its cost

■ = Actual reading
▨ = Estimated reading
☐ = Average customer

This chart shows your energy-use pattern over the last 13 months. It also shows the current month's usage by our average residential customer.

Electric Meter 87-099-474

DAILY AVERAGES		
	Last year	This period
Temp	13°	23°
kWh	10.6	11.8
Cost $	1.38	1.52

1. This bill is filled with numerical information, such as percents and rates. What other examples of numerical information can you find on this electric bill?

2. What time period does this bill represent?

3. Explain how the amount of electricity used for the time period of this bill was calculated.

4. What does each bar in the bar graph represent?

5. **a.** Which billing period had the most usage of electricity?

   b. Estimate the number of kilowatt-hours (kWh) used in that period.

6. **a.** Which billing period had the least usage?

   b. Estimate the number of kilowatt-hours used in that period.

7. How does your current electricity usage compare to that of the average residential customer? Express this comparison as a fraction.

8. Explain how the usage charge of $75.64 for this billing period was calculated.

Appendix

9. Explain how the sales tax of $1.88 was calculated.

10. **a.** How is the daily average usage for this billing period calculated?

b. Where is this amount indicated on the bill?

11. On a budget plan, you would pay the same amount each billing period for electricity. To do this, the utility company calculates the average usage over all billing periods during the previous year.

   a. If you choose this option for next year, calculate your average usage per billing period.

   b. Based on the current rate, calculate your usage charge for each billing period on the budget plan.

EXERCISES

1. List the different mathematical operations used in this activity.

2. Use the appropriate ideas you listed in Exercise 1 to calculate the following: You buy three CDs priced at $12.99, $17.99, and $19.99. If the sales tax rate is 7.5%, what is the total cost of your purchase?

3. You spend $13.48, $18.90, and $21.20 for your dinners on a three-day vacation and leave a 15% tip for each meal (calculated on the subtotal before taxes). The local sales tax is 7%.

   a. How much money do you spend on your meals, before tax and tip?

b. What is the total tax for all three meals?

c. How much do you leave in tips for all three meals?

d. What is the total cost of all three meals?

e. What is the average cost of a meal, tax and tips included?

4. At the bookstore you buy books and supplies for the semester. The five text-books that you need cost $42.00, $56.00, $34.50, $79.10, and $68.00. You also need to buy five spiral notebooks at $2.89 each, a journal book that costs $2.19, and a $94 graphics calculator for your mathematics class. The local sales tax is 7%. Your financial aid package provides you with a $400 bookstore account for the semester.

a. What is the average price of your textbooks?

b. What is your total bookstore bill?

c. Is there enough money in your bookstore account to pay the total bill? Explain.

5. Summer weather can vary, depending on the jet stream. The following chart gives daily high and low temperatures for a week in July.

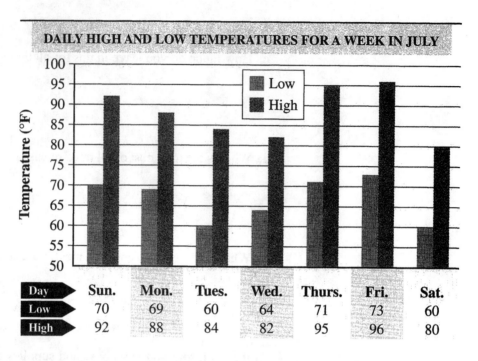

DAILY HIGH AND LOW TEMPERATURES FOR A WEEK IN JULY

Day	Sun.	Mon.	Tues.	Wed.	Thurs.	Fri.	Sat.
Low	70	69	60	64	71	73	60
High	92	88	84	82	95	96	80

a. Determine the average high temperature for the week.

b. Determine the average low temperature for the week.

c. Determine the average difference between the daily high and low temperatures for the week.

ACTIVITY 1.5

You and Your Calculator

Topics: *Properties of Real Numbers, Whole-Number Exponents, Scientific Notation with Large Numbers, Order of Operations, Grouping*

A calculator is a powerful tool for problem solving. A quick look at the desks of those around you should show you that calculators come in many sizes and shapes and with varying capabilities. Some calculators perform only basic operations such as addition, subtraction, multiplication, division, and square roots. Others also handle operations with exponents, perform operations with fractions, and do trigonometry and statistics. There are calculators that graph equations and generate tables of values; some even manipulate algebraic symbols.

Unlike people, however, calculators do not think for themselves and can only perform tasks in the way that you instruct them (or program them). Therefore, you need to understand the properties of numbers and become familiar with the way your calculator operates with numbers. In particular, you will learn how your calculator deals with very large numbers and the order in which it performs the operations you request.

Appendix

NOTE: Detailed information about using the TI-83 calculator for more complex tasks appears in Appendix D.

1. Use your calculator to determine the sum $146 + 875$.

2. **a.** Now, input $875 + 146$ into your calculator and evaluate. How does this sum compare to the sum in Problem 1?

   b. If you use numbers other than 146 and 875, does reversing the order of the numbers change the result? Explain by giving examples.

If the order in which two numbers are added is reversed, the sum remains the same. This property is called the **commutative property** of addition and can be written symbolically as

$$a + b = b + a$$

3. Is the commutative property true for the operation of subtraction? Multiplication? Division? Explain by giving examples for each operation.

It is sometimes convenient to do mental arithmetic (i.e., without the aid of your calculator). For example, to evaluate $4 \cdot 27$ without the aid of your calculator, think about the multiplication as follows: 27 can be written as $20 + 7$. Therefore, $4 \cdot 27$ can be written as $4 \cdot (20 + 7)$, which can be evaluated as $4 \cdot 20 + 4 \cdot 7$. The product $4 \cdot 27$ can now be thought of as $80 + 28$, or 108. To summarize,

$$4 \cdot 27 = \underline{4 \cdot (20 + 7)} = 4 \cdot 20 + 4 \cdot 7 = 80 + 28 = 108$$

The bracketed step involves a very important property called the *distributive property*. In particular, multiplication is distributed over addition or subtraction.

> The **distributive property** is written symbolically as:
>
> $$c \cdot (a + b) = c \cdot a + c \cdot b \text{ for addition,}$$
>
> or
>
> $$c \cdot (a - b) = c \cdot a - c \cdot b \text{ for subtraction.}$$

Note that $c \cdot (a + b)$ can also be written as $c(a + b)$ and $c \cdot (a - b)$ can also be written as $c(a - b)$. When a number is immediately followed by parentheses, the operation of multiplication is implied.

4. Another way to express 27 is $25 + 2$ or $30 - 3$.

   a. Express 27 as $25 + 2$ and use the distributive property to multiply $4 \cdot 27$.

   b. Express 27 as $30 - 3$ and use the distributive property to multiply $4 \cdot 27$.

5. Mentally evaluate the following multiplication problems using the distributive property. Verify your answer using your calculator.

   a. $7 \cdot 82$

   b. $5 \cdot 108$

6. **a.** Evaluate $5 + 6 \cdot 2$ in your head and record the result. Verify using your calculator.

   b. What operations are involved in this problem?

c. In what order did you and your calculator perform the operations to get the answer?

d. Evaluate $(5 + 6) \cdot 2$ and record the result. Verify using your calculator.

e. Why is the result in part d different from the result in part a?

Scientific and graphing calculators are programmed to perform operations in a universally accepted order as illustrated by the previous problems. Part of the **order of operations** priority convention is as follows:

1. Perform multiplication and division before addition and subtraction.
2. If both multiplication and division are present, perform the operations in order, from left to right.
3. If both addition and subtraction are present, perform the operations in order, from left to right.

For example: $10 - 2 \cdot 4 + 7 = 10 - 8 + 7 = 2 + 7 = 9$

7. Perform the following calculations without a calculator. Then use your calculator to verify your result.

a. $42 \div 3 + 4$

b. $42 \div (3 + 4)$

c. $(4 + 8) \div 2 \cdot 3 - 9$

d. $4 + 8 \div 2 \cdot 3 - 9$

8. a. Perform the calculation $\frac{24}{2 + 6}$ without your calculator.

b. Now use your calculator to evaluate $\frac{24}{2 + 6}$. Did you obtain 3 as the result? If not, then perhaps you entered the expression as $24 \div 2 + 6$ and your answer is 18.

c. Explain why the result of $24 \div 2 + 6$ is 18.

Note that $\frac{24}{2+6}$ is the same as the quotient $\frac{24}{8}$. Therefore, the addition in the denominator is done first, followed by the division. To write $\frac{24}{2+6}$ in a horizontal format, you must use parentheses to group the expression in the denominator to indicate that the addition is performed first. That is, write $24 \div (2 + 6)$.

9. Enter $24 \div (2 + 6)$ into your calculator using the parenthesis keys and verify that the result is 3.

> **Parentheses** are grouping symbols that are used to override the standard order of operations. Operations contained in parentheses are performed first.

For example, $2 \cdot (3 + 4 \cdot 5) = 2 \cdot (3 + 20) = 2 \cdot 23 = 46$.

10. Evaluate the following mentally and verify on your calculator.

a. $\dfrac{6}{3+3}$ **b.** $\dfrac{2+8}{4-2}$

c. $5 + 2 \cdot (4 \div 2 + 3)$ **d.** $10 - (12 - 3 \cdot 2) \div 3$

Calculators can easily perform repeated multiplication. Recall that $5 \cdot 5$ can be written as 5^2 (5 squared). There are two ways to square a number on your calculator.

11. a. One method to evaluate 5^2 is to use the $\boxed{x^2}$ key. Input $\boxed{5}$ and then press the $\boxed{x^2}$ key. Do this now and record your answer.

b. Another way you can evaluate 5^2 is by using the exponent key. Depending on your calculator, the exponent key may be $\boxed{x^y}$, $\boxed{y^x}$, or $\boxed{\wedge}$. To calculate 5^2, input $\boxed{5}$, press the exponent key, then enter the exponent as $\boxed{2}$ and press $\boxed{\text{ENTER}}$. Do this now and record your answer.

c. The exponent key can be used with any exponent. For example, $5 \cdot 5 \cdot 5$ can be written as 5^3. Evaluate $5 \cdot 5 \cdot 5$ as written, and evaluate 5^3 using the exponent key.

An expression such as 5^3 is called a **power** of 5. The base is 5 and the exponent is 3. Note that the exponent indicates how many times the base is multiplied by itself. Note also that 5^3 is read as "five raised to the third power." When a power (also known as an *exponential expression*) is contained in an expression, it is evaluated *before* any multiplication or division.

For example, to evaluate the expression $20 - 2 \cdot 3^2$, you can proceed as follows:

$$20 - 2 \cdot 3^2 =$$
$$20 - 2 \cdot 9 =$$
$$20 - 18 =$$
$$2$$

12. Enter the expression $20 - 2 \cdot 3^2$ into your calculator and verify the result.

13. Evaluate the following.

   a. $6 + 3 \cdot 4^3$ **b.** $2 \cdot 3^4 - 5^3$

14. a. Use the exponent key to evaluate the following powers: $3^0, 8^0, 23^0, 526^0$.

   b. Evaluate other nonzero numbers with a zero exponent.

   c. Evaluate 0^0. What is the result?

   d. Write a sentence describing the result of raising a nonzero number to a zero exponent.

15. a. Now use the exponent key to evaluate the following powers of 10: $10^2, 10^3, 10^4$, and 10^6. What relationship do you notice between the exponent and the number of zeros in the result?

   b. Evaluate 10^5. Is the result what you expected? How many zeros are in the result?

   c. Evaluate 10^0. Is the result what you expected? How many zeros are in the result?

16. a. Now use the exponent key to evaluate the following powers of 10: 10^{-1}, 10^{-2}, 10^{-3}, 10^{-4}, and 10^{-6}. What relationship do you notice between the exponent and the number of zeros in the result?

   b. Evaluate 10^{-5}. Is the result what you expected? How many zeros are in the result?

17. a. Because 5000 is 5×1000, the number 5000 can be written as 5×10^3. Use your calculator to verify this by evaluating 5×10^3.

   b. There is another way to evaluate a number times a power of 10, such as 5×10^3, on your calculator. Find the key labeled ⟨EE⟩ or ⟨E⟩ or ⟨EXP⟩; sometimes it is a second function. This key takes the place of the ⟨10⟩ ⟨^⟩ keys. To evaluate 5×10^3, enter ⟨5⟩, press the ⟨EE⟩ key, then enter ⟨3⟩. Try this now and verify the result.

> When a number is written as the product of a decimal number between 1 and 10 and a power of 10, it is expressed in **standard scientific notation.**

For example, 423 is expressed in scientific notation as 4.23×10^2.

The ⟨EE⟩ or ⟨E⟩ key on your calculator is used to enter a number in scientific notation. For example,

$$423 = 4.23 \times 100 = 4.23 \times 10^2 \text{ and can be entered as } 4.23 \,⟨EE⟩\, 02$$
$$147{,}000 = 1.47 \times 100{,}000 = 1.47 \times 10^5 \text{ and can be entered as } 1.47 \,⟨EE⟩\, 05$$

18. a. Input $4.23 \,⟨EE⟩\, 2$ into your calculator, press the ⟨ENTER⟩ or ⟨=⟩ key, and see if you obtain the result that you expect.

   b. Input $1.47 \,⟨EE⟩\, 5$ into your calculator, press the ⟨ENTER⟩ or ⟨=⟩ key, and see if you obtain the result that you expect.

One advantage of using scientific notation becomes evident when you have to work with very large numbers or very small numbers.

19. a. The average distance from Earth to the Sun is 93,000,000 miles. Write this number in words and in scientific notation. Then enter it into your calculator using the (EE) key.

b. Estimate 5 times the average distance from Earth to the Sun.

c. Now use your calculator to verify your estimate from part a. Write the answer in standard form, in scientific notation, and in words.

20. There are heavenly bodies that are thousands of times farther away from Earth than the Sun is. Multiply 93,000,000 miles by 1000. Write the result in scientific notation, in standard form, and in words.

21. a. You can approximate the distance that Earth travels in one orbit around the sun by multiplying 93,000,000 miles by $2 \times \pi$. (The Greek letter π, pronounced "pie," represents a specific number that, when rounded to the nearest hundredth, is 3.14). Use the (π) button on your calculator to calculate this distance.

b. In part a, you calculated the circumference of a circle whose radius is 93,000,000 miles. The calculator gives a result with many digits. Do you think it makes sense to report the distance with that much accuracy? Explain.

22. Use your calculator to perform each of the following calculations.

a. $12 - 2 \cdot (8 - 2 \cdot 3) + 3^2$ **b.** $5^4 + 2 \cdot 4^0$

c. $\dfrac{128}{16 - 2^3}$

d. $3.26 \times 10^4 \cdot 5.87 \times 10^3$.

Enter the numbers in scientific notation.

e. $10\pi \div (0.25\pi)$

f. $25 \times 10^{-2} + 750 \times 10^{-3}$

SUMMARY

1. If the order in which two numbers are added is reversed, the sum remains the same. This property is called the **commutative property** of addition and can be written symbolically as

$$a + b = b + a.$$

2. The **distributive property** of multiplication over addition or subtraction is written symbolically as

$$c \cdot (a + b) = c \cdot a + c \cdot b \text{ for addition}$$

or

$$c \cdot (a - b) = c \cdot a - c \cdot b \text{ for subtraction.}$$

3. The **Order of Operations** priority convention for parentheses, addition, subtraction, multiplication, division and exponentiation is:

   a. First priority: operations contained within parentheses (performed according to the accepted priority convention).

   b. Second priority: exponentiation.

   c. Third priority: multiplication or division (whichever comes first when read from left to right).

   d. Fourth priority: addition or subtraction (whichever comes first when read from left to right).

4. Any number, except zero, raised to the zero power equals 1. The symbol 0^0 is undefined.

5. A number is expressed in **standard scientific notation** when it is written as the product of a decimal number between 1 and 10 and a power of 10.

EXERCISES

1. The following numbers are written in standard notation. Convert each number to scientific notation.

   a. 213 040 000 000

   b. 0.000041324

Exercise numbers appearing in color are answered in the Selected Answers section of this book.

c. 555 140 500 000 000   **d.** 0.00000000000213749

2. The following numbers are written in scientific notation. Convert each number to standard notation.

a. 4.532×10^{11} **b.** 2.162×10^{-3}

c. 4.532×10^{7} **d.** 4.532×10^{-7}

3. Mentally evaluate each of the following expressions by performing the operations in the appropriate order. Use your calculator to check your results.

a. $6 + 18 \div 3 \cdot 4$ **b.** $5 \cdot 2^3 - 6 \cdot 2 + 5$

c. $48 \div 6 + 2 \cdot 2$ **d.** $5 + 5 \cdot 3 - 2 \cdot 2^2$

e. $5^3 \cdot 5^5$ **f.** $500 \div 25 \cdot 2 - 3 \cdot 2$

g. $\dfrac{7 - 3 \cdot 2}{5}$ **h.** $\dfrac{6}{8 - 2 \cdot 3}$

4. Solve the following problems by first changing the numbers to scientific notation and then performing the appropriate operations.

   a. The distance that light travels in 1 second is 186,000 miles. How far will light
   travel in 1 year? This distance is called a light-year. (There are approximately 31,500,000 seconds in 1 year.)

   b. The total area of the oceans of the world is about 140,000,000 square miles.
   An acre is about 0.00156 square mile. Determine the number of acres in
   the oceans of the world by dividing 140,000,000 by 0.00156. Express your
   answer in standard form and in words.

Target Heart Rate
Topics: *Algorithms, Percents*

NOTE: In preparation for this activity, you need to find your resting heart rate by taking your pulse for 60 seconds before getting out of bed in the morning.

You have joined a fitness center to get into shape and to lose a few pounds. You have chosen to use the Nautilus equipment as well as the aerobic machines. To maximize the benefit from your workout, you must increase and maintain your heart rate within a targeted range for a period of 10 to 20 minutes. Your instructor explains two different methods for determining this range.

1. Use method 1 to compute your target heart-rate range.

DETERMINING YOUR TARGET HEART RATE

Method 1

a. Calculate your resting heart rate by taking your pulse for 60 seconds before getting out of bed in the morning:

Resting heart rate = _____ beats per minute

b. Calculate your approximate maximum heart rate:

220 − age = _____ **maximum heart rate**

c. Calculate your approximate working heart rate:

Maximum heart rate − resting heart rate = _____ **working heart rate**

d. Calculate your approximate lower heart-rate limit by multiplying your approximate working heart rate by 60% and then adding the result to your resting heart rate:

Working heart rate · 60% + resting
heart rate = _____ **lower heart-rate limit**

e. Calculate your approximate upper heart-rate limit by multiplying your approximate working heart rate by 80%, then add the result to your resting heart rate.

Working heart rate · 80% + resting
heart rate = _____ **upper heart-rate limit**

f. Your target heart-rate range during aerobic exercise is defined by your lower and upper heart-rate limits:

Target heart-rate range is from _____ **(lower heart-rate limit)**
to _____ **(upper heart-rate limit)**

Source: YMCA

2. Use method 2 to compute your target heart-rate range.

DETERMINING YOUR TARGET HEART RATE

Method 2

  a. Calculate your approximate maximum heart rate:

      $220 - \text{age} =$ _____ beats per minute   **maximum heart rate**

  b. Calculate your lower heart-rate limit by multiplying your maximum heart rate by 70%

      Maximum heart rate $\cdot$ 70% = _____ **lower heart-rate limit**

  c. Calculate your upper heart-rate limit by multiplying your maximum heart rate by 85%:

      Maximum heart rate $\cdot$ 85% = _____ **upper heart-rate limit**

  d. Your target heart-rate range during aerobic exercise is defined by your lower and upper heart-rate limits:

      Target heart-rate range is from _____ **(lower heart-rate limit)**

          to _____ **(upper heart-rate limit)**

Source: YMCA

---

3. Compare the two methods. Which one do you think is more accurate? Explain in complete sentences.

4. When exercising, you take your pulse for only 10 seconds, not an entire minute. Use method 1 to compute your 10-second heart-rate range.

5. Why do the calculations in method 2 suggest that a person's target heart-rate range decreases as he or she gets older?

**PROJECT
ACTIVITY 1.7**

Income and Expenses

Topics: *Tables, Percents,
Bar Graphs*

You have just completed your two-year degree and are starting your first job as a salesperson at a sporting goods store. Your income consists of a base salary of $8.00 per hour, with time and a half for more than 40 hours per week and double time for holidays. You also receive a 3% commission on total sales.

1. Based on a 5-day week, 8-hour day, and 52-week year, determine your annual gross base salary.

2. You are paid biweekly. What is your gross base salary per pay period?

3. To determine your net (take-home) biweekly pay, the following must be deducted from your gross income: Social Security, Medicare, federal and state taxes, and union dues.

    a. If Social Security is 6.2% of gross income, determine the amount of your Social Security deduction.

    b. If Medicare is 1.45% of gross income, determine your Medicare deduction.

    c. Use the charts on pages 32–34 to find the federal and state biweekly deductions for a single person (claiming zero for withholding allowances).

    d. Ten dollars per pay period for union dues is also deducted. Determine the total of all deductions.

    e. What is your net base salary per pay period?

4. During the first pay period of a certain month, you work 10 days. Two of these days are holidays. During the second pay period, you work 10 days, and on four occasions you work overtime accumulating $2\frac{1}{4}$, $4\frac{2}{3}$, $5\frac{1}{2}$, and $3\frac{3}{4}$ hours overtime. Calculate your net pay for these pay periods by filling in the accompanying table on page 35.

SINGLE Persons—BIWEEKLY Payroll Period   FEDERAL

If the wages are—		And the number of withholding allowances claimed is—										
At least	But less than	0	1	2	3	4	5	6	7	8	9	10
		The amount of income tax to be withheld is—										
$0	$105	0	0	0	0	0	0	0	0	0	0	0
105	110	1	0	0	0	0	0	0	0	0	0	0
110	115	2	0	0	0	0	0	0	0	0	0	0
115	120	2	0	0	0	0	0	0	0	0	0	0
120	125	3	0	0	0	0	0	0	0	0	0	0
125	130	4	0	0	0	0	0	0	0	0	0	0
130	135	5	0	0	0	0	0	0	0	0	0	0
135	140	5	0	0	0	0	0	0	0	0	0	0
140	145	6	0	0	0	0	0	0	0	0	0	0
145	150	7	0	0	0	0	0	0	0	0	0	0
150	155	8	0	0	0	0	0	0	0	0	0	0
155	160	8	0	0	0	0	0	0	0	0	0	0
160	165	9	0	0	0	0	0	0	0	0	0	0
165	170	10	0	0	0	0	0	0	0	0	0	0
170	175	11	0	0	0	0	0	0	0	0	0	0
175	180	11	0	0	0	0	0	0	0	0	0	0
180	185	12	0	0	0	0	0	0	0	0	0	0
185	190	13	0	0	0	0	0	0	0	0	0	0
190	195	14	0	0	0	0	0	0	0	0	0	0
195	200	14	0	0	0	0	0	0	0	0	0	0
200	205	15	0	0	0	0	0	0	0	0	0	0
205	210	16	0	0	0	0	0	0	0	0	0	0
210	215	17	0	0	0	0	0	0	0	0	0	0
215	220	17	1	0	0	0	0	0	0	0	0	0
220	225	18	2	0	0	0	0	0	0	0	0	0
225	230	19	3	0	0	0	0	0	0	0	0	0
230	235	20	3	0	0	0	0	0	0	0	0	0
235	240	20	4	0	0	0	0	0	0	0	0	0
240	245	21	5	0	0	0	0	0	0	0	0	0
245	250	22	6	0	0	0	0	0	0	0	0	0
250	260	23	7	0	0	0	0	0	0	0	0	0
260	270	24	8	0	0	0	0	0	0	0	0	0
270	280	26	10	0	0	0	0	0	0	0	0	0
280	290	27	11	0	0	0	0	0	0	0	0	0
290	300	29	13	0	0	0	0	0	0	0	0	0
300	310	30	14	0	0	0	0	0	0	0	0	0
310	320	32	16	0	0	0	0	0	0	0	0	0
320	330	33	17	1	0	0	0	0	0	0	0	0
330	340	35	19	3	0	0	0	0	0	0	0	0
340	350	36	20	4	0	0	0	0	0	0	0	0
350	360	38	22	6	0	0	0	0	0	0	0	0
360	370	39	23	7	0	0	0	0	0	0	0	0
370	380	41	25	9	0	0	0	0	0	0	0	0
380	390	42	26	10	0	0	0	0	0	0	0	0
390	400	44	28	12	0	0	0	0	0	0	0	0
400	410	45	29	13	0	0	0	0	0	0	0	0
410	420	47	31	15	0	0	0	0	0	0	0	0
420	430	48	32	16	0	0	0	0	0	0	0	0
430	440	50	34	18	2	0	0	0	0	0	0	0
440	450	51	35	19	3	0	0	0	0	0	0	0
450	460	53	37	21	5	0	0	0	0	0	0	0
460	470	54	38	22	6	0	0	0	0	0	0	0
470	480	56	40	24	8	0	0	0	0	0	0	0
480	490	57	41	25	9	0	0	0	0	0	0	0
490	500	59	43	27	11	0	0	0	0	0	0	0
500	520	61	45	29	13	0	0	0	0	0	0	0
520	540	64	48	32	16	0	0	0	0	0	0	0
540	560	67	51	35	19	3	0	0	0	0	0	0
560	580	70	54	38	22	6	0	0	0	0	0	0
580	600	73	57	41	25	9	0	0	0	0	0	0
600	620	76	60	44	28	12	0	0	0	0	0	0
620	640	79	63	47	31	15	0	0	0	0	0	0
640	660	82	66	50	34	18	1	0	0	0	0	0
660	680	85	69	53	37	21	4	0	0	0	0	0
680	700	88	72	56	40	24	7	0	0	0	0	0
700	720	91	75	59	43	27	10	0	0	0	0	0
720	740	94	78	62	46	30	13	0	0	0	0	0
740	760	97	81	65	49	33	16	0	0	0	0	0
760	780	100	84	68	52	36	19	3	0	0	0	0
780	800	103	87	71	55	39	22	6	0	0	0	0

SINGLE Persons—BIWEEKLY Payroll Period   FEDERAL

If the wages are–		And the number of withholding allowances claimed is—										
At least	But less than	0	1	2	3	4	5	6	7	8	9	10
		The amount of income tax to be withheld is—										
$800	$820	106	90	74	58	42	25	9	0	0	0	0
820	840	109	93	77	61	45	28	12	0	0	0	0
840	860	112	96	80	64	48	31	15	0	0	0	0
860	880	115	99	83	67	51	34	18	2	0	0	0
880	900	118	102	86	70	54	37	21	5	0	0	0
900	920	121	105	89	73	57	40	24	8	0	0	0
920	940	124	108	92	76	60	43	27	11	0	0	0
940	960	127	111	95	79	63	46	30	14	0	0	0
960	980	130	114	98	82	66	49	33	17	1	0	0
980	1,000	133	117	101	85	69	52	36	20	4	0	0
1,000	1,020	136	120	104	88	72	55	39	23	7	0	0
1,020	1,040	139	123	107	91	75	58	42	26	10	0	0
1,040	1,060	142	126	110	94	78	61	45	29	13	0	0
1,060	1,080	145	129	113	97	81	64	48	32	16	0	0
1,080	1,100	151	132	116	100	84	67	51	35	19	3	0
1,100	1,120	156	135	119	103	87	70	54	38	22	6	0
1,120	1,140	162	138	122	106	90	73	57	41	25	9	0
1,140	1,160	167	141	125	109	93	76	60	44	28	12	0
1,160	1,180	173	144	128	112	96	79	63	47	31	15	0
1,180	1,200	179	149	131	115	99	82	66	50	34	18	2
1,200	1,220	184	154	134	118	102	85	69	53	37	21	5
1,220	1,240	190	160	137	121	105	88	72	56	40	24	8
1,240	1,260	195	165	140	124	108	91	75	59	43	27	11
1,260	1,280	201	171	143	127	111	94	78	62	46	30	14
1,280	1,300	207	177	146	130	114	97	81	65	49	33	17
1,300	1,320	212	182	152	133	117	100	84	68	52	36	20
1,320	1,340	218	188	158	136	120	103	87	71	55	39	23
1,340	1,360	223	193	163	139	123	106	90	74	58	42	26
1,360	1,380	229	199	169	142	126	109	93	77	61	45	29
1,380	1,400	235	205	174	145	129	112	96	80	64	48	32
1,400	1,420	240	210	180	150	132	115	99	83	67	51	35
1,420	1,440	246	216	186	155	135	118	102	86	70	54	38
1,440	1,460	251	221	191	161	138	121	105	89	73	57	41
1,460	1,480	257	227	197	167	141	124	108	92	76	60	44
1,480	1,500	263	233	202	172	144	127	111	95	79	63	47
1,500	1,520	268	238	208	178	148	130	114	98	82	66	50
1,520	1,540	274	244	214	183	153	133	117	101	85	69	53
1,540	1,560	279	249	219	189	159	136	120	104	88	72	56
1,560	1,580	285	255	225	195	164	139	123	107	91	75	59
1,580	1,600	291	261	230	200	170	142	126	110	94	78	62
1,600	1,620	296	266	236	206	176	145	129	113	97	81	65
1,620	1,640	302	272	242	211	181	151	132	116	100	84	68
1,640	1,660	307	277	247	217	187	157	135	119	103	87	71
1,660	1,680	313	283	253	223	192	162	138	122	106	90	74
1,680	1,700	319	289	258	228	198	168	141	125	109	93	77
1,700	1,720	324	294	264	234	204	173	144	128	112	96	80
1,720	1,740	330	300	270	239	209	179	149	131	115	99	83
1,740	1,760	335	305	275	245	215	185	155	134	118	102	86
1,760	1,780	341	311	281	251	220	190	160	137	121	105	89
1,780	1,800	347	317	286	256	226	196	166	140	124	108	92
1,800	1,820	352	322	292	262	232	201	171	143	127	111	95
1,020	1,840	358	328	298	267	237	207	177	147	130	114	98
1,840	1,860	363	333	303	273	243	213	183	152	133	117	101
1,860	1,880	369	339	309	279	248	218	188	158	136	120	104
1,880	1,900	375	345	314	284	254	224	194	164	139	123	107
1,900	1,920	380	350	320	290	260	229	199	169	142	126	110
1,920	1,940	386	356	326	295	265	235	205	175	145	129	113
1,940	1,960	391	361	331	301	271	241	211	180	150	132	116
1,960	1,980	397	367	337	307	276	246	216	186	156	135	119
1,980	2,000	403	373	342	312	282	252	222	192	161	138	122
2,000	2,020	408	378	348	318	288	257	227	197	167	141	125
2,020	2,040	414	384	354	323	293	263	233	203	173	144	128
2,040	2,060	419	389	359	329	299	269	239	208	178	148	131
2,060	2,080	425	395	365	335	304	274	244	214	184	154	134
2,080	2,100	431	401	370	340	310	280	250	220	189	159	137

$2,100 and over   Use Table 2(a) for a **SINGLE person** on page 34. Also see the instructions on page 32.

NY State—Single Persons—Biweekly Payroll Period

WAGES		EXEMPTIONS CLAIMED										10
At	But	0	1	2	3	4	5	6	7	8	9	or more
Least	Less Than	TAX TO BE WITHHELD										
$0	$200	$0.00										
200	210	0.00										
210	220	0.00										
220	230	0.00	$0.00									
230	240	0.00	0.00									
240	250	0.00	0.00									
250	260	0.00	0.00									
260	270	0.00	0.00	$0.00								
270	280	0.30	0.00	0.00								
280	290	0.70	0.00	0.00								
290	300	1.10	0.00	0.00								
300	320	1.70	0.10	0.00	$0.00							
320	340	2.50	0.90	0.00	0.00							
340	360	3.30	1.70	0.20	0.00	$0.00						
360	380	4.10	2.50	1.00	0.00	0.00						
380	400	4.90	3.30	1.80	0.30	0.00	$0.00					
400	420	5.70	4.10	2.60	1.10	0.00	0.00					
420	440	6.50	4.90	3.40	1.90	0.30	0.00	$0.00				
440	460	7.30	5.70	4.20	2.70	1.10	0.00	0.00	$0.00			
460	480	8.10	6.50	5.00	3.50	1.90	0.40	0.00	0.00			
480	500	8.90	7.30	5.80	4.30	2.70	1.20	0.00	0.00	$0.00		
500	520	9.70	8.10	6.60	5.10	3.50	2.00	0.40	0.00	0.00		
520	540	10.50	8.90	7.40	5.90	4.30	2.80	1.20	0.00	0.00	$0.00	
540	560	11.30	9.70	8.20	6.70	5.10	3.60	2.00	0.50	0.00	0.00	
560	580	12.10	10.50	9.00	7.50	5.90	4.40	2.80	1.30	0.00	0.00	$0.00
580	600	12.90	11.30	9.80	8.30	6.70	5.20	3.60	2.10	0.60	0.00	0.00
600	620	13.80	12.10	10.60	9.10	7.50	6.00	4.40	2.90	1.40	0.00	0.00
620	640	14.70	13.00	11.40	9.90	8.30	6.80	5.20	3.70	2.20	0.60	0.00
640	660	15.60	13.90	12.20	10.70	9.10	7.60	6.00	4.50	3.00	1.40	0.00
660	680	16.50	14.80	13.10	11.50	9.90	8.40	6.80	5.30	3.80	2.20	0.70
680	700	17.40	15.70	14.00	12.30	10.70	9.20	7.60	6.10	4.60	3.00	1.50
700	720	18.50	16.60	14.90	13.10	11.50	10.00	8.40	6.90	5.40	3.80	2.30
720	740	19.50	17.50	15.80	14.00	12.30	10.80	9.20	7.70	6.20	4.60	3.10
740	760	20.60	18.60	16.70	14.90	13.20	11.60	10.00	8.50	7.00	5.40	3.90
760	780	21.60	19.60	17.60	15.80	14.10	12.40	10.80	9.30	7.80	6.20	4.70
780	800	22.80	20.70	18.60	16.70	15.00	13.30	11.60	10.10	8.60	7.00	5.50
800	820	24.00	21.70	19.70	17.70	15.90	14.20	12.50	10.90	9.40	7.80	6.30
820	840	25.20	22.90	20.70	18.70	16.80	15.10	13.40	11.70	10.20	8.60	7.10
840	860	26.40	24.10	21.80	19.80	17.80	16.00	14.30	12.50	11.00	9.40	7.90
860	880	27.50	25.30	23.00	20.80	18.80	16.90	15.20	13.40	11.80	10.20	8.70
880	900	28.70	26.50	24.20	21.90	19.90	17.80	16.10	14.30	12.60	11.00	9.50
900	920	29.90	27.60	25.40	23.10	20.90	18.90	17.00	15.20	13.50	11.80	10.30
920	940	31.10	28.80	26.50	24.30	22.00	19.90	17.90	16.10	14.40	12.70	11.10
940	960	32.30	30.00	27.70	25.50	23.20	21.00	19.00	17.00	15.30	13.60	11.90
960	980	33.40	31.20	28.90	26.60	24.40	22.10	20.00	18.00	16.20	14.50	12.70
980	1,000	34.60	32.40	30.10	27.80	25.50	23.30	21.10	19.00	17.10	15.40	13.60
1,000	1,020	35.80	33.50	31.30	29.00	26.70	24.50	22.20	20.10	18.10	16.30	14.50
1,020	1,040	37.00	34.70	32.40	30.20	27.90	25.60	23.40	21.10	19.10	17.20	15.40
1,040	1,060	38.30	35.90	33.60	31.40	29.10	26.80	24.50	22.30	20.20	18.20	16.30
1,060	1,080	39.60	37.10	34.80	32.50	30.30	28.00	25.70	23.50	21.20	19.20	17.20
1,080	1,100	41.00	38.40	36.00	33.70	31.40	29.20	26.90	24.60	22.40	20.30	18.20
1,100	1,120	42.40	39.80	37.20	34.90	32.60	30.40	28.10	25.80	23.50	21.30	19.30
1,120	1,140	43.80	41.10	38.50	36.10	33.80	31.50	29.30	27.00	24.70	22.50	20.30
1,140	1,160	45.10	42.50	39.90	37.30	35.00	32.70	30.40	28.20	25.90	23.60	21.40
1,160	1,180	46.50	43.90	41.20	38.60	36.20	33.90	31.60	29.40	27.10	24.80	22.50
1,180	1,200	47.90	45.20	42.60	40.00	37.30	35.10	32.80	30.50	28.30	26.00	23.70
1,200	1,220	49.20	46.60	44.00	41.30	38.70	36.30	34.00	31.70	29.40	27.20	24.90
1,220	1,240	50.60	48.00	45.30	42.70	40.10	37.40	35.20	32.90	30.60	28.40	26.10
1,240	1,260	52.00	49.30	46.70	44.10	41.40	38.80	36.30	34.10	31.80	29.50	27.30
1,260	1,280	53.30	50.70	48.10	45.40	42.80	40.20	37.50	35.30	33.00	30.70	28.40
1,280	1,300	54.70	52.10	49.50	46.80	44.20	41.50	38.90	36.40	34.20	31.90	29.60
1,300	3,460	6.85% (.0685) of the excess over $1,300 plus:										
		55.40	52.80	50.10	47.50	44.90	42.20	39.60	37.00	34.80	32.50	30.20
$3,460 & OVER		Use Method II, "Exact Calculation Method," on page T-13 of this booklet										

REMINDER: Use 6.2% for Social Security, 1.45% for Medicare, and the tables for federal and state taxes. Don't forget the union dues.

	FIRST PAY PERIOD	SECOND PAY PERIOD
GROSS BASE		
GROSS OT/HOL.		
TOTAL GROSS		
FEDERAL INCOME TAX		
STATE INCOME TAX		
SOCIAL SECURITY TAX		
MEDICARE		
UNION DUES		
TOTAL NET		

5. You sell $10,000 worth of merchandise during each pay period.

   a. What is your total commission?

   b. Your commission is paid to you in a separate paycheck. Calculate your take-home pay for commission for this month. (Remember that federal and state tax tables are based on *biweekly* payroll periods.)

   c. What is your total take-home pay for the month, including commission?

   d. What percent of your gross income this month is from commission?

   e. What percent of your gross income this month comes from overtime/holiday hours?

f. Create a bar graph to show a graphical view of your month's total gross income. Include these three categories: gross overtime/holiday, gross commission, and gross base salary.

6. a. You want to purchase a new TV that costs $549 plus 7% sales tax. You plan to save your overtime pay to purchase the TV outright and not pay monthly installments on the bill. Estimate the number of hours you need to work to yield enough net overtime pay to purchase the TV.

b. Your overtime hours for the month in Problem 4 are a reasonable estimate of the hours you work each month. How many months of saving will it take for you to purchase the TV?

7. You are trying not to go any further into debt, and you want to pay off some of your college debts. Each month you analyze how you spend your money and categorize your expenses under the following headings: (1) household, (2) medical, (3) entertainment, (4) loans, (5) insurance, (6) personal, and (7) miscellaneous.

Your actual expenses incurred for one month are shown in the following list. The number in parentheses indicates the category of the expense.

car payment (4), $125	rent (1), $300
car insurance (5), $72	phone (1), $60
parking (7), $50	movies (3), $20
bowling (3), $60	towels (1), $22
shoes (6), $43	student loan (4), $60
dentist (2), $30	film (7), $5
groceries (1), $150	savings (6), $100
credit-card debt (4), $50	medicines (2), $47
bank charges (7), $7	clothes (6), $110
gas/car (7), $80	

If computers are accessible, create a spreadsheet; otherwise, use the accompanying table to group the information. List the given expenses in the appropriate columns in the table.

HOUSEHOLD [1]	MEDICAL [2]	ENTERTAINMENT [3]	LOANS [4]	INSURANCE [5]	PERSONAL [6]	MISC. [7]

8. Do you think that the expenses you incurred this month will be consistent with other months' expenses? Explain.

9. What are the total expenses for the month?

10. What percent of the total is used for household expenses? What percent is for entertainment? Create a bar graph showing the percentages for all of the categories.

11. Will you have enough income to cover your expenses this month? Explain.

12. You are considering a move to another apartment that has two bedrooms. How much more do you think you can afford to pay, based on your calculated income and expenses? Will the move be possible?

What Have I Learned?

The activities in this cluster gave you an opportunity to use mathematics to solve problems in several different contexts. Fractions, decimals, and percents were involved, as well as tables, bar graphs, and calculators. If you need to brush up on some of these skills, you can find many practice problems in the Appendices. Apply the skills you used in this cluster to solve the following problem.

1. You are shopping for new clothes for the semester and decide to buy a sweater priced at $63, shoes for $74, and pants priced at $39. All items in the store are on sale at 30% off the tag price. If the total cost of your purchase after the discount is more than $100, you may deduct an additional $25. The 7% sales tax is computed on the final cost after all the discounts have been taken. You have $100 to spend.

   a. Organize these data in a way that makes sense to you.

   b. Will $100 cover your purchases? Explain in complete sentences. Include the calculations that you used to determine your answer.

2. George Polya's book *How to Solve It* outlines a four-step process for solving problems.

   1. Understand the problem (see clearly what is involved).
   2. Make a plan (look for connections to obtain the idea of a solution).
   3. Carry out the plan.
   4. Look back at the completed solution (review and discuss it).

Describe how your procedures in Problem 1 correspond with Polya's suggestions.

How Can I Practice?

1. a. Estimate the average temperature in your hometown for each month from January to December.

MONTH	AVERAGE TEMPERATURE
January	
February	
March	
April	
May	
June	
July	
August	
September	
October	
November	
December	

b. Draw a bar graph to represent your data.

2. a. Write four million three hundred thousand forty-two in standard form.

    b. Write 12,578 in words.

3. Use pencil and paper to perform the following calculations. Then use your calculator to verify your results.

    a. $4 \cdot (6 + 3) - 9 \cdot 2$

    b. $5 \cdot 9 \div 3 - 3 \cdot 4 \div 6$

    c. $2 + 3 \cdot 4^3$

    d. $\dfrac{256}{8 + 6^2}$

4. a. Write 214,000,000,000 in scientific notation.

    b. Write 7.83×10^4 in standard notation.

5. The sales tax in Erie County, New York, is 8%. Determine the cost of a new car, including sales tax, if the sticker price is $12,073.

6. The summer of 1999 was exceptionally hot and dry throughout the eastern seaboard and Midwest of the United States. The bad news was that crop yields for corn were poor, but the good news was that mosquitoes were scarce. During July 1999, scientists in Monmouth County, New Jersey, counted 1711 mosquitoes in their traps, which was only about one-fifth of the typical July catch they averaged in the previous six years. About how many mosquitoes were trapped in Monmouth County during a typical July?

7. A newly discovered binary star, Shuart1, is located 185 light-years from Earth. One light-year is 9,460,000,000,000 kilometers.

   a. Express the distance to Shuart1 in kilometers. Write the answer in scientific notation.

   b. The speed of light in a vacuum is approximately 300,000 kilometers per second. Approximately how many years does it take light to travel to Earth from Shuart1? Assume that there are 365 days per year. Write your result in scientific notation.

8. A professional softball player was injured partway through the season. She played 75% of her games before the injury and 25% of them after she recuperated and returned to play. Her batting average was .420 in the first part of the season and .360 when she returned. What was her average for the entire season?

CLUSTER 2

Problem Solving with Fractions

ACTIVITY 1.8

How Much Do I Owe?

Topics: *Equivalent Fractions, Addition, Subtraction, and Multiplication of Fractions*

You decide to have friends over to watch some videos. After the first movie, you call the local sub shop to order three giant submarine sandwiches, which are on sale for $9.95 each (tax included, free delivery). When the subs are delivered, you pay the bill of $29.85, plus a $4.00 tip, and everyone agrees to reimburse you, depending on how much they eat.

Because some friends are hungrier than others, you cut one sub into three equal (large) parts, a second sub into six equal (medium) parts, and the third sub into twelve equal (small) parts.

Sub 1: Large pieces

Sub 2: Medium pieces

Sub 3: Small pieces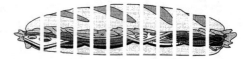

Because the first sub is divided into three equal parts, each part (large piece) represents $\frac{1}{3}$ of a giant sub.

1. a. What fraction of giant sub 2 does each medium piece represent? Explain.

b. What fraction of giant sub 3 does each small piece represent? Explain.

The following table represents the number and size of the portion(s) that each friend consumes. You will complete the remaining columns as you proceed through this activity.

NAME	LARGE PIECES ($\frac{1}{3}$ SUB)	MEDIUM PIECES ($\frac{1}{6}$ SUB)	SMALL PIECES ($\frac{1}{12}$ SUB)	FRACTIONAL PART OF SUB	AMOUNT OWED
Pete	1	0	0		
Joaquin	0	0	4		
Halima	0	2	0		
Leah	1	0	1		
Pat	0	2	0		
Marty	0	1	2		
Jennifer	0	1	1		
You	1	0	0		

2. What fractional part of a giant sub does Pete eat? Record your result in column 5 of the table.

3. In computing how much Halima owes, you notice that two medium pieces placed end to end measure the same as one large piece. What single fraction of a sub represents Halima's combined portion? Explain how you obtained your answer. Compare your method with those used by your classmates.

You could have used either of two different approaches to obtain your answer in Problem 3:

Add the fractions: $\frac{1}{6} + \frac{1}{6} = \frac{1+1}{6} = \frac{2}{6}$

Use multiplication to do repeated addition: $\frac{1}{6} + \frac{1}{6} = 2 \cdot \frac{1}{6} = \frac{2}{1} \cdot \frac{1}{6} = \frac{2 \cdot 1}{1 \cdot 6} = \frac{2}{6}$

Appendix

If you find you need some review with fractions and operations with fractions, refer to Appendix A, which contains several examples with solutions and practice exercises.

4. Because two medium-sized pieces equal one large piece, $\frac{2}{6}$ should be equivalent to $\frac{1}{3}$. Describe a procedure to write $\frac{2}{6}$ equivalently as $\frac{1}{3}$.

5. Use the procedure you described in Problem 4 to compare Joaquin's portion with Pete's piece. Use the following diagrams to help support your answer.

Pete's portion —

Joaquin's portion —

In Problems 4 and 5, you determined that the fractions $\frac{1}{3}$, $\frac{2}{6}$, and $\frac{4}{12}$ are **equivalent.** These fractional parts of a sub all represent the same portion. When $\frac{2}{6}$ and $\frac{4}{12}$ are written as $\frac{1}{3}$, the fractions $\frac{2}{6}$ and $\frac{4}{12}$ are said to be written in **reduced form** (lowest terms).

PROPERTY OF EQUIVALENT FRACTIONS

If the numerator and denominator of a fraction are both multiplied (or divided) by the same nonzero number, an **equivalent fraction** is obtained.

---

6. Write each fraction as an equivalent fraction in lowest terms.

    a. $\frac{10}{12}$ **b.** $\frac{18}{24}$

7. There are many fractions that are equivalent to $\frac{1}{3}$. For each of the following, determine the value of the missing numerator or denominator so that the resulting fraction is equivalent to $\frac{1}{3}$.

    a. $\dfrac{1}{3} = \dfrac{?}{15}$ **b.** $\dfrac{1}{3} = \dfrac{6}{?}$

    c. $\dfrac{1}{3} = \dfrac{?}{33}$ **d.** $\dfrac{1}{3} = \dfrac{90}{?}$

8. Leah has one large piece and one small piece of a sub. What single fraction of a sub represents Leah's combined portions? *Recall:* To add fractions, each fraction must have the same denominator.

9. You have expressed Pete's, Halima's, Joaquin's, and Leah's portions as a single fraction of a sub. Compute the fractional part for your remaining friends (and yourself!) and record your results in column 5 of the table following Problem 1. Show your work below.

10. a. Determine how much Pete owes. Remember to include the tip in the total cost of the order before calculating the cost of one sub. Round your final answer to the nearest cent.

b. Determine the amount each additional person owes, and record your answers in the last column of the table. Round your answers to the nearest cent.

c. Do you have enough money to reimburse yourself? Explain.

d. What fractional part of a sub is left over?

11. What total fractional part of the sandwich order did Pete, Joaquin, Halima and Marty eat?

12. Use the sandwich diagrams on page 42 to help answer the following.

a. How many sandwiches do Leah, Pete, Joaquin, and Marty consume altogether? Express this answer in twelfths.

b. The fraction that is your answer to part a is called an **improper fraction**. What characterizes improper fractions?

Appendix

c. You can also express your answer to part a as a **mixed number**. Explain how to convert between an improper fraction and a mixed number.

    d. Express the number of sandwiches consumed by Marty, Leah, Jennifer, Halima, and Pete as a mixed number.

13. Suppose that you and Pete are the only ones who show up to eat the subs and you each eat the portions reported in the table. You divide the remaining portions into two equal parts to take home. How much do you each take home?

Appendix

14. Leah likes this method of cutting sandwiches and orders the same three subs the next day for her sorority gathering.

    a. The sorority sisters eat $1\frac{5}{12}$ subs. How much is left?

    b. Some friends arrive later and eat $\frac{5}{6}$ more. How much remains to feed to the dog?

E X E R C I S E S

1. Your stock goes up $\frac{1}{8}$ of a point (1 point = $1). If you own 220 shares, how much money do you make?

2. The winnings from a horse race are distributed among the owners. You own $\frac{4}{25}$ share of the horse, Mulligan, who won $235,000 at Rolling Hills Raceway. How much money will you receive for your share?

3. At the end of the semester, the bookstore will buy back books that will be used again in courses the next semester. Usually, they will give you $\frac{1}{6}$ the original cost of the book. If you spend $243 on books this semester and the bookstore will buy back all your books, how much money can you expect to receive?

4. You use $\frac{1}{3}$ of your take-home pay each week for rent, $\frac{1}{5}$ for food, and $\frac{1}{10}$ for insurance. What part of your paycheck is left for your other expenses and savings?

5. List at least five fractions that are equivalent to $\frac{3}{5}$. Explain or show why they are equivalent.

6. Perform the indicated operations.

   a. $\dfrac{4}{9} + \dfrac{7}{3}$ b. $\dfrac{6}{7} - \dfrac{1}{4}$

   c. $\dfrac{3}{8} \cdot \dfrac{4}{9}$ d. $\dfrac{7}{3} + \dfrac{4}{5}$

7. Your youngest brother, who is in elementary school, asks you why $\frac{3}{4}$ and $\frac{6}{8}$ are equivalent. How would you answer his question?

ACTIVITY 1.9

Fractions Invade Campus Life

Topics: *Adding, Subtracting, Multiplying, and Dividing Fractions*

Fractions are a part of everyday life, and many calculators support operations with fractions. In this activity, you will calculate with fractions that you are likely to encounter during your college career and beyond. Your goal is to become comfortable doing arithmetic operations with fractions manually, as well as with the aid of your calculator. Both ways of dealing with fractions are important for your future success in using math to solve problems.

1. In the course of a typical day (24 hours), you, as a student, expect to spend $\frac{1}{4}$ of the time sleeping, $\frac{1}{6}$ of the time in class, $\frac{1}{3}$ of the time studying, and $\frac{1}{8}$ of the time eating. What fraction of your day is left as "free time"? Explain how you arrived at your result.

2. As part of your life as a college student, you decide to try some baking. Your favorite muffin recipe calls for $2\frac{2}{3}$ cups of flour, 1 cup of sugar, $\frac{1}{2}$ cup of crushed cashews, and $\frac{5}{8}$ cup of milk, plus assorted spices. How many cups of mixture do you have?

Go to Appendix A if you need help to review mixed numbers.

3. The syllabus for your history course contains the following information about the fractional parts that will be used to calculate your course grade.

Quiz average	$\frac{1}{5}$
Exam average	$\frac{1}{2}$
Final exam	$\frac{1}{5}$

The rest of your grade is based on in-class participation. What fraction of your course grade does in-class participation represent?

a. Show your manual calculations.

b. Explain how you used your calculator to verify your result.

4. You correctly answer $\frac{2}{3}$ of the 75 questions on your first psychology exam. How many questions do you answer incorrectly? Show your manual work. Explain the steps you followed using your calculator.

5. You are taking five 3-credit courses this semester. On the average, you spend 35 hours per week outside of class doing course work. You use about 10 of these 35 hours to work on math.

   a. What fraction of your study time is devoted to your math course?

   b. If you spend equal time on each course, what fraction of your study time should you allot to the math course?

6. You must take medicine in four equal doses each day. Each day's medicine comes in a single container and measures $3\frac{1}{3}$ tablespoons. How much medicine is in each dose?

7. The wall space for bookshelves in your dorm room is $4\frac{1}{2}$ feet across. A board you have measures $12\frac{2}{3}$ feet in length.

   a. Without calculating, roughly estimate how many shelves you can cut from the board.

   b. Check your estimate by calculating $12\frac{2}{3} \div 4\frac{1}{2}$.

   c. Did the calculation verify your estimate? Explain why or why not.

EXERCISES

Recall that Appendix A contains examples of operations with fractions, including solutions and practice exercises.

   1. The year that you enter college, your freshman class consists of 760 students. According to statistical studies, about $\frac{4}{7}$ of these students will actually graduate. Approximately how many of your classmates will receive their degree?

2. You rent an apartment for the academic year (two semesters) with three of your college friends. The rent for the entire academic year is $10,000. Each semester you receive a bill for your share of the rent. If you and your friends divide the rent equally, how much must you pay each semester?

3. Your residence hall has been designated a quiet building. This means that there is a no-noise rule from 10:00 P.M. every night to noon the next day. During what fraction of a 24-hour period is one allowed to make noise?

4. You would like to learn to play the harp but are concerned with time constraints. A friend of yours plays and for three consecutive days before a recital, she practices for $1\frac{1}{4}$ hours, $2\frac{1}{2}$ hours, and $3\frac{2}{3}$ hours. What is her total practice time before a recital?

5. You are planning a summer cookout and decide to serve $\frac{1}{4}$-pound hamburgers. If you buy $5\frac{1}{2}$ pounds of hamburger meat, how many burgers can you make?

6. Perform the indicated operations.

   a. $4\frac{2}{3} - 1\frac{6}{7}$

   b. $5\frac{1}{2} + 2\frac{1}{3}$

   c. $2\frac{1}{6} \cdot 4\frac{1}{2}$

   d. $2\frac{3}{7} + \frac{14}{5}$

   e. $\dfrac{4}{5} \div \dfrac{8}{3}$

   f. $4\frac{1}{5} \div \frac{10}{3}$

ACTIVITY 1.10

Delicious Recipes

Topics: *Adding, Subtracting, Multiplying, and Dividing Fractions*

Appendix

The recipes in this activity are for foods to be served at a party. Use these recipes to help plan the party by answering the questions following the recipes. Reduce each fraction, using mixed numbers when appropriate.

NOTE: You may not have worked extensively with fraction operations for some time. Appendix A contains many practice problems involving adding, subtracting, multiplying, and dividing fractions.

Crab Supreme

4 small (6 oz) cans crab meat	2 dashes of Tabasco sauce
1 egg, hard-boiled and mashed	$3\frac{1}{2}$ tbsp chopped fresh chives
$\frac{1}{2}$ cup mayonnaise	$\frac{1}{4}$ tsp salt
$2\frac{1}{2}$ tbsp chopped onion	$\frac{1}{2}$ tsp garlic powder
$3\frac{2}{3}$ tbsp plain yogurt	1 tsp lemon juice

Drain and rinse crab in cold water. Mash crab and egg together. Add all remaining ingredients except chives. Stir well. Chill, top with chives, and serve with chips or crackers. SERVES 6.

---

1. Determine the ingredients for one-half of this recipe. Fill in the blanks below.

   _____ small (6 oz) cans crab   _____ dashes Tabasco

   _____ egg, hard boiled and mashed   _____ tbsp chives

   _____ cup(s) mayonnaise   _____ tsp salt

   _____ tbsp, chopped onion   _____ tsp garlic powder

   _____ tbsp, plain yogurt   _____ tsp lemon juice

2. List the ingredients needed for the crab recipe if 18 people attend the party.

   _____ small (6 oz) cans crab   _____ dashes Tabasco

   _____ egg, hard-boiled and mashed   _____ tbsp chives

   _____ cup(s) mayonnaise   _____ tsp salt

   _____ tbsp chopped onion   _____ tsp garlic powder

   _____ tbsp plain yogurt   _____ tsp lemon juice

3. If a container of yogurt holds 1 cup, how many batches of crab appetizer can you make with one container? (1 cup = 16 tbsp)

4. If each person drinks $2\frac{2}{3}$ cups of soda, how many cups of soda will be needed for 18 people?

Apple Crisp

4 cups tart apples	$\frac{1}{3}$ cup softened butter
peeled, cored, and sliced	$\frac{1}{2}$ tsp salt
$\frac{2}{3}$ cup packed brown sugar	$\frac{3}{4}$ tsp cinnamon
$\frac{1}{4}$ cup rolled oats	$\frac{1}{8}$ tsp allspice or nutmeg
$\frac{1}{2}$ cup flour	

Preheat oven to 375°. Place apples in a greased 8-inch square pan. Blend remaining ingredients until crumbly, and spread over the apples. Bake approximately 30 minutes uncovered, until the topping is golden and the apples are tender. SERVES 4.

---

5. List the ingredients needed for the apple crisp recipe if 18 people attend the party.

6. How many times would you need to fill a $\frac{2}{3}$-cup container to measure 4 cups of apples?

7. If it takes $\frac{3}{4}$ tsp of cinnamon to make one batch of apple crisp and you have only 6 tsp of cinnamon left in the cupboard, how many batches can you make?

EXERCISES

Use the two preceding recipes in this activity, as well as the following recipe for potato pancakes, to answer the questions.

Potato Pancakes

6 cups potato	$\frac{1}{3}$ cup flour
(pared and grated)	$3\frac{3}{8}$ tsp salt
9 eggs	$2\frac{1}{4}$ tbsp grated onion

Drain the potatoes well. Beat eggs and stir into the potatoes. Combine and sift the flour and salt, then stir in the onions. Add to the potato mixture. Shape into patties and sauté in hot fat. Best served hot with applesauce. MAKES 36 3-inch pancakes.

1. If you were to make one batch of each of the three recipes, how much salt would you need? How much flour? How much onion?

2. If you have 2 cups of flour in the cupboard before you start cooking for the party and you make one batch of each recipe, how much flour will be left in the cupboard?

What Have I Learned?

Spend some time to reflect on operations with fractions by answering the following questions.

1. To add or subtract fractions, they must be written in equivalent form with common denominators. However, to multiply or divide fractions you do not need a common denominator. Why is this reasonable?

2. The operation of division can be viewed from several different points of view. For example, 24 ÷ 3 has at least two meanings:

   - 24 can be written as the sum of how many 3s?
   - If 24 is divided into 3 equal-sized parts, how large is each part?

   These interpretations can be applied to fractions as well as to whole numbers.

   a. Calculate $2 \div \frac{1}{2}$ by answering this question: 2 can be written as the sum of how many $\frac{1}{2}$s?

   b. Calculate $\frac{1}{5} \div 2$ by answering this question: If you divide $\frac{1}{5}$ into 2 equal parts, how large is each part?

   c. Do your answers to parts a and b agree with the results you would obtain by using the procedures for dividing fractions reviewed in this cluster? Explain.

How Can I Practice?

1. You are in a golf tournament and there is a prize for driving the green on the sixth hole, with the drive closest to the hole winning. You drive the ball to within 4 feet $2\frac{3}{8}$ inches of the hole and your nearest competitor is 4 feet $5\frac{1}{4}$ inches from the hole. By how many inches did you win?

2. One of your jobs as the assistant to a weather reporter is to determine the average thickness of the ice in a bay on the St. Lawrence River. Ice fishermen use this report to determine if the ice is safe for fishing. You must chop holes in five different areas, measure the thickness, and take the average. During the first week in January, you record the following measurements: $2\frac{3}{8}$, $5\frac{1}{2}$, $6\frac{3}{4}$, 4, and $5\frac{7}{8}$ inches. What do you report as the average thickness of the ice in this area? Do you think the ice is safe?

3. You and two others in your family will divide 120 shares of a computer stock left by a relative who died. The stock is worth $\$10\frac{9}{16}$ per share. If you decide to sell your share of the stock, how much money will you receive?

4. You are about to purchase a rug for your college dorm room. The rug's length is perfect for your room. The width of the rug you want to purchase is $6\frac{1}{2}$ feet. If you center the rug in the middle of your 10-foot-wide room, how much floor space will you have on each side of the rug?

5. A plumber has $12\frac{1}{2}$ feet of plastic pipe. He uses $3\frac{2}{3}$ feet for the sink line and $5\frac{3}{4}$ feet for the washing machine. How much does he have left? He needs approximately $3\frac{1}{2}$ feet for a disposal. Does he have enough pipe left for a disposal?

6. Perform the following operations.

   a. $\frac{5}{7} + \frac{2}{7}$

   b. $\frac{3}{4} + \frac{3}{8}$

   c. $\frac{3}{8} + \frac{1}{12}$

   d. $\frac{4}{5} + \frac{5}{6}$

   e. $\frac{1}{2} + \frac{3}{5} + \frac{4}{15}$

   f. $\frac{11}{12} - \frac{5}{12}$

   g. $\frac{7}{9} - \frac{5}{12}$

   h. $\frac{2}{3} - \frac{1}{4}$

   i. $\frac{7}{30} - \frac{3}{20}$

j. $\frac{4}{5} - \frac{3}{4} + \frac{1}{2}$　　　　**k.** $\frac{3}{5} \cdot \frac{1}{2}$　　　　**l.** $\frac{2}{3} \cdot \frac{7}{8}$

m. $\frac{15}{8} \cdot \frac{24}{5}$　　　　**n.** $5 \cdot \frac{3}{10}$　　　　**o.** $\frac{3}{8} \div \frac{3}{4}$

p. $8 \div \frac{1}{2}$　　　　**q.** $\frac{5}{7} \div \frac{20}{21}$　　　　**r.** $4\frac{5}{6} + 3\frac{2}{9}$

s. $12\frac{5}{12} - 4\frac{1}{6}$　　　　**t.** $6\frac{2}{13} - 4\frac{7}{26}$

u. $2\frac{1}{4} \cdot 5\frac{2}{3}$　　　　**v.** $6\frac{3}{4} \div 1\frac{2}{7}$

EXPLORING NUMERACY

Suppose that each of the 263,814,032 residents of the United States skipped one meal per week for a year. Estimate the number of hungry people in the world who could be fed three meals per day for a year.

CLUSTER 3

ACTIVITY 1.11

Which One Is Better?

Topics: *Ratios, Equivalent Ratios, Proportions, Fractions, Decimals, Percent*

Comparisons and Proportional Reasoning

The following table summarizes Michael Jordan's statistics during the six games of the 1996 National Basketball Association (NBA) championship series.

GAME	POINTS	FIELD GOALS	FREE THROWS
1	28	9 out of 18	9 out of 10
2	29	9 out of 22	10 out of 16
3	36	11 out of 23	11 out of 11
4	23	6 out of 19	11 out of 13
5	26	11 out of 22	4 out of 5
6	22	5 out of 19	11 out of 12

1. What was his points-per-game average over the six-game series?

2. In which game did he score the most points?

3. In which game(s) did he score the most field goals? The most free throws?

Problem 3 focused on the *actual* number of Jordan's successful field goals and free throws in these six games. Another way of assessing Jordan's performance is to *compare* the number of successful shots to the total number of attempts for each game. This comparison gives you information on the *relative* success of his shooting. For example, in each of games 1 and 2, Jordan made 9 field goals. Relatively speaking, you could argue that he was more successful in game 1 because he made 9 out of 18 attempts; in game 2, he only made 9 out of 22 attempts.

4. Use the free-throw data from the six games to express Jordan's *relative* performance in the given comparison formats (verbal, fraction, division, and decimal). The data from the first game have been entered for you.

JORDAN'S RELATIVE FREE-THROW PERFORMANCE

	VERBAL	FRACTION	DIVISION	DECIMAL
GAME 1	9 out of 10	$\frac{9}{10}$	$9 \div 10$ or $10\overline{)9}$	0.90
GAME 2				
GAME 3				
GAME 4				
GAME 5				
GAME 6				

5. a. For which of the six games was his relative free-throw performance highest?

b. Which comparison format did you use to answer part a? Why?

6. For which of the six games was Jordan's *actual* free-throw performance the lowest?

7. For which of the six games was Jordan's *relative* free-throw performance the lowest?

> When relative comparisons using quotients are made between different values or quantities of the same kind (e.g., number of baskets to number of baskets), the comparison is called a **ratio**. Ratios can be expressed in any of several forms—verbal, fraction, division, or decimal, as you saw in Problem 4.

Proportional reasoning, a critically important quantitative skill, is the ability to recognize when two ratios are equivalent, that is, when equivalent ratios represent the same relative performance level.

> Two ratios are said to be **equivalent** if the ratios have equal numerical (e.g., decimal or fraction) values. The mathematical statement that two ratios are equivalent is called a **proportion**. In fraction form, the proportion is written $\frac{a}{b} = \frac{c}{d}$.

You can find *equivalent* ratios the same way you find equivalent fractions. For example, 3 out of 4 is equivalent to 6 out of 8, because $\frac{3}{4} \cdot \frac{2}{2} = \frac{6}{8}$.

8. Fill in the blanks in each of the following proportions.

a. 3 out of 4 is equivalent to _____ out of 12

b. 3 out of 4 is equivalent to _____ out of 32

c. 3 out of 4 is equivalent to _____ out of 100

d. Write the resulting proportion from part c using a fraction format.

9. a. Which of the following ratios are equivalent?

    i. 28 out of 40   **ii.** 175 out of 250   **iii.** 75 out of 100

b. Explain the method you used to answer part a.

c. Write each of the equivalent ratios from part a in fraction form.

d. Determine the "reduced" form of the equivalent fractions from part c. What do you observe?

10. a. Explain why the following ratios are equivalent.

    i. 27 out of 75   **ii.** 63 out of 175   **iii.** 36 out of 100

b. Write each ratio in fraction form.

c. Determine the "reduced" form of the equivalent fractions from part b.

d. With which of the equivalent ratios in part a do you feel most comfortable? Explain.

The number 100 is a very familiar quantity of comparison: There are 100 cents in a dollar and frequently 100 points on a test. Therefore, people feel most comfortable with a ratio such as 70 out of 100 or 36 out of 100.

> The phrase "out of 100" is commonly referred to by its Latin equivalent, *percent*. Per means "division" and cent means "100," so **percent** means "divide by 100."

Therefore, 70 out of 100 can be rephrased as 70 percent and written in the familiar notation 70%, which equals $70 \div 100 = \frac{70}{100} = 0.70$. Similarly, 36 out of 100 can be rephrased as 36 percent and written in the familiar notation $36\% = 36 \div 100 = \frac{36}{100} = 0.36$.

11. Complete the following table using Michael Jordan's field goal data from the beginning of the activity.

JORDAN'S RELATIVE FIELD GOAL PERFORMANCE

	VERBAL	FRACTION	DECIMAL	PERCENT
GAME 1	9 out of 18	$\frac{9}{18}$	0.50	50%
GAME 2				
GAME 3				
GAME 4				
GAME 5				
GAME 6				

SUMMARY

When comparisons using quotients are made between different quantities of the same kind, the comparison is called a **ratio.**

Ratios can be expressed verbally (4 out of 5), as a fraction $\left(\frac{4}{5}\right)$, as a division $(5\overline{)4})$, as a decimal (0.80), or as a percent (80%).

Two ratios are said to be *equivalent* if the ratios have equal numerical values. The mathematical statement that two ratios are equivalent is called a **proportion.**

Finding equivalent ratios is often accomplished by finding equivalent fractions.

EXERCISES

1. Complete the following table by representing each comparison in all four formats.

VERBAL	REDUCED FRACTION	DECIMAL	PERCENT
	$\frac{1}{3}$		
	$\frac{4}{5}$		
	$\frac{16}{25}$		
5 out of 8			
250 out of 600			
144 out of 48			
		0.75	
		0.375	
		0.6	
			40%
			0.25%
			500%

Exercise numbers appearing in color are answered in the Selected Answers section of this book.

2. There are 1240 females out of 2200 freshmen at the local community college. Compare the number of females to the total number of freshmen in the following formats.

    a. As a fraction **b.** As a decimal **c.** As a percent

3. At the state university near the community college in Exercise 2, the freshman class consists of 1480 males and 1620 females. In which freshman class, the community college or the university, is the relative number of females larger? Explain your reasoning.

4. At competitive colleges, the admissions office often compares the number of students accepted to the total number of applications received. This comparison is known as the *selectivity index*. The admissions office also compares the number of students who actually attend to the number of students who have been accepted for admission. This comparison is known as the *yield*. Complete the following table to determine the selectivity index and yield (in percent format) for colleges A, B, and C.

	NUMBER OF APPLICANTS	NUMBER ACCEPTED	NUMBER ATTENDING	SELECTIVITY INDEX	YIELD (AS A %)
COLLEGE A	5500	3500	1000		
COLLEGE B	8500	4800	2100		
COLLEGE C	4200	3200	900		

   Which college do you think is the most competitive? The least competitive? Explain.

5. Here are your scores on three graded assignments. On which assignment did you perform best?

    a. 25 out of 30 **b.** 30 out of 40 **c.** 18 out of 25

6. In a typical year, 3884 million kilograms of the plastic PVC is produced in the United States and 9 million kilograms is recycled. What percent of the PVC manufactured in this country is recycled?

7. Baseball batting averages are the ratio of hits to at bats. They are reported as three-digit decimals. Compare the batting average of three players with the given records.

   a. 24 hits out of 70 at bats   **b.** 35 hits out of 124 at bats

   c. 87 hits out of 273 at bats

8. In their championship 1999 season, the New York Yankees won 98 and lost 64 of their regular season games. What percent of the games played did they win?

9. The win-loss records of three pitchers are given below. Use the data to rank the three pitchers by their relative performances. Explain how you determined your answer. Compare your results and methods with those of your learning partners. Did you arrive at the same conclusion? Why or why not?

	WINS	LOSSES
BOB	14	14
DAN	26	11
TOM	17	7

Social Issues

Topics: *Fractions, Percent, Ratio and Proportion, Contingency Tables, Relative Frequency, Probability*

In an effort to increase the education level of their police officers, many municipalities are requiring new recruits to have at least a two-year college degree. A recent survey indicated that 1 out of 5 New York City (NYPD) police officers holds a four-year college degree.

1. There are approximately 41,000 NYPD officers. Based on the ratio above, estimate (i.e., without making an actual calculation) how many NYPD officers hold a four-year college degree. Explain how you made the estimation.

2. To calculate the number of four-year college degree holders more precisely, you can start with the proportion statement

$$1 \text{ out of } 5 \ = \ \underline{\ \ ?\ \ } \ \text{ out of } 41{,}000$$

   a. Rewrite this proportion in fraction form.

   b. Solve the proportion using equivalent fractions. (Recall your work in Activity 1.11.)

There are several ways to solve proportion equations.

For example, consider the proportion

$$2 \text{ out of } 5 = \underline{\ \ \ \ \ } \text{ out of } 6000$$

As in Problem 2, the proportion can be written in fraction form, this time as

$$\frac{2}{5} = \frac{n}{6000},$$

where n is the unknown quantity of the proportion. You can determine the value of the unknown numerator n by writing $\frac{2}{5}$ as an equivalent fraction with denominator 6000:

$$6000 \div 5 = 1200,$$

so,

$$\frac{2}{5} \cdot \frac{1200}{1200} = \frac{2400}{6000}.$$

Therefore, the unknown value is 2400.

Another method of solving proportions uses the fact that the two mathematical statements

$$\frac{a}{b} = \frac{c}{d} \quad \text{and} \quad a \cdot d = b \cdot c$$

are equivalent.

The act of transforming the statement on the left (containing two fractions) into the statement on the right is customarily called **cross-multiplication** because the numerator of the first fraction is multiplied by the denominator of the second and the numerator of the second fraction is multiplied by the denominator of the first.

3. Use cross-multiplication to determine which pair(s) of fractions are equal.

    a. $\frac{11}{15}$ and $\frac{5}{8}$ **b.** $\frac{5}{9}$ and $\frac{65}{117}$ **c.** $\frac{3}{10}$ and $\frac{14}{45}$

You can use cross-multiplication to solve proportions. The proportion $\frac{2}{5} = \frac{n}{6000}$ is equivalent to $2 \cdot 6000 = 5 \cdot n$. You can then view the resulting equation, $12{,}000 = 5n$, as a scale whose arms are in balance. The equal sign can be thought of as the balance point.

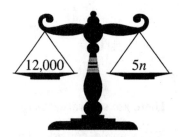

If you divide both sides of the equation by 5, the balance is maintained. Then the unknown number is isolated on one side of the equal sign and its value appears on the other side. The entire process can be written as follows:

Original proportion:	$\dfrac{2}{5} = \dfrac{n}{6000}$
Cross-multiply:	$2 \cdot 6000 = 5 \cdot n$
Divide both sides by 5:	$\dfrac{2 \cdot 6000}{5} = \dfrac{\cancel{5} \cdot n}{\cancel{5}}$
Simplify:	$2400 = n$

4. Use the cross-multiplication method to verify your result in Problem 2b.

In the original statement 2 out of 5 = _____ out of 6000, you are given a known ratio, $\frac{2}{5}$, and asked to determine what "part" of the total, 6000, will represent the same relative ratio, $\frac{2}{5}$. This "part" can be expressed mathematically as $\frac{2}{5}$ of 6000, and is calculated as

$$\frac{2}{5} \ times\ 6000 = \frac{2}{5} \cdot 6000 = 2400.$$

5. Redo Problem 2b using the multiplication approach just described. Compare your results from all three methods. Which method do you prefer for Problem 2? Why?

6. Solve the following proportions.

   a. 2 out of 3 = _____ out of 36

   b. $\dfrac{2}{3} = \dfrac{n}{45}$

New York State has taken a leading position in raising the standards of its high school graduates. By the year 2003, every graduate will need to have passed a series of rigorous subject-matter tests called regents exams. Currently, in your cousin's county, only 6 out of 10 graduates receive regents diplomas.

7. If 5400 students in your cousin's county earned a regents diploma last year, estimate (without actually doing a calculation) the total number of high school graduates in that county last year.

This situation differs from the NYPD situation at the beginning of the activity because the total number is not known. The 5400 represents that part of the total number of high school graduates who earned a regents diploma. Written as a proportion,

6 out of 10 = 5400 out of _____

8. a. Rewrite this proportion in fraction form.

   b. To determine the total number of students, use cross-multiplication to calculate the unknown denominator in part a.

9. Solve these proportions.

a. 2 out of 3 = 80 out of _____.

b. $\frac{2}{3} = \frac{216}{n}$

c. Tuition at a local community college is $1250 per term for a full-time student. This is 53% of the estimated cost of attending classes (tuition, books, transportation, lunch) published in the college catalog. What would be the total estimated cost for attending classes at the college?

Data are collected every day by agencies large and small. The Internal Revenue Service and the Congressional Budget Office collect data, as do college registrars. Data are usually organized into tables to help answer questions and make decisions. When conjectures are made based on data, it is assumed that the sample is representative of the entire population.

The following table of data was generated as a result of a survey you were asked to conduct in your new job at the county social services agency.

	MALE	FEMALE
SMOKER	154	139
NONSMOKER	238	201

10. a. How many males are represented in this table?

b. How many females?

c. How many smokers?

d. How many nonsmokers?

e. How many female nonsmokers?

f. How many male smokers?

g. How many people were surveyed?

11. The table provides *actual* numbers for your answers in Problem 10. In many applications, *relative* numbers provide more information. Find the following *relative* numbers, expressed as a percent. Round your answer to the nearest percent.

a. What percent of the people surveyed are smokers?

b. What percent of the people surveyed are female?

c. What percent of the people surveyed are male smokers?

d. What percent of the males surveyed are smokers?

e. Explain why you should get different relative numbers in parts c and d.

The percents you determined in Problem 11 are sometimes referred to as **relative frequencies** (for example, the frequency of women relative to all people in the survey). A relative frequency is often used to estimate the probability (chance) of something occurring. For example, the probability that a randomly chosen person in your county is a nonsmoking female is expressed as the ratio $\frac{201}{732}$, which may also be represented as 0.27 when rounded to the nearest hundredth or as 27% when rounded to the nearest whole percent.

12. Estimate the following probabilities by finding the relative frequency. Express as a decimal rounded to the nearest hundredth and then as a percent.

a. Determine the probability that a randomly chosen person in your county is a smoker.

b. Determine the probability that a randomly chosen person in your county is a male.

    c. Determine the probability that a randomly chosen male in your county is a smoker.

    d. Determine the probability that a randomly chosen female in your county is a smoker.

    e. Who apparently smokes more in your county, men or women? Use the data from the survey to support your conclusion.

13. Assume that your survey responses are representative of the 125,300 adult residents of your county. Use proportional reasoning to approximate (to the nearest hundred) the number of people in your county who are

    a. Female

    b. Smokers

    c. Female smokers

SUMMARY

1. A proportion expressed in fraction form, $\frac{a}{b} = \frac{c}{d}$, is equivalent to the statement $ad = bc$.

2. Problems that involve **proportional reasoning** usually include a known ratio $\frac{a}{b}$ and a given piece of information, either a "part" or a "total" value, resulting in the proportion:

$$\frac{a}{b} = \frac{part}{total}$$

The missing value can be determined by constructing equivalent fractions or by cross-multiplying and solving the resulting equation.

EXERCISES

1. Determine the value of each of the following.

   a. $\frac{3}{2} \cdot 32$

   b. $\frac{5}{4}$ of 200

   c. $45\% \cdot 40$

   d. 15% of 24

   e. $\frac{3}{8}$ of 40

   f. $\frac{5}{8} \cdot 56$

   g. 7.5% of 80

   h. $0.3\% \cdot 60{,}000$

2. Solve the following proportions.

   a. 3 out of 5 = _____ out of 20

   b. $\frac{3}{5} = \frac{n}{765}$

   c. 3 out of 5 = 27 out of _____

   d. 3 out of 5 = 1134 out of _____

In Exercises 3–19, write a proportion that represents the situation and then determine the unknown value in the proportion.

3. You correctly answered two-thirds of the questions on your psychology exam. There were 75 questions on the exam. How many questions did you answer correctly?

Exercise numbers appearing in color are answered in the Selected Answers section of this book.

4. At the end of the semester, the bookstore will buy back books that will be used again in the courses the next semester. The bookstore will usually pay 15% of the original cost of the book. If you spend $246 on books this semester and the bookstore will buy back all your books, how much money can you expect to receive? (Recall that 15% can be thought of as the ratio $\frac{15}{100}$.)

5. During a recent downsizing, 20% of a company's workforce received pink slips. If this represents 500 job losses, how many people had been employed by this company?

6. On a recent mathematics exam, 80% of the class received a grade above 70. If 28 students performed at this C level and above, how many students are in the class?

7. The 8% sales tax on your cousin's new car is $1250. What is the actual price of the car?

8. During a recent infestation by beetles, $\frac{2}{3}$ of the ash trees in a local park were destroyed. If this represents 120 trees, how many ash trees were originally in the park?

9. In the 1996 merger of the Boeing and McDonnell Douglas corporations, McDonnell Douglas shareholders received a $\frac{2}{3}$ share of Boeing stock for each share of McDonnell Douglas stock they owned. If you owned 240 shares of McDonnell Douglas stock, how many shares of Boeing did you receive?

10. If 35% of the 2200 employees brown-bag their lunch at their desk, how many employees does this represent?

11. The sales tax rate on taxable items in Nassau County, New York, is 8.5%. Determine the tax on a new $25,000 car.

12. The expected tip on waiter service in a restaurant is now approximately 20% of the food and beverage cost. What is the customary tip on a dinner for two costing $45?

13. You invest $2500 in an account paying an annual interest of 5%. How much interest will you earn at the end of one year?

14. Your freshman class consists of 760 students. In recent years, only 4 out of 7 students actually graduated in four years. Approximately how many of your classmates are expected to graduate in four years?

15. In a very disappointing season, your softball team won only 30% of its games. If this represents 6 games, how many games were played?

16. You were given a job stuffing envelopes. After completing a box of 440 envelopes, you are told that you are only $\frac{2}{5}$ done. How many envelopes (total) are you expected to stuff?

17. A local businessman contributes $63,000 to a candidate's political campaign. This will cover 15% of the candidate's expenses. What are the total expenses in running this campaign?

18. In a recent classroom survey, the following table of data was generated. Students were categorized by their major—general studies or other (all other majors).

	MALES	FEMALES	TOTAL
GENERAL STUDIES	10	8	
OTHER	14	18	
TOTAL			

a. What percent of the people surveyed were general studies majors?

b. What percent of the males surveyed were in the category of Other?

c. What percent of the people surveyed were female?

Suppose your survey is representative of the whole college. There are 3230 students at this campus.

d. Approximate the number of people at the college who are general studies majors.

e. Approximate the number of males at the college.

f. What is the relative frequency of male general studies majors?

g. Based on the table, what is the probability of selecting at random, from the entire student body, a female general studies major?

h. What is the probability of selecting a male?

ACTIVITY 1.13

Did You Buy Enough Paint?

Topics: *Rates, Proportions, Unit Analysis*

Did you know that 1 gallon of paint covers approximately 400 square feet of wall? You plan to paint all the walls and ceilings in your new home. The total surface area that needs to be painted is 6000 square feet.

1. a. Assuming that you apply just one coat of paint, will 10 gallons be enough? 20 gallons?

    b. Estimate (without actually calculating) the number of gallons of paint you will need to purchase.

To answer Problem 1 more precisely, you need to apply the same proportional reasoning you used in Activity 1.12. In this case, however, "number of gallons of paint" to "number of square feet of surface to be painted" is properly called a **rate**, since the units of measurement are different. In fact, such a rate is usually expressed as number of gallons of paint *per* square foot of surface, where *per* signifies division.

2. Determine the amount of paint you need by solving the following proportion:

$$\frac{1 \text{ gal}}{400 \text{ sq ft}} = \frac{n \text{ gal}}{6000 \text{ sq ft}}$$

Notice that when setting up a proportion involving rates, the two numerators must have the same units of measurement (in this case, number of gallons). Likewise, the denominators must also have the same units of measurement (in this case, the number of square feet).

3. Any rate can also be expressed in its reciprocal form, in this case $\frac{400 \text{ sq ft}}{1 \text{ gal}}$. Given your total surface area of 6000 square feet, set up and solve the proportion with this reciprocal rate. Compare your answer to the number of gallons of paint calculated in Problem 2.

4. Now suppose that you are given 5 gallons of a superior paint, which covers better because it is much thicker. However, 1 gallon only covers 250 square feet of wall surface.

   a. How much wall space will your 5 gallons cover?

   b. Solve a proportion to determine how much of this superior paint you need to cover your 6000 square feet of wall surface.

To solve the proportion in the original paint problem, you may have used cross-multiplication.

$$\frac{1 \text{ gal}}{400 \text{ sq ft}} = \frac{n \text{ gal}}{6000 \text{ sq ft}}$$

Cross multiply: $1 \text{ gal} \cdot 6000 \text{ sq ft} = n \text{ gal} \cdot 400 \text{ sq ft}$

Divide both sides by 400 sq ft: $\dfrac{6000 \,(\cancel{\text{sq ft}}) \,(\text{gal})}{400 \,(\cancel{\text{sq ft}})} = \dfrac{n \cdot 400 \,(\cancel{\text{sq ft}})(\text{gal})}{400 \,(\cancel{\text{sq ft}})}$

Simplify: $15 \text{ gal} = n \text{ gal}$

Notice that you can treat the units of measurement as factors in the fractions, dividing out the common units where possible and leaving the desired units of measurement. This technique is the key to **unit analysis** (sometimes called *dimensional analysis*). Pay close attention to the units of measurement in a problem and apply the strategy of unit analysis to more effectively find correct solutions.

Unit analysis provides a convenient shortcut to the paint problem. To determine the number of gallons of paint corresponding to 6000 square feet of wall space, you need only to multiply 6000 square feet by the appropriate fractional form of the rate:

$$6000 \text{ sq ft} \cdot \frac{1 \text{ gal}}{400 \text{ sq ft}} = \frac{6000 \,(\cancel{\text{sq ft}})(\text{gal})}{400 \,(\cancel{\text{sq ft}})} = 15 \text{ gal}$$

Notice here that the rate $\frac{1 \text{ gal}}{400 \text{ sq ft}}$ was chosen rather than $\frac{400 \text{ sq ft}}{1 \text{ gal}}$ because the unit of measurement square feet divides out, leaving the correct unit of measurement, namely gallons.

5. Your car averages 24 miles to the gallon. The 180-mile route you are planning to take across the mountain has no gas stations along the way. How many gallons should be in your gas tank to allow you to make it safely across? (In each part, show how the units of measurement divide out.)

   a. Solve by setting up a proportion, using the rate 24 miles per 1 gallon.

   b. Solve by setting up a proportion, using the rate 1 gallon per 24 miles.

   c. Solve by multiplying 180 miles by the appropriate rate.

   d. Which method from parts a–c do you prefer? Why?

6. You are still driving your trusty 24-mile-per-gallon car, planning for a 320-mile trip. Gasoline currently costs $1.12 per gallon. How much will you expect to pay on your trip for gas? *Hint:* You will need to multiply the 320 miles by two appropriate rates. Write down your calculation, and show how the units of measurement divide out.

7. As a nurse in the county hospital, you have received an order to administer 50 milligrams of a drug. The drug is available at a strength of 15 milligrams per milliliter. How many milliliters would you administer?

8. A Ford Taurus averages 380 miles on a 14-gallon tank of gas. You run out of gas on a deserted highway, but have $\frac{1}{2}$ gallon of lawn mower gas with you. Will you be able to reach the nearest gas station 15 miles away?

SUMMARY

- A **ratio** is a comparison between two quantities with the same unit of measurement (or perhaps no units).
- A **rate** is a comparison between two quantities with different units of measurement.
- **Unit analysis** is a strategy for performing calculations by treating units of measurement as factors in fractions. Common units in the fractions are divided out (cancelled) to leave desired units for the result.

EXERCISES

In the following exercises, first estimate the answer by taking an educated guess. Then solve precisely, recording your calculations with the units of measurement. Check your answer against your original estimate, making sure your final answer is reasonable.

1. As part of your job as a quality-control worker in a factory you can check 16 parts in 3 minutes. How long will it take you to check 80 parts?

$$\frac{16}{3} \qquad \frac{x}{80}$$

2. Your car averages about 27 miles per gallon on highways. With gasoline priced at $1.25 per gallon, how much will you expect to spend on gasoline during your 500-mile trip?

3. You currently earn $11.50 per hour. Assuming that you work 40-hour weeks with no raises, what total gross salary will you earn in the next five years?

4. You have an order to administer 0.2 milligram per kilogram of a drug to a patient who weighs 28 kilograms. How many milligrams would you administer?

5. You are traveling at 75 miles per hour on a straight stretch of highway in Nevada. It is noon now. When will you arrive at the next town 120 miles away?

ACTIVITY 1.14

Uncle Sam's Place
Topics: *Unit Analysis, Metric System, U.S. System, Unit Conversion*

According to the USDA Natural Resources Conservation Service, federally owned land totaled 408 million acres in 1992. This was 21% of the total area of the United States.

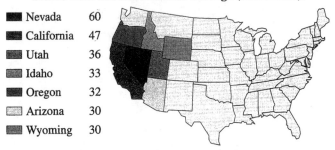

FEDERALLY PROTECTED LAND

States with the most federal acreage (in millions):

Nevada	60
California	47
Utah	36
Idaho	33
Oregon	32
Arizona	30
Wyoming	30

1. What percent of the total federally owned acreage is contained in the top seven states? (Round your answer to the nearest tenth of a percent.)

2. Nevada alone contains what percent of the total federally owned acreage? (Round your answer to the nearest tenth of a percent.)

The total area of the state of Nevada is 110,567 square miles. You will use this fact plus the information in the chart above to determine what percent of the total area of the state of Nevada is federally owned.

Note that to correctly compare the area of federally owned land to the total area of Nevada, both measurements must be expressed in the same units, either acres or square miles. You can use unit analysis to convert either measurement.

The conversion fact that you need is 1 square mile = 640 acres. As a rate, this fact can be expressed in two ways:

$$\frac{1 \text{ sq mi}}{640 \text{ acres}} \quad \text{or} \quad \frac{640 \text{ acres}}{1 \text{ sq mi}}$$

To convert a measurement from square miles to acres, multiply by the appropriate conversion factor. For example, to convert 20 square miles to acres, multiply by the conversion factor that will result in square miles dividing out, leaving acres in the numerator:

$$20 \text{ sq mi} \cdot \frac{640 \text{ acres}}{1 \text{ sq mi}} = 12,800 \text{ acres}$$

3. The total area of the state of Nevada is 110,567 square miles. What percent of the total acreage of the state of Nevada is federally owned?

   a. Use unit analysis to express both measurements in acres, and then calculate the requested percent.

   b. Use unit analysis to express both measurements in square miles, and then calculate the requested percent.

Refer to the U.S. system of measurement inside the front cover to determine the conversion facts needed for Problems 4–7. Write down your calculations, and show how the units of measurement divide out.

4. A 52-foot-long string is more than 600 inches long. What conversion fact is used to convert feet to inches? Determine the exact length of the string in inches.

5. How many feet are there in 3.2 miles?

6. How many ounces are there in 5 tons? (You will need to multiply by two conversion factors.)

7. Find the number of gallons in 360 fluid ounces.

Refer to the metric system of measurement inside the front cover to determine the conversion facts needed for Problems 8–11. Write down your calculations and show how the units of measurement divide out.

8. Convert 5.6 kilometers to meters.

9. Convert 5,250,000 milligrams to kilograms.

10. How many milliliters are there in 7.35 liters?

11. Describe the difference between the metric conversions and the U.S. conversions. In which system do you find the conversions easier to perform?

Unit analysis is used extensively to convert between U.S. system measurements and metric measurements. Refer to the conversion facts inside the front cover to solve the following problems.

12. Your car weighs 2504 pounds. What is its mass in kilograms?

13. You need to mail a box to Venezuela, but to be processed at the Venezuelan post office, the box must have no single dimension longer than 120 centimeters, and the sum of the three dimensions must not exceed 200 centimeters. All you can find is a tape measure in inches, and your box is 24 by 18 by 40 inches. Will your package be accepted by the post office in Venezuela?

Unit analysis is especially useful when the required conversion does not have a direct equivalent in a table. For example, suppose you want to convert 500 fluid ounces of soda into liters (abbreviated as ℓ). The table on the inside cover does not directly give conversion facts for fluid ounces and liters. However, you can relate fluid ounces to cups, cups to pints, pints to quarts and quarts to liters. Thus, the problem requires four conversion factors. They can be used all at once as follows:

$$500 \text{ fl-oz} \cdot \frac{1 \text{ cup}}{8 \text{ fl-oz}} \cdot \frac{1 \text{ pt}}{2 \text{ cups}} \cdot \frac{1 \text{ qt}}{2 \text{ pt}} \cdot \frac{1 \ell}{1.06 \text{ qt}} = \frac{500}{8 \cdot 2 \cdot 2 \cdot 1.06} \ell = 14.74 \ell$$

Note how all of the units "divided out" leaving you with the desired unit of liters. Each successive unit fraction was chosen to eliminate the units remaining from the previous fraction.

14. How many grams are there in 1 ton?

15. You are traveling in Canada at 70 miles per hour. The speed limit is given metrically as 100 kilometers per hour. Are you exceeding the speed limit?

16. How many millimeters are there in a length of 0.0045 inch?

17. If you are traveling at 90 feet per second, will you be exceeding the 100 km/hr Canadian speed limit?

18. Assume that the distance across a flat United States is approximately 3000 miles. How many pennies laid edge to edge would it take to span the country? What measurement of a penny must you use here?

EXERCISES

In Exercises 1–4, refer to the graphic of federally owned land on page 79.

1. How many acres of land are there in the United States? (State your answer using scientific notation.)

2. There are 43,560 square feet in 1 acre. Determine the number of square feet of land in the United States. (State your answer using scientific notation.)

3. Assume that there are about 250 million people in the United States. If everyone spread out uniformly across the country and claimed his or her own personal space, how many square feet would each person have?

4. Under the assumptions given in Exercise 3, how many people would there be in each square mile?

5. The distance between Earth and the Sun is 92,960,000 miles. Convert this distance to kilometers.

6. The height of the Empire State Building is 1414 feet. The height of the Eiffel Tower in Paris is 300.12 meters. Which is taller?

7. Compare the height of the Empire State Building to the height of the Oriental Pearl Television Tower in China, which is 468.18 meters tall.

8. a. How tall are you (in feet)?

b. Convert your height to inches.

c. What is your height in centimeters?

9. You buy a 2-liter bottle of diet cola.

   a. How many quarts do you have?

   b. Convert the quarts to pints.

   c. Do you have enough to give 8-ounce cups to each of your six companions? Explain.

10. The equatorial diameter of Earth is 12,756 kilometers. Convert this length to miles.

ACTIVITY 1.15

Grade Point Averages: Who Improved More?

Topics: *Actual Change, Relative Change, Growth Factor, Decay Factor*

You and your friend are discussing your grade point averages (GPAs) over the past two semesters. The GPAs are summarized in the following table.

	YOUR GPA	YOUR FRIEND'S GPA
FALL	2.10	3.00
SPRING	2.55	3.50

1. Determine your actual change in GPA from the fall to the spring.

2. Determine your friend's actual change in GPA.

You see that your friend has improved more than you have and you congratulate her. She thanks you for the compliment, but says that based on the fall semester, you in fact improved more than she did. Who is right?

It is possible that you are both correct. You and your friend are discussing two different types of change: actual change and relative change. **Actual change** is the actual numerical difference by which a quantity has changed. When a quantity *increases* in value, the actual change is *positive*. When the quantity *decreases,* the actual change is *negative*. For example, if a quantity has decreased by 10, you can describe this as an actual change of -10: the magnitude, 10 (absolute value), states the size of the change, and the negative sign denotes the direction of the change.

The word *relative* used in this situation indicates that two quantities are being compared in terms of the ratio of their values. Recall that a ratio is commonly written in fraction or percent format.

> The ratio formed when calculating **relative change** always compares the actual change (numerator) to the original (or earlier) amount (denominator).

Your GPA during the fall semester, 2.10, is your original amount. Your actual change is 0.45. Therefore, your relative change is

$$\frac{0.45}{2.10} \approx 0.214 = 21.4\%$$

3. Determine the relative change in your friend's GPA. Was she justified in her claim that you have improved more than she has?

4. Determine the actual change in each of the following.

   a. The price of a share of stock was $24 last week and is now $30.

b. The number of violent crimes reported in your precinct was 40 in 1997 and 35 in 1998.

c. Miscellaneous household expenses last month were $250. This month they were $150.

5. Determine the relative change in the quantities from Problem 4. Express this ratio in both fraction and percent format.

   a.   **b.**

   c.

6. Suppose that the market value of your house has increased $10,000 since you purchased it. How significant is this actual change?

   a. What is the relative change (expressed as a percent) if the original purchase price was $50,000?

   b. What is the relative change (expressed as a percent) if your purchase price was $500,000?

7. Suppose that inflation is running at a fixed rate of 8% per year.

   a. By how much will the cost of a $22,000 car increase in the next year?

   b. What will the $22,000 car cost next year?

In Problem 7, you determined the new cost of the car by first computing the actual increase (8% of $22,000) and then adding this increase to the original cost of the car. It is often useful to compute the new value directly, bypassing the intermediate step of calculating the actual increase.

8. a. If a quantity increases by 50%, how does its new value compare to its original value? That is, what is the ratio of new value to original value? Complete the following table to discover/confirm your answer.

ORIGINAL VALUE	NEW VALUE (INCREASED BY 50%)	RATIO OF NEW VALUE TO ORIGINAL VALUE		
		FRACTION FORMAT	PERCENT FORMAT	DECIMAL FORMAT
20	30	$\frac{30}{20} = \frac{3}{2} = 1\frac{1}{2}$	150%	1.50
50				
100				

b. What is the ratio of new value to original value of any quantity that increases by 50%? Express this ratio in reduced fraction and decimal formats.

The ratio of a new value to an original value, which depends on a specified percent increase, is called the **growth factor.** A growth factor is obtained by adding the percent increase to 100%. For example, in Problem 8, the quantities increase by 50%, so the growth factor is 100% (the original amount) plus 50% (the increase) or 150% = 1.50.

Multiplying an original value by a growth factor results in the new value. For example, in Problem 8, if an original value, 20, increases by 50%, then the new value is $20 \cdot 1.50 = 30$.

9. a. What is the growth factor of any quantity that increases by 25%? Use this growth factor to determine the new value when an original value, 60, increases by 25%.

b. What is the growth factor of any quantity that increases by 8%? Use this growth factor to answer the question in Problem 7b.

10. It is often useful to determine the percent increase represented by a given growth factor. That is, if the growth factor is 1.40, then what percent increase of the original quantity does this represent?

11. Complete the following table.

PERCENT INCREASE	5%		7.3%	
GROWTH FACTOR		1.45		1.027

When a quantity increases in value by a fixed percent, say 10%, multiply its original value by the growth factor 1.10 to obtain its new value.

$$\text{Growth Factor} \cdot \text{Original Value} = \text{New Value}$$

Example: Acme Corporation is planning to expand its current workforce of 1500 by 20%. What is the anticipated size of its new workforce?

$$1.20\,(1500) = 1800 \text{ employees}$$

If a quantity has already increased by a fixed percent, say 10%, divide its new (larger) value by the growth factor (1.10) to obtain the original value.

$$\frac{\text{New Value}}{\text{Growth Factor}} = \text{Original Value}$$

Example: Acme's chief competitor, Arco, has already increased its workforce by 25% and currently employs 2400 workers. What was the previous size of its workforce?

$$\frac{2400}{1.25} = 1920 \text{ employees}$$

An alternate method to solve the above problems is to set up and solve a percent proportion. The growth factor represents the ratio of the new value to the original value. Thus, if the growth factor is $1.10 = 110\% = \frac{110}{100}$, then the percent proportion is

$$\frac{110}{100} = \frac{\text{New Value}}{\text{Original Value}}.$$

12. Since last year, housing prices have appreciated (increased) by 25% in your neighborhood. A house just sold for $300,000.

   a. What is the growth factor associated with a 25% increase?

   b. Is $300,000 the new value or the original value?

   c. What was last year's market value?

13. The past year has seen tremendous growth in the stock market. Your stock's price has increased 35% since you bought it last January, and the value of your investment is now $6000. How much did you invest in this stock last January?

In this next section, you will examine the process of calculating percent decrease.

14. A suit, originally priced at $400, is on sale for 30% off.

   a. Determine the amount of discount on the suit. This represents the actual decrease in the cost of the suit.

   b. What is the new ticketed price of the suit?

In Problem 14, you first determined the actual decrease (30% of 400) in the cost of the suit and then subtracted this decrease from the original value. As you did in the growth factor calculations done earlier, you can bypass the intermediate step of calculating the actual decrease by multiplying the original value by the **decay factor.**

15. a. Complete the following table to determine the decay factor of a quantity that *decreases* by 20%.

| ORIGINAL VALUE | NEW VALUE | RATIO OF NEW VALUE TO ORIGINAL VALUE: DECAY FACTOR | | |
		FRACTION FORMAT	PERCENT FORMAT	DECIMAL FORMAT
20	16	$\frac{16}{20} = \frac{4}{5}$	80%	0.80
50				
100				

   b. What is the decay factor of any quantity that decreases by 75%? Express this ratio in reduced fraction and decimal formats.

   c. If the percent decrease is 5%, what is the decay factor?

It is important to note that although a percent decrease usually describes a portion that has been removed, the corresponding decay factor represents the percent remaining. Therefore, a 20% decrease is represented by a decay factor of 80%, or 0.80.

Multiplying the original value by a decay factor always produces the value that remains, not the amount that has been removed.

When a quantity decreases in value by a fixed percent, say 10%, multiply its original value by the decay factor 0.90 to obtain its new (smaller) value.

Decay Factor · Original Value = New Value

If a quantity has already decreased by 10%, divide its new (smaller) value by 0.90 to obtain the original value.

$$\frac{\text{New Value}}{\text{Decay Factor}} = \text{Original Value}$$

Note that you can also solve problems involving a decay factor by setting up and solving a percent proportion. The decay factor represents the ratio of the new value to the original value. Thus, if the decay factor is $0.90 = 90\% = \frac{90}{100}$, then the percent proportion is

$$\frac{90}{100} = \frac{\text{New Value}}{\text{Original Value}}$$

16. Complete the following table.

PERCENT DECREASE	45%			6%	15%		3.2%	
NEW TO OLD RATIO: DECAY FACTOR		.55	.75			.34		.986

17. A suit, originally priced at $400, is on sale for 30% off.

   a. Determine the decay factor.

   b. Use this decay factor to calculate the new ticketed price of the suit. Compare your results with your answer to Problem 14b.

18. You have been able to trim this year's budget by 22% over last year's expenses. Last year's budget was $170,000. Determine the decay factor, and use this factor to calculate this year's budget.

19. After several years of downsizing, a company now employs 1500 people. This represents a decrease of 35% from the 1997 level. How many employees worked for the company back in 1997?

> ### SUMMARY
>
> **Actual change** is the actual numerical difference by which a quantity has changed. It may be positive or negative and has the same unit of measurement as the quantity itself.
>
> **Relative change** is the ratio that compares the actual change (numerator) to the original, or earlier, amount (denominator). This ratio has no unit of measure associated with it.
>
> If the ratio of a new value to an original value is greater than 1, it is called a **growth factor.**
>
> If the ratio of a new value to an original value is less than 1, it is called a **decay factor.**

EXERCISES

1. A house that cost $175,000 in 1990 was priced at $300,000 in 1999.

   a. Determine the actual increase in price.

   b. Calculate the percent increase in price.

2. Your school's enrollment was 8250 last year. This year the enrollment went down to 7650.

   a. Determine the actual change in enrollment.

   $$\begin{array}{r} 8250 \\ -7650 \\ \hline 600 \end{array}$$

   b. Find the percent decrease in enrollment.

   $$\frac{600}{8250} = 0.0727 = 7.3\%$$

3. In 1998, the average price of gasoline in your neighborhood was $1.12 per gallon. By the end of 1999, the average price rose to $1.26 per gallon. Determine the percent increase in the price of gasoline.

4. Your hourly wage at your part-time job is $6.30 per hour, up from last year's wage of $5.95 per hour. What percent raise did you receive?

5. The number of applications to the local state college have soared by 40% since 1995. At that time, there were 4500 applicants. How many applications are anticipated this year?

6. The size of this year's graduating class represents an increase of 25% over the 1995 graduating class. This year, 2200 students are receiving their diplomas. How many graduates were there in 1995?

7. The number of homicides in your city has dramatically decreased in the past five years, down by approximately 80%. If there were 42 homicides on record for the last calendar year, approximately how many homicides were committed five years ago?

8. At the end of the season, your favorite label jacket is finally on sale for 70% off the original list price of $120. What is its current ticketed price?

9. Last year's rental cost of a power saw was $16.20 per hour. This year, the rental fee was increased by 5%. How much will you pay this summer for a 4-hour rental?

10. You have been burning 420 calories during each session on the StairMaster. Your trainer claims that you will burn off 30% more calories on the treadmill. How many calories do you expect to burn off on the treadmill?

PROJECT ACTIVITY 1.16

Take an Additional 10% Off

Topics: *Fractions, Decimals, Percent, Ratio, Growth Factor, Decay Factor, Consecutive Percent Change*

Homer was walking home from work one day when he noticed a $5 bill on the sidewalk. There was no one nearby, so he picked it up and placed it in his pocket. His other pocket already contained a $10 bill. Homer grinned and thought to himself, "My wealth has just increased by 50%."

Unfortunately, Homer was unaware that the pocket that held the $5 bill had a large hole in it. When he arrived home, he sadly discovered that the $5 was missing. "That's not so bad," he explained to his disappointed wife. "Earlier our wealth increased by 50%, but now it has decreased by only $33\frac{1}{3}$%. We're still ahead by nearly 17%!"

1. a. Show how Homer calculated his increase of 50%. Was he correct?

   b. Explain how Homer calculated his decrease of $33\frac{1}{3}$%. Was he correct?

   c. Explain how Homer calculated his net gain of nearly 17%. Was he correct?

When a sequence of consecutive changes occurs in the value of a quantity, such as Homer's short-lived wealth, you often need to calculate the overall change.

> The total change is the *sum* of the individual actual changes that occur.

2. Suppose you track the price of a stock over two weeks. The starting price is $24, and the changes in price are an increase of $6 the first week and $6 the second week.

   a. Determine the actual change in stock price over these two weeks.

   b. Now, calculate the relative change in stock price over the *first* week. Express this relative change in both fraction and percent format.

   c. At the end of the first week, the price has risen to _____. Calculate the relative change in stock price over the *second* week. Express this relative change in both fraction and percent format.

d. Determine the relative change in stock price over the full two-week period. That is, compare the actual two-week change to the starting price. Express this relative change in both fraction and percent format.

e. Do the relative changes over each week sum to the relative change over the two-week period?

> The calculations you have just done demonstrate that the numerical values (in percent, decimal, or fraction format) of a sequence of relative changes do *not* sum.

The following example should be familiar to anyone who shops during storewide sales.

3. You have just clipped an "additional 10% off" coupon from the newspaper. Your favorite shirt is already on sale for 30% off the original price of $36.00. The store will apply these discounts consecutively.

a. Determine the decay factor corresponding to each discount.

b. Apply these decay factors one at a time to calculate the final sale price if the 30% discount is taken first, followed by the 10% discount.

c. Apply these decay factors one at a time to calculate the final sale price if the 10% discount is taken first, followed by the 30% discount.

d. In which order would you prefer these discounts to be taken? Explain.

e. Calculate the ratio of the final sale price to the original price and write it in decimal form. Compare it with the product of the two decay factors you determined in part a. What do you observe?

4. The average score on a fourth-grade reading test in your district was 65 in 1980. By 1990, the average score had fallen by 60%. After a decade of extensive curriculum changes, the superintendent proudly announced that the average 1999 score was up 70% since 1990.

   a. What is the growth or decay factor from 1980 to 1990? What was the 1990 average reading score?

   b. What is the growth or decay factor from 1990 to 1999? What is the 1999 average reading score?

   c. What was the relative (percent) change from 1980 to 1999?

   d. What percent of the 1980 score is the 1999 score?

   e. Compare your result from part d with the product of the two factors you found in parts a and b.

> The previous problems have demonstrated that the cumulative effect of a sequence of relative changes is the **product** of the associated growth or decay factors.

To give another example, if a value is increased by 50%, followed by an increase of 20%, then the cumulative effect is given by the product $1.50 \cdot 1.20 = 1.80$. Therefore, the net effect of consecutively applying the 50% and 20% increases is an increase of 80%. Notice that the order in which these increases are applied has no effect on the cumulative growth factor. Why?

5. Suppose an item's value is decreased by 50%, followed by a decrease of 20%. What is the cumulative percent decrease?

6. Suppose an item's value is decreased by 30%, followed by an increase of 30%.

   a. Does its value return to the original level? Explain by giving an example.

b. Suppose instead that the 30% increase were taken first, followed by the 30% decrease. Would the item's value return to the original level? Explain.

7. Homer's wealth increased by 50%, only to decrease by $33\frac{1}{3}\%$. What is the cumulative result of these changes? Show how you obtained the result mathematically. Does the result you obtain here agree with your initial reaction to Homer's plight?

8. Homer was eyeing a beautiful diamond pendant for his wife, but the $2000 list price was far too high for his modest budget. During the next several weeks, he rejoiced as he witnessed the following successive discounts on the pendant:

20% off list price

30% off marked price

an additional 50% off marked price of every item in the display case

At this point, he rushed into the store, expecting to purchase the pendant for 100% off!

a. How do you think Homer calculated the total discount?

b. For what price is the store actually selling the pendant?

c. How would the final price differ if the discounts had been taken in the reverse order (50% off, 30% off, and then 20% off)?

9. The accompanying graph is adapted from *USA Today* (January 5, 1996). Answer the following questions concerning the graph.

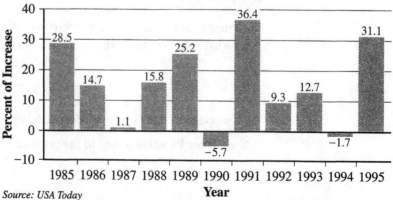

Mutual Funds Performance

Average Total Return for General Stock Funds

Source: USA Today

a. Describe what the graph represents.

b. Which year had the highest average percent return?

c. Which year had the lowest average percent return?

d. If Homer had invested money in 1990, does the graph imply that he would have lost money on his investment for that year? Explain.

e. Based on the past performance of the mutual funds, is it possible for Homer to make any predictions for 1996?

f. In 1994, Homer invested $1200 in mutual funds. Using the average return for that year, what is his net gain or loss on this investment for 1994?

g. Homer invested $1000 at the beginning of 1989. Assuming that he received the average return as indicated on the graph, what was the value of his investment by the end of 1990?

h. If Homer invested $3000 in January 1988 and left his earnings or losses in the same mutual fund until December 1991, what would be his expected average total percent return? Assume that he received the percents shown on the graph.

What Have I Learned?

1. On a 75-question practice exam, you were able to answer 61 questions correctly. On the exam itself you managed to answer 39 out of 45 correctly. Explain the distinction between your actual performance and relative performance on each of these exams.

2. Fifteen out of 25 students in your mathematics class commute to school by car.

   a. Express this ratio in reduced fraction form, as a decimal, and as a percent.

$$5 \quad \frac{15}{25} = \frac{3}{5} \qquad\qquad 0.6 \qquad\qquad 60\%$$

   b. Suppose this ratio accurately represents the commuting habits of the entire student body. Explain the strategy you would use to answer the following questions.

      i. Suppose there are 4500 students at your college. How many students commute by car?

      ii. Suppose there are 4500 students on campus who commute by car. What is the total enrollment at your college?

   c. Determine the answers to questions i and ii.

3. In converting from inches to centimeters, do you multiply or divide by 2.54? Use an example to illustrate how you can be sure of your answer.

4. a. Explain how to determine the growth factor associated with any percent increase.

b. Explain how to determine the decay factor associated with any percent decrease.

5. Which numbers represent possible growth factors and which represent possible decay factors? Explain. Determine the percent increase or decrease corresponding to each of these factors.

a. 1.35   **b.** 107%   **c.** 0.97

d. 86%   **e.** 2.00

6. You deposited $1000 in a special bank account for your child. The yearly rate of interest is 5.6% as long as you do not remove any money from the account for three years. How much is in your account at the end of the third year? Show how you obtained your answer.

How Can I Practice?

1. In a class of 27 students, 16 are female. What percent of students are female? (Round your answer to the nearest whole number.)

$$\frac{16}{27} \approx 59\%$$

2. If a student answered 67 questions correctly out of 80 questions on an exam, what percent of the questions did the student answer correctly? (Round your answer to the nearest whole number.)

$$\frac{67}{80} \approx 84\%$$

3. A total of 2365 students on your campus are commuters. The remaining 1325 live in the college dormitories. What percent of students are commuters?

$$\frac{2365}{2365 + 1325} \rightarrow \frac{2365}{3690} = 64\%$$

4. If the sales tax in your county is 7.5%, how much tax will you pay on books and supplies costing $185?

5. You are planning a weekend trip to New York City. You estimate that the round trip is 400 miles. Your car gets 24 miles per gallon and gas costs $1.26 per gallon. Compute your gas costs for the round trip.

6. The blueprint for your new home is on a scale of 0.25 in. : 1 ft. This means that every $\frac{1}{4}$ inch on the blueprint represents 1 foot of actual space. You have just purchased a $6\frac{1}{2}$ foot sofa that you will place against the long wall in your family room. On the blueprint, the wall measures $3\frac{1}{2}$ inches. How much space is left along the wall for end tables?

7. The taxes on a house assessed at $22,000 are $900. At the same tax rate, what are the taxes (to the nearest dollar) on a house assessed at $30,000?

8. In Suffolk County on Long Island, 6152 mosquitoes were trapped in July 1999, compared with 27,161 the previous July. If the number of trapped mosquitoes accurately represents the mosquito population in the county, determine the percent decrease in the mosquito population from 1998 to 1999.

9. Ample storage space is an important factor in the design and building of modern structures. It seems as if there are never enough closets to keep all those "essential" items we all love to store. Museums are not immune to these problems.

   Did you ever wander through a museum and wonder how much of the museum's collection you are viewing? According to *New York* magazine (July 10, 1995), many New York City museums display only a small percent of their total number of holdings.

MUSEUM	TOTAL NUMBER OF ITEMS IN THE COLLECTION	ITEMS ON DISPLAY
Whitney Museum	10,000	200
Museum of Modern Art	78,000	600
New York Historical Society Museum	150,000	2000
Guggenheim Museum	5000	75
Brooklyn Museum	1,500,000	6000
Jewish Museum	2700	1000
Frick Museum	1500	1425

a. For each museum, express the number of items on display as a percent of the total number of items in the collection.

b. Change these percents to decimals, and order them from smallest to largest.

c. Which museum displays the smallest percent? The largest?

d. If the collections from all seven museums are combined, express the number of items on display as a percent of the total number of items in the collection.

e. Is the percent in part d the same as the average of the percents in part a? Explain in complete sentences.

f. If you were writing a newspaper article about these museums, which of the two numbers discussed in part e best expresses the average percent of the number of items on display in the seven museums?

10. You have a friend in graduate school who is completing a master's thesis. You decide to help her out by offering to type her paper for a small fee.

   a. You make 8 mistakes in typing on the first 6 pages. If the thesis is 324 pages long, how many mistakes can you expect to make?

   b. If you can type 11 pages per hour, how long will it take you to finish the 324-page thesis?

    c. If you charge your friend 50 cents per page, what is the total your friend owes you?

    d. Your friend's thesis is due in three days. Is there enough time to finish the typing? Explain.

11. You decide to buy a new beach ball for the summer, but you cannot remember whether the diameter is 60 centimeters, or 60 kilometers. Which diameter is reasonable? Explain.

12. A friend from Canada is visiting for Thanksgiving. Your friend wants to know how much the 18-pound turkey you bought weighs in kilograms. You also want to tell her the amount in liters of the 3 quarts of eggnog you have made. Calculate these values.

13. Your patient is supposed to receive 500 milligrams of medication in an elixir at a strength of 875 milligrams per 5 milliliters of solution. How many milliliters would you administer?

14. A stamping machine punches out 10 parts per minute. How many parts are stamped out during a continuous 8-hour shift?

15. a. A sweater that sold for $32 before Christmas is selling for 30% off during an after-Christmas sale. What is the sale price of the sweater?

b. In January, the sweater is still available but has been reduced an additional 60%. What will it cost to buy the sweater in January? What is the total percent savings from the original cost of the sweater?

16. You used to drink 67.6 ounces (2 liters) of diet cola each day. Now you drink four 12-ounce cans a day. By what percent have you decreased your diet cola consumption?

17. **a.** You used to maintain your weight at 130 pounds. This year you put on some weight and tip the scale at 138 pounds. By what percent has your weight increased?

    b. If you lose 1% of what you weigh each week while following a diet and exercise program, how many weeks will it take you to reduce back to 130 pounds?

18. Your new diet requires you to decrease your daily caloric intake from 1800 to 1400 calories. By what percent do you need to decrease your caloric intake?

19. It is customary for the tax and tip at a restaurant to come to 25% of the actual food and beverage charge. What is the total cost, including tax and tip, of a meal whose food and beverage charge is $48.50?

20. A generous diner left 30% to cover the tax and tip on his meal. If his total expense came to $110, what was his food and beverage charge?

1. Subtract 187 from 406.

2. Multiply 68 by 79.

3. Write 16.0709 in words.

4. Write three thousand four hundred two and twenty-nine thousandths in standard form.

5. Round 567.0468 to the nearest hundredth.

6. Round 2.59945 to the nearest thousandth.

7. Add 48.2 + 36 + 2.97 + 0.743.

8. Subtract 0.48 from 29.3.

9. Multiply 2.003 by 0.36.

10. Divide 28.71 by 0.3.   *95.7*

11. Change 0.12 to a percent.   *12 %*

12. Change 3 to a percent.   *300%*

13. The sales tax rate in some states is 6.5%. Write this percent as a decimal.   *.065*

14. Write 360% in decimal form.   *3.6*

15. Write $\frac{2}{15}$ as a decimal.   *0.1\overline{3}*

16. Write $\frac{3}{7}$ as a percent. Round the percent to the nearest tenth.   *42.9*

17. The membership in the Nautilus Club increased by 12.5%. Write this percent as a fraction.

18. Write the following numbers in order from smallest to largest:
3.027   3.27   3.0027   3.0207

19. Find the average of 43, 25, 37, and 58.

20. In a recent survey, 14 of the 27 people questioned preferred Coke to Pepsi. What percent of the people preferred Coke?

21. If the sales tax is 7%, what is the cost, including tax, of a new baseball cap that is priced at $8.10?

22. If you spend $63 a week for food and you earn $800 per month, what percent of your monthly income is spent on food?

23. The enrollment at a local college has increased 5.5%. Last year's enrollment was 9500 students. How many students are expected this year?

24. You decide to decrease the number of calories in your diet from 2400 to 1500. Determine the percent decrease.

25. The area of the land masses of the world is about 57,000,000 square miles. If the area of 1 acre is about 0.00156 square mile, determine the number of acres of land in the world.

26. You and a friend have been waiting for the price on a winter coat to come down sufficiently from the manufacturer's suggested retail price (MSRP) of $500 so you each could afford to buy one. The retailer always discounts the MSRP by 10%. Between Thanksgiving and New Year's, the price was further reduced by 40%, and in January, it was again reduced by 50%.

    a. Your friend remarked that it looks like you can get the coat for free in January. Is that true? Explain.

    b. What does the coat cost before Thanksgiving, in December, and in January?

c. How would the final price differ if the discounts had been taken in the reverse order (50% off, 40% off, and 10% off)? How would the intermediate prices be affected?

27. A local education official proudly declares that although in the 1980s math scores fell by nearly 55%, they have since rebounded over 65%. This sounds like great news for your district, doesn't it? Determine how the current math scores actually compare with the pre-1980 scores.

28. Last year, the MIA Corporation showed a 10.8% increase in retail sales in January, a 4.7% decrease in February, and a 12.4% increase in March. If retail sales at the beginning of January were approximately 6 million dollars, what were the sales at the beginning of April?

29. Each year, Social Security payments are adjusted for cost of living. Your grandmother relies on Social Security for a significant part of her retirement income. In 1996, her Social Security income was approximately $1100 per month. If cost of living increases were 1.7% for 1997, 1.6% for 1998, and 2.6% for 1999, what was the amount of your grandmother's monthly Social Security checks in 2000?

CLUSTER 4

Problem Solving with Signed Numbers

ACTIVITY 1.17

Celsius Thermometers

Topic: *Adding and Subtracting Signed Numbers*

So far, the activities in this book have mostly involved positive numbers and zero. In the real world, you also encounter negative numbers.

1. What are some situations in which you have encountered negative numbers?

> The collection of positive counting numbers, negative counting numbers, and zero is basic to our number system. For easy referral, this collection is called the set of **integers.**

A good technique for visualizing the relationship between positive and negative numbers is to use a number line, scaled with integers, much like a thermometer's scale.

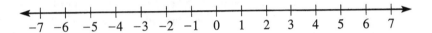

On a number line, 0 separates the positive and negative numbers. Recall that numbers increase in value as you move to the right. Thus, -1 has a value greater than -4, which makes sense in the thermometer model, since $-1°$ is a warmer temperature than $-4°$.

In this activity, a thermometer model illustrates addition and subtraction of signed numbers. On a Celsius thermometer, $0°$ represents the temperature at which water freezes, and $100°$ represents the temperature at which water boils. The following thermometers show temperatures from $-10°C$ to $+10°C$.

2. a. What is the practical meaning of positive numbers in the Celsius thermometer model?

b. What is the practical meaning of negative numbers in the Celsius thermometer model?

You can use signed numbers to represent a change in temperature. A rise in temperature is indicated by a positive number, and a drop in temperature is indicated by a negative number. As shown on the following thermometers, a rise of 6° from −2° results in a temperature of 4°, symbolically written as −2° + 6° = 4°.

3. Answer the following questions, using the thermometer models.

a. What is the result if a temperature starts at 5° and rises 3°? Symbolically, you are calculating 5° + 3°. Use the thermometer below to demonstrate your calculation.

b. If a temperature starts at −5° and rises 3°, what is the result? Write the calculation symbolically. Use the thermometer below to demonstrate your calculation.

c. If a temperature starts at 5° and drops 3° (−3), the resulting temperature is 2°. Symbolically, you are calculating 5° + (−3°). Use the thermometer below to demonstrate your calculation.

d. What is the result when a temperature drops 3° from −5°? Write the calculation symbolically. Use the thermometer below to demonstrate your calculation.

4. a. In what direction did you move on the thermometer when you added positive degrees to a starting temperature in Problem 3?

b. In each case, was the result greater or less than the starting number?

5. a. When you added negative degrees to a starting temperature in Problem 3, in what direction did you move on the thermometer?

b. In each case, was the result greater than or less than the starting number?

6. a. Evaluate each of the following mentally. Check your result using a calculator.

$4 + 6 =$ $6 + 8 =$ $-7 + (-2) =$

$-16 + (-10) =$ $(-0.5) + (-1.4) =$

$-\frac{5}{2} + \left(-\frac{3}{2}\right) =$

b. In each calculation in part a, what do you notice about the signs of the two numbers being added?

c. How do the signs of the numbers being added determine the sign of the result?

d. How do you calculate the numerical part of the result from the numerical parts of the numbers being added?

7. a. Evaluate each of the following mentally. Check your result using a calculator.

$$4 + (-6) \qquad\qquad -6 + 8 \qquad\qquad 7 + (-2)$$

$$-16 + 10 \qquad\qquad -\tfrac{6}{2} + \tfrac{7}{2} = \qquad\qquad 0.5 + (-2.8)$$

b. In each calculation in part a, what do you notice about the signs of the numbers being added?

c. How do the signs of the numbers being added determine the sign of the result?

d. How do you calculate the numerical part of the result from the numerical parts of the numbers being added?

8. Evaluate each of the following. Check your result using a calculator.

a. $-8 + (-6)$ **b.** $9 + (-12)$ **c.** $6 + (-8)$ **d.** $-7 + (-9)$

e. $16 + 10$ **f.** $16 + (-10)$ **g.** $-9 + 8$ **h.** $-2 + (-3)$

i. $9 + (-5)$ **j.** $3 + (-6)$ **k.** $-\tfrac{5}{8} + \tfrac{1}{8}$ **l.** $-\tfrac{5}{6} + \left(-\tfrac{1}{6}\right)$

m. $\tfrac{3}{4} + \left(-\tfrac{1}{4}\right)$ **n.** $\tfrac{1}{2} + \tfrac{1}{3}$ **o.** $-5.9 + (-4.7)$ **p.** $0.50 + 0.06$

q. $(-5.75) + 1.25$ **r.** $-12.1 + 8.3$ **s.** $-6 + \left(-\tfrac{2}{3}\right)$ **t.** $5 + \left(-1\tfrac{3}{4}\right)$

Suppose you know the starting and ending temperatures for a certain period of time and that you are interested in the *change* in temperature over that period.

> **Change in value** is calculated by subtracting the initial (original) value from the final value. That is,
>
> Final number − initial number = change in value (difference).

For example, the change in value from 2° to 9° is 9° − 2° = 7°. Here, 9° is the final temperature, 2° is the original, or initial, temperature, and 7° is the change in temperature. Notice that the temperature has risen; therefore, the change in temperature of 7° is positive, as shown on the thermometer on the left.

Suppose that −6° is the final temperature and 5° is the original, or initial temperature.

Symbolically, this is written −6° −5° producing a result of −11°, as indicated on the thermometer on the right. The significance of a negative change is that the temperature has fallen.

9. a. What is the change in temperature from 3° to 5°? That is, what is the difference between the final temperature, 5°, and the initial temperature 3°? Symbolically you are calculating +5° − (+3°). Use the thermometer below to demonstrate this calculation. Has the temperature risen or fallen?

b. The change in temperature from 3° to −5° is −8°. Symbolically, you write −5° − (3°) = −8°. Use the thermometer below to demonstrate this calculation. Has the temperature risen or fallen?

c. A temperature in Montreal last winter rose from $-3°$ to $5°$. What was the change in temperature? Write the calculation symbolically and determine the result. Use the thermometer below to demonstrate your calculation.

d. The temperature on a March day in Montana was $-3°$ at noon and $-5°$ at 5 P.M. What was the change in temperature? Write the calculation symbolically and determine the result. Use the thermometer below to demonstrate your calculation. Has the temperature risen or fallen?

10. When calculating a change in value, in which position in the subtraction calculation must the initial value be placed—to the left or to the right of the subtraction symbol?

Problem 9 showed that you use subtraction to calculate the *change* or *difference* in value between two numbers and Problem 3 demonstrated that addition is used to move from an initial number to another number.

You can use the concept of opposites to relate the operations of addition and subtraction of integers.

Opposites are numbers that when added together give a sum of zero.

For example, 10 and -10 are opposites because $10 + (-10) = 0$.

11. a. What is the opposite of 5?

b. What is the opposite of -8?

c. $0 - 5 =$ $\qquad$ $0 + (-5) =$

d. $0 - 12 =$ $\qquad$ $0 + (-12) =$

e. $0 - (-8) =$ $\qquad$ $0 + 8 =$

f. $0 - (-6) =$ $\qquad$ $0 + 6 =$

g. From your experience in parts c–f, what can you conclude about the result of subtracting a number from zero? about adding a number to zero?

h. From your experience with parts c–f, is it reasonable to believe that subtracting a number gives the same result as adding its opposite? Explain.

Subtracting a signed number is equivalent to adding its opposite.

For example, $-4 - 6$ becomes $(-4) + (-6)$ and equals -10 by the addition of signed numbers.

12. Convert each of the following to an equivalent addition problem and evaluate. Check your result using a calculator.

a. $4 - 11$ $\qquad$ **b.** $-8 - (-6)$ $\qquad$ **c.** $9 - (-2)$

d. $-7 - 1$ $\qquad$ **e.** $10 - 15$ $\qquad$ **f.** $6 - (-4)$

g. $-8 - 10$ $\qquad$ **h.** $-2 - (-5)$ $\qquad$ **i.** $-\frac{5}{8} - \frac{1}{8}$

j. $\frac{5}{6} - \left(-\frac{1}{6}\right)$ $\qquad$ **k.** $-\frac{3}{4} - \left(-\frac{1}{4}\right)$ $\qquad$ **l.** $\frac{1}{2} - \frac{1}{3}$

m. $5.9 - (-4.7)$ $\qquad$ **n.** $-3.75 - 1.25$

o. $-6 - \left(-\frac{2}{3}\right)$ $\qquad$ **p.** $5 - \left(-1\frac{3}{4}\right)$

Number lines and models such as thermometers provide a good visual approach to adding and subtracting signed numbers. However, you will find it more efficient to use a general method when dealing with signed numbers in applications. A convenient way of adding and subtracting signed numbers is to use the concept of absolute value.

The **absolute value** of a number represents the distance that the number is from zero on the number line. For example, $+9$ and -9 are both 9 units from 0 but in opposite directions so they have the same absolute value, 9. Symbolically we write $|9| = 9$, and $|-9| = 9$ and $|0| = 0$. Notice that opposites have the same absolute value. More generally, the absolute value of a number represents the size or magnitude of the number.

The procedures you have developed in this activity for adding and subtracting signed numbers can be restated using absolute value.

> **ADDING AND SUBTRACTING SIGNED NUMBERS**
>
> When *adding* two numbers with the *same* sign, add the absolute values of the numbers. The sign of the sum is the same as the sign of the numbers being added.
>
> When *adding* two numbers with *opposite* signs, find their absolute values and then subtract the smaller from the larger. The sign of the sum is the same as the sign of the number with the larger absolute value.
>
> Subtracting a signed number is equivalent to *adding the opposite* of the signed number. Two changes must be made. The subtraction symbol is changed to an addition symbol, and the number following the subtraction symbol is replaced by its opposite. The new addition problem is evaluated using the addition rule.

EXERCISES

1. Another illustration of adding signed numbers can be found on the gridiron—that is, on the football field. On the number line, a gain is represented by a move to the right, while a loss results in a move to the left. For example, a 7-yard loss and a 3-yard gain results in a 4-yard loss. This can be written symbolically as $-7 + 3 = -4$.

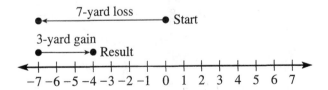

Use the number line to complete the following.

a. A 6-yard gain and a 3-yard gain results in a _____.

b. A 5-yard gain and a 2-yard loss results in a _____. $5 + -2 = 3$

c. A 4-yard loss and a 3-yard loss results in a _____. $-4 + -3 =$

d. A 1-yard gain and an 8-yard loss results in a _____.

Exercise numbers appearing in color are answered in the Selected Answers section of this book.

2. Write each of the situations in Problem 1 as an addition problem

    a.   **b.**

    c.   **d.**

3. The San Francisco 49ers are famous for selecting their first ten plays before the game begins. If the yardage gained or lost from each play is totaled, the sum represents the total yards gained (or lost) for those plays. One play sequence proceeded as follows:

PLAY	1	2	3	4	5	6	7	8	9	10
YARDS	Lost 5	Gained 7	Gained 9	Lost 5	Gained 15	Gained 4	Lost 6	Gained 20	Lost 1	Gained 5

What was the total yards gained (or lost) for these ten plays?

4. Evaluate each of the following. Use a calculator to verify your result.

    a. $-3 + (-7)$ **b.** $-6 + 2$ **c.** $4 + (-10)$ **d.** $16 - 5$

    e. $7 - 12$ **f.** $-2 - 8$ **g.** $-5 + (-10)$ **h.** $(-6) + 9$

    i. $-8 - 10$ **j.** $-4 - (-5)$ **k.** $0 - (-6)$ **l.** $-3 + 0$

    m. $9 - 9$ **n.** $9 - (-9)$ **o.** $0 + (-7)$ **p.** $-4 + (-5)$

    q. $-8 - (-3)$ **r.** $(-9) - (-12)$ **s.** $5 - 8$ **t.** $(-7) - 4$

    u. $-\frac{5}{9} + \frac{4}{9}$ **v.** $2.56 - 3.14$ **w.** $-75 - 30.5$ **x.** $33\frac{1}{3} - 66\frac{2}{3}$

5. The current temperature is $-12°C$. If the forecast is that it will be 5° warmer tomorrow, write a symbolic expression and evaluate it to determine tomorrow's predicted temperature.

6. The current temperature is $-4°C$. If the forecast is that it will be $7°$ colder tomorrow, write a symbolic expression and evaluate it to determine tomorrow's predicted temperature.

7. On a cold day in April, the temperature rose from $-5°C$ to $7°C$. Write a symbolic expression and evaluate it to determine the change in temperature.

8. A heat wave hits New York City, increasing the temperature an average of $3°C$ per day for five days, starting with a high of $20°C$ on June 6. What is the approximate high temperature on June 11?

ACTIVITY 1.18

Gains and Losses in Business

Topic: *Multiplying and Dividing Signed Numbers*

Situation 1

Stock values are reported daily in some newspapers. Reports usually state the values at both the opening and the closing of a business day. Suppose you own 220 shares of Corning Incorporated stock.

1. Your stock opens today valued at $31.00 per share, but goes down to $30.50 per share by the end of the day. What is the total change in the value of your shares today? State your answer in words and as a signed number.

2. Your stock opens another day at $42.00 per share and goes up $1.25 per share by the end of the day. What is the total value of your shares at the end of the day?

Situation 2

You are one of three equal partners in a company.

3. Your company made a profit of $300,000 in 1999. How much money did you and your partners make each? Write the answer in words and as a signed number.

4. Your company experienced a loss of $150,000 in 1998. What was your share of the loss? Write the answer in words and as a signed number.

5. Over the two-year period from January 1, 1998, to December 31, 1999, what was the net profit for each partner? Express your answer in words and as a signed number.

6. Suppose that in 2000, your corporation suffered a further loss of $180,000. Over the three-year period from January 1, 1998, to December 31, 2000, what was the net change for each partner? Express your answer in words and as a signed number.

Situation 3

Each individual account in your small business has a current dollar balance, which can be either positive (a credit) or negative (a debit). To find your current total account balance, you simply add all the individual balances.

7. Suppose your records show the following individual balances.

$$-220 \quad -220 \quad 350 \quad 350 \quad -220 \quad -220 \quad -220 \quad 350$$

a. What is the total of the individual positive balances?

b. What is the total of the individual negative balances?

c. In part b, did you sum the five negative balances? Or did you multiply -220 by 5? Which method is more efficient? What is the sign of the result of your calculation?

d. What is the total balance for these accounts?

8. From past experience, you know that multiplication is repeated addition. (See Problem 7c.) Represent the following as repeated addition.

For example, $2(-3) = -3 + -3 = -6$

a. $4(-12)$ b. $3(9)$

You can use the concept of opposites when representing multiplication as repeated addition. Think of $-2(3)$ as the opposite of $2(3) = 6$. Then $-2(3) = -6$.

9. Use your calculator to determine the following. Compare the results of parts a–d.

a. $9 \cdot (-5) =$

b. $-5 \cdot 9 =$

c. $-9 \cdot 5 =$

d. $5 \cdot (-9) =$

10. Evaluate the following **mentally,** then check using your calculator.

a. $-2 \cdot 6$

b. $(-4)(5)$

c. $6 \cdot (-6)$

d. $3(-9)$

e. $-8 \cdot 11$

f. $(-5.1) \cdot 7$

g. From your experience in this activity, what is the sign of the product of a positive number and a negative number?

11. a. Fill in the blanks to complete the pattern begun in the first few equations.

$$3 \cdot -2 = -6$$
$$2 \cdot -2 = -4$$
$$1 \cdot -2 = \rule{2cm}{0.4pt}$$
$$0 \cdot -2 = \rule{2cm}{0.4pt}$$
$$-1 \cdot -2 = 2$$
$$-2 \cdot -2 = \rule{2cm}{0.4pt}$$
$$-3 \cdot -2 = \rule{2cm}{0.4pt}$$

b. What do you conclude is the sign of the product of two negative numbers?

The rule you discovered in Problem 11 can also be obtained using the ideas of repeated addition and opposites. Because $3(-2) = -6$, we know that $-3(-2)$ is the opposite of -6, which is 6. Thus, $-3(-2) = 6$.

12. Evaluate the following mentally. Then check using your calculator.

a. $-5 \cdot (-7)$

b. $-3 \cdot (-6)$

c. $-4 \cdot 6$

d. $-8(-2)$

e. $-1 \cdot 2.718$

f. $-3.14 \cdot (-1)$

g. $-6(0)$

h. $4(-7)$

i. $(-3)(-8)$

Once you know how to multiply signed numbers, division of signed numbers follows naturally. Recall that division is "undoing" multiplication. For example, $12 \div 4 = 3$ because $4 \cdot 3 = 12$. Similarly, $12 \div -4 = -3$ because $(-4) \cdot (-3) = 12$. (Check this on your calculator.)

13. Evaluate the following mentally. Then check using your calculator.

    a. $25 \div (-5)$ **b.** $32 \div (-8)$ **c.** $(-12) \div 6$

    d. $16 \div (-2)$ **e.** $-48 \div 6$ **f.** $-36 \div (-9)$

    g. $-11 \cdot (-3)$ **h.** $-6 \div 3$ **i.** $0 \div (-5)$

    j. $-6 \div 0$ **k.** $-63 \div (-1)$ **l.** $-7 \cdot 4$

SIGNED NUMBER MULTIPLICATION AND DIVISION

The product of two numbers with the same sign is positive.

The product of two numbers with different signs is negative.

The quotient of two numbers with the same sign is positive.

The quotient of two numbers with different signs is negative.

EXERCISES

1. Calculate mentally or use your calculator. Compare the results for similarities and differences.

    a. $12 \cdot (-6)$ **b.** $12 - 6$ **c.** $12 \div (-6)$ **d.** $-6 \div 12$

2. Calculate mentally and check using your calculator. Compare the results for similarities and differences.

    a. $\frac{1}{2} \div 2$ **b.** $\frac{1}{2} \div (-2)$ **c.** $-2 \div \frac{1}{2}$ **d.** $2 \div \left(-\frac{1}{2}\right)$

3. Evaluate each of the following. Use a calculator to verify your answers.

  a. $2.1(-8)$ **b.** $-8 \cdot (-7)$ **c.** $11(-3)(-4)$ **d.** $-125 \div 25$

  e. $10{,}000 \div (-250)$ **f.** $-6 \cdot 9$ **g.** $-24 \div (-3)$

  h. $-12 \div 4$ **i.** $0.2 \cdot (-0.3)$ **j.** $-1.6 \div (-4)$

  k. $\left(-\frac{3}{4}\right)\left(-\frac{2}{9}\right)$ **l.** $-4\frac{2}{3} \div \left(-\frac{7}{9}\right)$

4. Yesterday, you wrote five checks for $25 each.

  a. What was the total amount of the checks?

$$\frac{\begin{array}{r}25\\5\end{array}}{125}$$

  b. You originally had $98 in your checking account. What was your balance after you wrote the five checks?

   $125 + 98 = 223$

5. A cold front moves through your hometown in January, dropping the temperature an average of 3° per day. If the temperature is 7° on January 1, what will the temperature be five days later?

   $3°$

6. You own 180 shares of Bell Atlantic stock. The following table lists the changes in a given week for a single share. Did you earn a profit or suffer a loss on the value of your shares during the given week? How much profit or loss?

DAY	MON.	TUES.	WED.	THURS.	FRI.
DAILY CHANGE	+0.38	−0.75	−1.25	−1.13	2.55

Order of Operations Revisited

Topics: *Order of Operations with Signed Numbers, Negative Exponents, Scientific Notation*

You can combine the procedures for adding and subtracting signed numbers with those for multiplying and dividing signed numbers by using the order of operations you learned in Activity 1.5, You and Your Calculator. That order of operations is valid for *all* numbers, positive and negative, including decimals, fractions, and numerical expressions with exponents. Your ability to follow these procedures correctly with all numbers will help you use the formulas that you will encounter in applications.

1. Calculate the following expressions by hand. Then check your answer using your calculator.

   a. $6 + 4 \cdot (-2)$ **b.** $-6 + 2 - 3$ **c.** $(6 - 10) \div 2$

   d. $-3 + (2 - 5)$ **e.** $(2 - 7) \cdot 5$ **f.** $-3 \cdot (-3 + 4)$

   g. $-2 \cdot 3^2 - 15$ **h.** $(2 + 3)^2 - 10$ **i.** $-7 + 8 \div (5 - 7)$

   j. $2.5 - (5.2 - 2.2)^2 + 8$ **k.** $4.2 \div 0.7 - (-5.6 + 8.7)$

   l. $\frac{1}{4} - \left(\frac{2}{3} \cdot \frac{9}{8}\right)$ **m.** $\frac{5}{6} \div (-10) + \frac{7}{12}$

2. Evaluate $5 - 3^2$ by hand and then check using your calculator. Which operation must be performed first?

3. Evaluate $0 - 3^2$ by hand and then check using your calculator.

4. Evaluate -3^2 by hand. Did you obtain the same answer as in Problem 3?

In Problem 4, two operations are performed on the number 3: exponentiation and negation. This means that, by order of operations, you first square 3—that is, $3^2 = $ ___9___. Then you write the opposite of 9 (negate the 9), which is _____.

Problems 3 and 4 together show that you can interpret a leading negative sign as subtraction by simply subtracting from zero. For example: $-16 = 0 - 16$. Therefore,

$$-4^2 = 0 - 4^2$$
$$= 0 - 16$$
$$= -16.$$

5. Evaluate -7^2 by using this technique.

6. **a.** Evaluate $(-3)^2$ by hand and then check with your calculator.

   b. Is $(-3)^2$ the same as -3^2?

The base for the exponent in the expression $(-3)^2$ is -3. You are calculating the square of -3. In the expression -3^2, the base for the exponent is 3. You are calculating the opposite of the square of 3.

7. Evaluate the following expressions by hand. Check each one using your calculator before going on to the next.

   a. -5^2 **b.** $(-5)^2$ **c.** $(-3)^3$

   d. -1^4 **e.** $2 - 4^2$ **f.** $(2 - 4)^2$

   g. $-5^2 - (-5)^2$ **h.** $(-1)^8$ **i.** $-5^2 + (-5)^2$

   j. $-\left(\frac{1}{2}\right)^2 + \left(\frac{1}{2}\right)^2$ **k.** $-1.5^2 - (1.5)^2$ **l.** $(-1.5)^2 - (1.5)^2$

So far in this book, you have been using only zero or positive integers as exponents. Are numbers with negative exponents meaningful? How would you calculate an expression such as 10^{-2}? In the following problems, you will discover answers to these questions.

8. a. Complete the following table.

EXPONENTIAL FORM	EXPANDED FORM	VALUE
10^5	$10 \times 10 \times 10 \times 10 \times 10$	100,000
10^4	$10 \times 10 \times 10 \times 10$	10,000
10^3	$10 \times 10 \times 10$	1000
10^2		
10^1		
10^0		
10^{-1}		
10^{-2}	$\frac{1}{10} \times \frac{1}{10}$	
10^{-3}		$\frac{1}{1000}$ or 0.001
10^{-4}		

b. What is the relationship between each negative exponent in column 1 and the number of zeros in the denominator of the corresponding fraction in column 3? In the decimal result? List and explain everything you observe.

9. What is the meaning of the expression, 10^{-6}? That is, write 10^{-6} as a fraction and as a decimal number.

10. Evaluate each of the following expressions.

    a. 10^3 **b.** 1×10^3 **c.** 5×10^3 **d.** 2.72×10^3

    e. 10^{-3} **f.** 1×10^{-3} **g.** 5×10^{-3} **h.** 2.72×10^{-3}

11. a. Recall from Activity 1.5 that you used the (EE) key on your calculator to enter numbers written in scientific notation. For example, $10^2 = 1 \times 10^2$ is entered as (1) (EE) (2). Try it.

    b. Now enter $10^{-2} = 1 \times 10^{-2}$ as (1) (EE) (−) (2). What is the result written as a decimal? Written as a fraction?

    c. Use the (EE) key to enter the numbers in Problem 10 into your calculator. Record your results and compare them with your results in Problem 10.

12. Pluto takes 247.7 years to circumnavigate the sun.

   a. How many seconds does it take Pluto to circumnavigate the sun?

   b. Round your result to the nearest million seconds.

   c. Write the rounded result in standard scientific notation.

13. Tests show that the unaided eye can detect objects that have a diameter of 0.1 millimeter. What is the diameter in inches (1 in. = 25.4 mm)? Write your result in decimal form and in scientific notation.

14. The wavelength of x-rays is 1×10^{-8} centimeter, and that of ultraviolet light is 2×10^{-5} centimeter.

   a. Which wavelength is shorter?

   b. How many times shorter? Write your answer in standard form and in scientific notation.

15. Use your calculator to evaluate the following expressions.

   a. $\dfrac{16}{4 \times 10^{-2} - 2 \times 10^{-3}}$

   b. $\dfrac{3.2 \times 10^{3}}{(8.2 \times 10^{-2})(3.0 \times 10^{2})}$

EXERCISES

1. Complete the following table and compare with the table in Problem 8 of the activity.

EXPONENTIAL FORM	EXPANDED FORM	VALUE
2^5	$2 \times 2 \times 2 \times 2 \times 2$	32
2^4	$2 \times 2 \times 2 \times 2$	16
2^3		8
2^2		
2^1		
2^0		
2^{-1}		
2^{-2}	$\frac{1}{2} \times \frac{1}{2}$	
2^{-3}		$\frac{1}{8}$
2^{-4}		

2. Evaluate the following expressions by hand or by calculator as you see fit. Estimate your results to see if your answers are reasonable.

   a. $(8 - 17) \div 3 + 6$ **b.** $-7 + 3(1 - 5)$ **c.** $-3^2 \cdot 2^2 + 25$

   d. $1.6 - (1.2 + 2.8)^2$ **e.** $\frac{5}{16} - 3\left(\frac{3}{16} - \frac{7}{16}\right)$ **f.** $\frac{3}{4} \div \left(\frac{1}{2} - \frac{5}{12}\right)$

   g. -1^{-2} **h.** $4^3 - (-4)^3$ **i.** $\left(\frac{2}{3}\right)^2 - \left(\frac{2}{3}\right)^2$

   j. $\dfrac{-3 \times 10^2}{3 \times 10^{-2} - 2 \times 10^{-2}}$ **k.** $\dfrac{1.5 \times 10^3}{\left(-5.0 \times 10^{-1}\right)\left(2.6 \times 10^2\right)}$

Exercise numbers appearing in color are answered in the Selected Answers section of this book.

3. In 1994, the U.S. government paid 296.3 billion dollars in interest on the national debt.

   a. Write this number in standard notation and in scientific notation.

   b. Assume that there were approximately 250 million people in the United States in 1994. How much of the debt could we say each person owed on the interest?

4. You have found 0.4 gram of gold while panning for gold on your vacation.

   a. How many pounds of gold do you have $(1 \text{ g} = 2.2 \times 10^{-3} \text{ lb})$? Write your result in decimal form and in scientific notation.

   b. If you were to tell a friend how much gold you have, would you state the quantity in grams or in pounds? Explain.

5. You are doing an experiment in a chemistry research lab and have to calculate the molecular weight of the compound you have isolated from the other compounds in the experiment. This leads you to the following numerical expression:

   $$\text{Molecular weight of the compound (grams per mole)} = \frac{(0.134)(0.082)(371)}{(0.9697)(0.0532)}$$

   Use your calculator to evaluate the expression, and write your result to the nearest thousandth.

What Have I Learned?

Your study group is preparing for a test on Cluster 4.

1. Explain how you would add two signed numbers and how you would subtract two signed numbers. Use examples to illustrate each.

2. Explain how you would multiply two signed numbers and how you would divide two signed numbers. Use examples to illustrate each.

3. What would you suggest to your classmates to avoid confusing addition and subtraction procedures with multiplication and division procedures?

4. a. Without actually performing the calculation, determine the *sign* of the product $(-0.1)(+3.4)(6.87)(-0.5)(+4.01)(3.9)$. Explain.

   b. Determine the *sign* of the product $(-0.2)(-6.5)(+9.42)(-0.8)(1.73)(-6.72)$. Explain.

   c. Determine the *sign* of the product $(-1)(-5.37)(-3.45)$. Explain.

d. Determine the *sign* of the product
$(-4.3)(+7.89)(-69.8)(-12.5)(+4.01)(-3.9)(-78.03)$. Explain.

e. What rule do the results you obtained in parts a–d suggest?

5. a. If -2 is raised to the power 4, what is the sign of the result? What is the sign if -2 is raised to the sixth power?

b. Raise -2 to the eighth power, tenth power, and twelfth power.

c. What general rule involving signs is suggested by the preceding results?

6. a. Raise -2 to the third power, fifth power, seventh power, and ninth power.

b. What general rule involving signs is suggested by the preceding results?

7. The following table contains the daily midnight temperatures in Batavia, NY, for a week in January.

DAY	SUN.	MON.	TUES.	WED.	THURS.	FRI.	SAT.
TEMPERATURE (°F)	−7°F	11°F	11°F	11°F	−7°F	−7°F	11°F

a. Determine the average daily temperature for the week.

b. Did you use the most efficient way to do the calculation? Explain.

8. a. What is the value of 3^2, 3^0, and 3^{-2}?

b. What is the value of any nonzero number raised to the zero power?

c. What is the meaning of any nonzero number raised to a negative power? Give two examples using -2 as the exponent.

9. a. The diameter of raindrops in drizzle near sea level is reported to be approximately 30×10^{-2} millimeter. Write this number in standard decimal notation and in standard scientific notation.

b. What is the measurement of these raindrops in centimeters (10 mm = 1 cm)? Write your answer in standard notation and in scientific notation.

c. From your experience with scientific notation, explain how to convert numbers from standard form to scientific form and vice versa.

How Can I Practice?

Calculate by hand or using your calculator.

1. $15 + (-39)$

2. $-43 + (-28)$

3. $-0.52 + 0.84$

4. $-7.8 + 2.9$

5. $-32 + (-45) + 68$

6. $-46 - 63$

7. $53 - (-64)$

8. $8.9 - (-12.3)$

9. $-75 - 47$

10. $-34 - (-19)$

11. $-4.9 - (-2.4) + (-5.6) + 3.2$

12. $16 - (-28) - 82 + (-57)$

13. $-1.7 + (-0.56) + 0.92 - (-2.8)$

14. $\frac{2}{3} + \left(-\frac{3}{5}\right)$

15. $-\frac{3}{7} + \left(\frac{4}{5}\right) + \left(-\frac{2}{7}\right)$

16. $-\frac{5}{9} - \left(-\frac{8}{9}\right)$

17. $2 - \left(\frac{3}{2}\right)$

18. $1 - \left(\frac{3}{4}\right) + \left(-\frac{3}{4}\right)$

19. $0 - \left(-\frac{7}{10}\right) + \left(-\frac{1}{2}\right) - \frac{1}{5}$

20. $\frac{-48}{12}$

21. $\frac{63}{-9}$

22. $\frac{121}{-11}$

23. $\frac{-84}{-21}$

24. $-125 \div -25$

25. $-2.4 \div 6$

26. $\frac{24}{-6}$

27. $-\frac{24}{6}$

28. $-0.8(12)$

29. $4(-0.06)$

30. $-9(-11)$

31. $-4(-0.6)(-5)(-0.01)$

32. $0.5(-7)(-2)(-3)$

33. $-4(-4)$

34. $(-4)(-4)$

35. $4(-4)$

36. You have $85.30 in your bank account. You write checks for $23.70 and $35.63. You then deposit $325.33. Later, you withdraw $130.00. What is your final balance?

37. You lose 4 pounds, then gain 3 pounds back. Later you lose another 5 pounds. If your aim is to lose 12 pounds, how many more pounds do you need to lose?

38. You and your friend Patrick go on vacation. When you are at sea level, Patrick decides to go scuba diving, but you prefer to do some mountain climbing. You decide to separate part of the day and do your individual activities. While you climb 2567 feet, Patrick is 49 feet underwater. What is the vertical distance between you and Patrick?

39. a. The temperature is 2°C in the morning but drops to −5°C by night. What is the change in temperature?

    b. The temperature is −12°C in the morning, but is expected to drop 7° during the day. What will be the evening temperature?

    c. The temperature is −17°C this morning, but is expected to rise 9° by noon. What will be the noon temperature?

    d. The temperature is −8°C in the morning but drops to −17°C by night. What is the change in temperature?

    e. The temperature is −14°C in the morning and −6°C at noon. What is the change in temperature?

40. a. $-6 \div 2 \cdot 3$ **b.** $(-3)^2 + (-7) \div 2$

c. $(-2.5)^3 + (-9) \div (-3)$ d. $(-14 - 4) \div 3 \cdot 2$

e. $(-4)^2 - [-8 \div (2 + 6)]$ f. $-4.4 \div (-0.2)^2 + 1.8$

g. $(-3)^3 \div 9 - 6$

41. a. At sea level, fog droplets on the average measure 20×10^{-3} millimeter in diameter. How many inches is this (1 mm = 0.03037 in.)?

b. At sea level, the average diameter of raindrops is approximately 1 millimeter. How many inches is this?

c. How many times larger are raindrops than fog droplets?

Problem Solving with Geometry

LAB ACTIVITY 1.20

Geometric Shapes
Topics: *Measurement, Perimeter, Area, Empirical Verification of Formulas*

You encounter problems involving geometric shapes every day. For example, you may wish to determine the amount of paint needed to redecorate a room, calculate the length of fencing needed for a new kennel for your dog, or design the shapes of pieces to make a quilt. These are all situations that involve measuring objects and calculating perimeters and areas. In the following problems, you will measure basic geometric figures and develop the formulas for calculating the perimeters and areas of these figures.

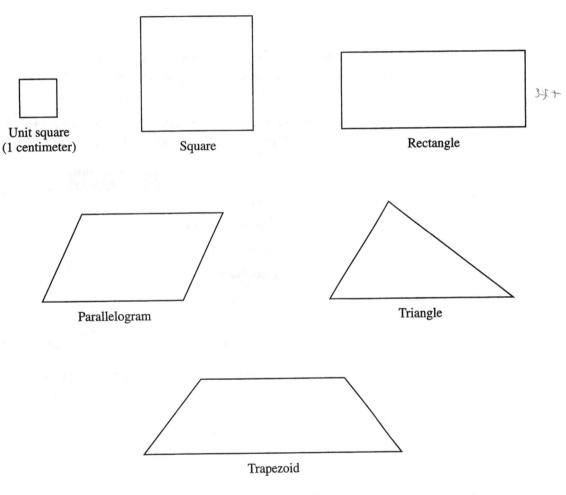

Unit square
(1 centimeter)

Square

Rectangle

Parallelogram

Triangle

Trapezoid

1. Measure each side of each of the preceding geometric figures. Use a metric ruler and use centimeters for the unit of measure. Label each side with its measure. Note that 1 centimeter is abbreviated 1 cm.

2. Each basic geometric figure has its own special features. Study each geometric figure preceding Problem 1 and note what features it has. Put a check in each box of the following table where a feature applies.

	ALL SIDES EQUAL	OPPOSITE SIDES EQUAL	RIGHT ANGLE	BOTH PAIRS OF OPPOSITE SIDES PARALLEL	ONE PAIR OF OPPOSITE SIDES PARALLEL
TRAPEZOID					
PARALLELOGRAM					
RECTANGLE					
SQUARE					
TRIANGLE					

> The **perimeter** of a geometric figure is the measure of the distance around the figure. Perimeter is measured in linear units such as meters, feet, or miles.

3. Use your measurements from Problem 1 to determine the perimeter of each of the geometric figures. Be sure to include the unit of measurement.

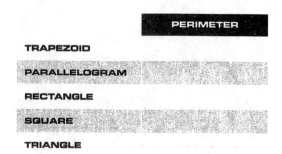

	PERIMETER
TRAPEZOID	
PARALLELOGRAM	
RECTANGLE	
SQUARE	
TRIANGLE	

Sometimes you can use a formula as a shortcut to measuring the perimeter of a figure.

4. Draw a square and represent each side with the letter *s*. Write a formula for the perimeter *P* in terms of *s*.

5. Draw a rectangle. Let the longest side of the rectangle be represented by *l* (length), and let the shorter side be represented by *w* (width). Write a formula for the perimeter *P* of the rectangle in terms of *l* and *w*.

6. Draw a triangle and label its sides *a*, *b* and *c*. Write a formula for the perimeter of the triangle.

The formulas for the perimeters of a square, rectangle, and triangle are listed on the inside back cover of this text. Compare your answers to Problems 4, 5, and 6 with those formulas.

7. Use the appropriate geometric formula to answer each of the following.

   a. The side of a square, *s*, measures 5 centimeters. Determine the perimeter of the square.

   b. The length *l* and width *w* of a rectangle are 6 inches and 4 inches, respectively. Determine the perimeter of the rectangle.

   c. The lengths of the sides of a triangle are 3 feet, 4 feet, and 5 feet. What is the perimeter of the triangle?

> The **area** of a geometric figure is the measure of the space enclosed by the sides of the figure. Area is measured in square units such as square meters, square feet, or square miles.

A unit square is one whose side length is 1 unit of measure. In this activity, you will use centimeters as your unit of measure, so the unit square will have a side length of 1 centimeter and an area of 1 square centimeter.

8. Draw copies of the unit square to fill the space enclosed by the sides of the larger square as seen on page 135. To determine the area of the larger square, simply count the number of whole and partial unit squares you drew. The total number of unit squares you drew is the area of the larger square in square centimeters. Record the area of the square. Be sure to use the correct units.

9. Your drawing in Problem 8 should suggest to you a way to obtain the area of a square from the measure of one of its sides, *s*. There is a shortcut formula for finding the area of a square. Determine a shortcut formula for the area *A* of a square in terms of *s*.

10. Draw copies of the unit square to fill the space enclosed by the sides of the rectangle on page 135. Determine the area of the rectangle by counting the number of unit squares you drew. Record the area of the rectangle. Be sure to use the correct units.

11. There is a shortcut formula for finding the area of a rectangle. Use your drawing from Problem 10 to determine the formula for the area *A* of a rectangle in terms of the measures of its length *l* and its width *w*.

12. Estimate the number of unit squares and fractions of unit squares you can draw in the space enclosed by the sides of the parallelogram on page 135. Use this estimate to approximate the area of the parallelogram. Record your result using the correct units.

13. **a.** In the accompanying figure, a shaded rectangle is placed over the original parallelogram. The length of the rectangle is the base *b* of the parallelogram, and the width of the rectangle is *h*, the height of the parallelogram. Measure *h* and *b* and then calculate the area of the shaded rectangle.

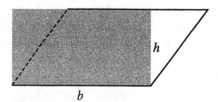

   b. Compare your result for the area of the shaded rectangle with your estimate for the area of the parallelogram from Problem 12. Explain why the area of the shaded rectangle is the same as the area of the original parallelogram.

14. Write a formula for the area *A* of the parallelogram in terms of *b* and *h*.

15. Estimate the number of unit squares and fractions of unit squares you can draw in the space enclosed by the sides of the triangle on page 135. Use this estimate to approximate the area of the triangle. Record your result using the correct units.

16. a. In the accompanying figure, a shaded parallelogram is placed over the original triangle. Measure h, and calculate the area of the shaded parallelogram.

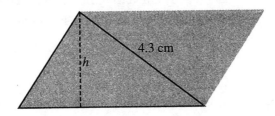

b. How is the area of the original triangle related to the area of the shaded parallelogram?

17. a. Write a formula for the area A of a triangle in terms of the base b and the height h.

b. Use the formula from part a to calculate the area of the triangle, and compare your answer with your estimate from Problem 15.

18. a. Estimate the number of unit squares and fractions of unit squares you can draw in the space enclosed by the sides of the trapezoid on page 135. Use this estimate to approximate the area of the trapezoid. Record your result with the correct units.

b. The shortcut formula for the **area of a trapezoid** is

$$A = \frac{b + B}{2} \cdot h,$$

where b and B are measures of the two parallel sides, or bases, and h is the distance between the bases. You can think of the formula as the average of the bases times the height. Use this formula to calculate the area of the trapezoid. Compare your result with your estimate from part a.

The shortcut formulas for the area of a square, rectangle, parallelogram, triangle, and trapezoid are listed on the inside back cover of this text. Check the formulas you obtained in this lab activity with the formulas printed there.

19. Use the appropriate geometric formula to answer each of the following.

    a. A square measures 1 foot 6 inches on each side. Calculate the area of the square in square feet by converting first to feet. Then convert the side measure to inches and calculate the area in square inches.

    b. Use unit conversions to show that the two areas obtained in part a are equivalent.

    c. The base of a triangle measures 5 inches and its height measures 3 inches. Calculate the area of the triangle.

    d. The bases of a trapezoid measure 2.2 meters and 4.6 meters and its height measures 1.8 meters. Calculate the area of the trapezoid.

    e. The length of a rectangle is 7.5 inches and the width is 2.3 inches. What is the area of the rectangle?

EXERCISES

Use a metric ruler to measure the dimensions of the following geometric figures, and use the applicable shortcut formula to calculate the perimeter and area of each figure.

1.

2.

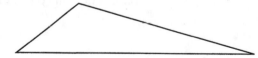

3.

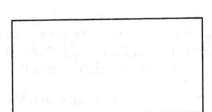

4.

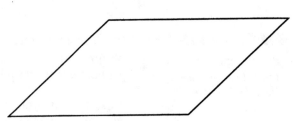

5.

6.

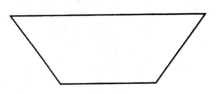

7.

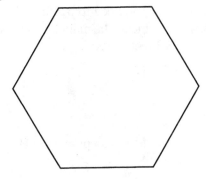

ACTIVITY 1.21

Home Improvements

Topic: *Using Geometry Formulas in Context*

Every summer you do some home improvement. This year you have $1000 budgeted for this purpose and the list looks like this: Replace the kitchen floor, add a wallpaper border to the third bedroom, seed the lawn, and paint the walls in the family room.

To stay within your budget, you need to determine the cost of each of these projects. You expect to do this work yourself.

1. The kitchen floor is divided into two parts. The first section is 12 by 14 feet, and the second section is a breakfast area, triangular in shape, which extends 5 feet out from the 12-foot side along a window. The cost of linoleum is $21 per square yard plus 6% sales tax. Linoleum is sold in 12-foot widths.

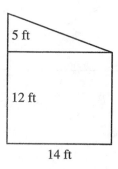

14 ft

a. How long a piece of linoleum will you need to purchase if you want only one seam, where the breakfast area meets the main kitchen area, as shown? Remember that the linoleum is 12 feet wide.

b. How many square feet of linoleum must you purchase? How many square yards is that? (9 sq ft = 1 sq yd)

c. How much will the linoleum cost?

d. How many square feet of waste will you have?

2. The third bedroom is rectangular in shape and has dimensions of $8\frac{1}{2}$ by 13 feet. On each 13-foot side, there is a window that measures 3 feet 8 inches wide and 4 feet high. The door is located on an $8\frac{1}{2}$-foot side and measures 3 feet wide from casing to casing. You are planning to put up the border around the room about halfway up the wall.

a. How many feet of wallpaper border will you need to purchase?

b. The border comes in rolls 5 yards in length. How many rolls will you need to purchase?

c. The wallpaper border costs $10.56 per roll plus 6% sales tax. Determine the cost of the border.

d. How much waste will you have (in feet)?

3. Your lawn needs to be seeded.

a. Using the following scale, determine the size of your lot and your home. Determine how many square feet of lawn you need to seed.

Scale: $\frac{1}{4}$ in. = 16 ft

b. Grass seed comes in bags of 5, 10, or 25 pounds. The 5-pound bag covers 2000 square feet of lawn and costs $12 a bag. The 10-pound bag covers twice as much lawn as the 5-pound bag and costs $23 a bag. The 25-pound bag costs $55, but since the label was ripped, you will need to determine proportionally how many square feet of lawn will be covered by the 25-pound bag.

c. Which bags of grass seed will you purchase?

d. What will be the total cost of your purchase? Remember to include the 6% sales tax.

4. Your family room needs to be painted. It has a cathedral ceiling. The front and back walls look like the diagram below. The two side walls measure 14 feet long and 12 feet high. The walls will need two coats of paint. The ceiling does not need paint.

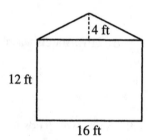

a. How many square feet will you be painting? (Remember, it will need two coats.)

b. Each gallon covers approximately 400 square feet. How many gallons of paint will you need to purchase?

c. Paint costs $19.81 per gallon plus 6% sales tax. What is the cost of the paint you need for the family room?

5. What is the total cost for all your home improvement projects?

6. Can you afford to do all the projects?

E X E R C I S E S

1. Your driveway is rectangular in shape and measures 15 feet wide and 25 feet long. Calculate the area of your driveway.

2. A flower bed is in the corner of your yard and is in the shape of a right triangle. The sides of the bed measure 6 feet 8 inches and 8 feet 4 inches. Calculate the area of the flower bed.

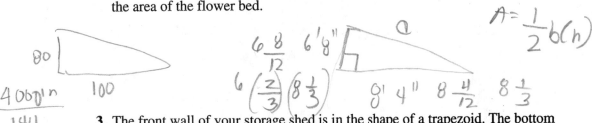

$$A = \frac{1}{2}b(h)$$

$6 \frac{8}{12}$ $6'8''$

$6 \left(\frac{2}{3}\right) \left(8\frac{1}{3}\right)$ $8' 4''$ $8\frac{4}{12}$ $8\frac{1}{3}$

80

4000'n

100

144

3. The front wall of your storage shed is in the shape of a trapezoid. The bottom measures 12 feet, the top measures 10 feet, and the height is 6 feet. Calculate the area of the front wall of your shed.

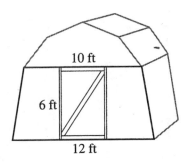

4. You live in a small, one-bedroom apartment. The bedroom is 10 by 12 feet, the living room is 12 by 14 feet, the kitchen is 8 by 6 feet, and the bathroom is 5 by 9 feet. Calculate the total floor space (area) of your apartment.

5. A stop sign is in the shape of a regular octagon. A regular octagon can be created using eight triangles of equal area. One triangle that makes up a stop sign has a base of 16 inches and a height of 18 inches. Calculate the area of the stop sign.

LAB ACTIVITY 1.22

Circles Are Everywhere
Topics: *Measurement,*
Circumference and Area
Formulas

Objects in the shape of circles of varying sizes are found in abundance in everyday life. Coins, dart boards, and ripples made by a raindrop in a pond are just a few examples. The size of a circle is customarily described by the length of a line segment that passes through the center and starts and ends on the circle. You may recall that this line segment is called the **diameter** of the circle. Recall also that the **radius** of a circle is the line segment starting at the center of the circle and ending on the circle. The length of the radius is one-half the length of the diameter.

In this laboratory activity, you will estimate the perimeter (more commonly known as the **circumference**) and area of circles. You will then develop formulas to calculate the circumference and area of a circle, given its radius or diameter.

1. Find four objects that are circular in shape and list them in column 1 of the accompanying table.

   a. Use a tape measure or a piece of string and ruler to measure (in centimeters) the circumference C of each object. Record these numbers in column 2 of the table.

   b. The diameter is more difficult to measure accurately than is the circumference. Devise a method for measuring the length of the diameter and explain why your method will actually measure diameter.

   Now use your method to measure the diameters of your chosen objects and record the measurements in column 3 of the table.

   c. Use the information from parts a and b to complete columns 4 and 5 in the table.

COLUMN 1 OBJECT USED	COLUMN 2 CIRCUMFERENCE C, FOUND BY MEASURING	COLUMN 3 DIAMETER d, FOUND BY MEASURING	COLUMN 4 $\frac{C}{d}$, EXPRESSED AS A FRACTION	COLUMN 5 $\frac{C}{d}$, EXPRESSED AS A DECIMAL
1.				
2.				
3.				
4.				

   d. Are the four values in column 5 approximately the same? Should they be?

   e. Calculate the average of the four decimal values in column 5, and compare your average with the averages obtained by your classmates. What do you conclude?

In every circle, the ratio of the circumference to the diameter is the same. This ratio is represented by π, the Greek letter "pi." Locate the $\boxed{\pi}$ key on your calculator and enter it to determine the numerical value of π. _____ The exact value of π is a non-repeating decimal. You may recall two familiar approximations of π: the two-decimal place approximation, 3.14 and the fraction approximation, $\frac{22}{7}$. It is most accurate to use the $\boxed{\pi}$ key when performing any calculation with π, and to round your final answer to the specified decimal place.

> In every circle, the ratio of the circumference to the diameter is always the same. This ratio of circumference to diameter is represented by the Greek letter π.
>
> $$\frac{C}{d} = \pi$$
>
> The formula for the circumference of the circle is given by
>
> $$C = \pi d \quad \text{or since } d = 2r, \quad C = 2\pi r.$$

NOTE: These formulas are also found on the inside back cover of the book.

For example, the circumference of a circle with radius 2 centimeters is given by

$$C = 2\pi r = 2\pi(2 \text{ cm}) = 4\pi \text{ cm} \approx 12.57 \text{ cm}.$$

Recall: $\approx$ means "is approximately equal to."

2. Calculate the circumference of a circle with diameter 11 feet.

3. The area of a circle is defined as the space inside the circle and is measured in square units.

   a. For each of the four circles in Problem 1, estimate how many 1-by-1-centimeter unit squares and fractions of unit squares can fit in each circle by drawing these squares on the circles. Place these estimates in column 2 of the accompanying table.

   b. Calculate the radius of each circle from the diameter measurement in Problem 1b and record the result in column 3.

   c. Compute πr^2 for each circle, and place your answers in column 4.

COLUMN 1 OBJECT USED	COLUMN 2 ESTIMATED AREA	COLUMN 3 RADIUS, $r = \frac{d}{2}$	COLUMN 4 πr^2
1.			
2.			
3.			
4.			

d. Compare your answers in columns 2 and 4. What do you notice?

The **area** A of any circle of radius r is $A = \pi r^2$.

For example, the area of a circle with radius 3 centimeters is determined as follows:

$$A = \pi r^2 = \pi(3 \text{ cm})^2 = 9\pi \text{ cm}^2 \approx 28.27 \text{ cm}^2$$

4. Calculate the area of a circle with radius 4.6 feet.

5. You can demonstrate why the formula $A = \pi r^2$ for the area of a circle is reasonable.

a. Cut a circle into eight equal pieces (called sectors). Rearrange the sectors into an approximate parallelogram (see accompanying figure).

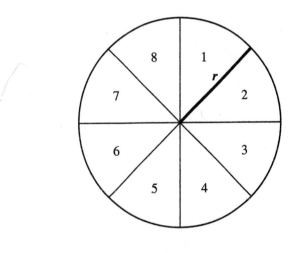

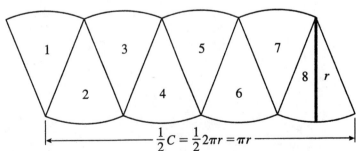

b. What measurement on the circle approximately represents the height of the parallelogram?

c. What measurement on the circle approximately represents the base of the parallelogram?

d. Recall that the area of a parallelogram is given by the product of its base and its height. Use your answers to parts b and c to determine the area of the parallelogram. What is the resulting expression?

A New Pool

Topic: *Circumference and Area Formulas in Context*

You are the proud owner of a new circular swimming pool of diameter 25 feet and are eager to dive in. However, you quickly discover that having a new pool requires making many decisions about other purchases.

1. Your first concern is a solar cover. You do some research and find that circular covers come in the following sizes: 400, 500, and 600 square feet. Which size is best for your needs? Explain.

2. You decide to build a circular concrete patio 6 feet wide all around your pool. What is the area covered by your patio? Explain.

3. State law requires that all pools be enclosed by a fence to prevent accidents. You decide to fence all around your pool and patio. How many feet of fencing do you need? Explain.

4. Your pool is uniformly 8 feet deep. How many cubic feet of water do you need to fill the pool? (Hint: Multiplying the area of the pool by its depth produces the volume of the pool, measured in cubic feet of water.) Explain.

EXERCISES

1. You have put on weight, and the radius of your waist has increased by an inch (assume that your waist is approximately circular). How much has your waist measurement increased?

Exercise numbers appearing in color are answered in the Selected Answers section of this book.

2. A Norman window has the shape of a rectangle with a semicircular top. If the rectangle is 4 feet wide and 5 feet tall, what is the area of the window?

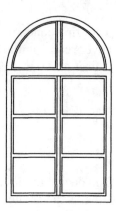

3. You want to know how much space is available between a basketball and the rim of the basket. One way to find out is to measure the circumference of each and use the circumference formula to determine the corresponding diameters. The distance you want to determine is the difference between the diameter of the rim and the diameter of the ball. Try it!

LAB ACTIVITY 1.24

Carpenter's Square

Topics: *Right Triangles, Pythagorean Theorem, Measurement, Angles, Square Roots*

In this activity you will experimentally verify an important right-triangle geometric formula used by surveyors, architects, and builders to check that two lines are perpendicular, that is, intersect at a 90° angle. You will need a protractor and ruler.

Recall that in a right triangle two sides (called *legs*) are perpendicular to each other. The side opposite the right angle is called the *hypotenuse* and is often denoted by the letter c; the legs are usually denoted by the letters, *a* and *b*.

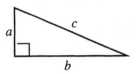

1. Use a protractor to construct three right triangles, one with legs of length 1 in. and 5 in., a second with legs of length 3 inches and 4 inches, and a third with legs of length 2 inches each.

2. Use a ruler to measure (in inches) the hypotenuse of each triangle, and record the lengths in the following table.

	a	b	c	a^2	b^2	c^2
TRIANGLE 1	1	5				
TRIANGLE 2	3	4				
TRIANGLE 3	2	2				

3. There does not appear to be a relationship between *a*, *b*, and *c*, but investigate further. Square *a*, *b*, and *c* and enter the values in the appropriate columns in the table in Problem 2.

4. What is the relationship between a^2, b^2, and c^2? Explain.

The Pythagorean theorem gives the relationship between the legs of a right triangle, *a* and *b*, and the hypotenuse, *c*. In words, the theorem states that the sum of the squares of the leg lengths is equal to the square of the hypotenuse length.

Symbolically, the theorem is written as: $c^2 = a^2 + b^2$ or $c = \sqrt{a^2 + b^2}$

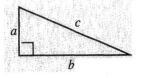

For example, if a right triangle has legs $a = 4$ centimeters and $b = 7$ centimeters, you can calculate the length of the hypotenuse as follows:

$$c = \sqrt{a^2 + b^2} = \sqrt{(4 \text{ cm})^2 + (7 \text{ cm})^2} = \sqrt{16 \text{ cm}^2 + 49 \text{ cm}^2}$$
$$= \sqrt{65 \text{ cm}^2} = \sqrt{65} \text{ cm} \approx 8.06 \text{ cm}$$

5. A right triangle has legs measuring 5 centimeters and 16 centimeters. Use the Pythagorean theorem to calculate the length of the hypotenuse. Check your answer by constructing the triangle and measuring its hypotenuse.

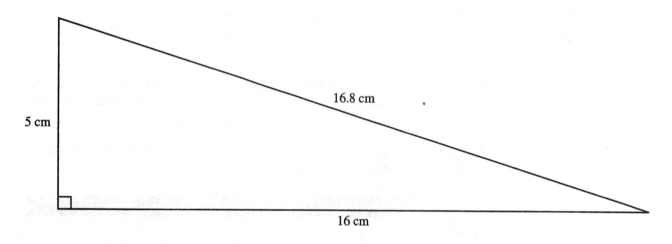

16.8 cm

5 cm

16 cm

6. In a right triangle, the sum of the measures of the two nonright angles is 90°. Verify this fact by using your protractor to obtain and then sum the measures of the nonright angles in each of the three right triangles in Problem 1.

	ONE ANGLE	OTHER ANGLE	SUM
TRIANGLE 1			
TRIANGLE 2			
TRIANGLE 3			

7. The experiment in Problem 6 also demonstrates that the sum of the three angles in a right triangle is 180°. This fact generalizes to any triangle. Verify this fact experimentally on each of the following three triangles:

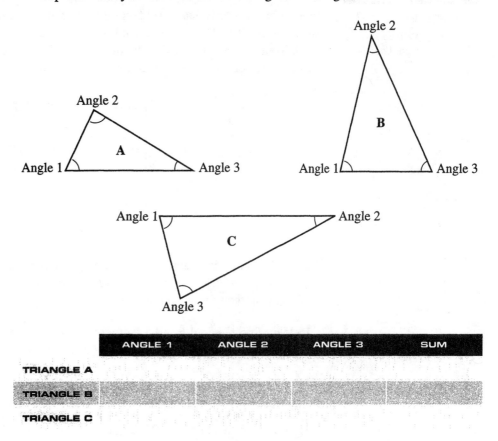

	ANGLE 1	ANGLE 2	ANGLE 3	SUM
TRIANGLE A				
TRIANGLE B				
TRIANGLE C				

The sum of the measures of the angles of a triangle is 180 degrees.

Septic Tank

Topics: *Pythagorean Theorem, Square Roots*

You are putting in a septic tank for your house. The building code in your area states that there must be at least 100 feet between the well and the septic tank. To make sure you meet code, you must find the distance between the septic tank and the well. Your house is located in the direct line of measurement from the well to the septic tank (see figure) preventing you from measuring this distance.

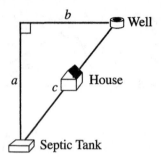

In this diagram, the distance between the well and the septic tank, represented by c, is the hypotenuse of a right triangle whose legs are a and b. Therefore, the Pythagorean theorem is applicable.

1. If $a = 65$ feet and $b = 85$ feet, do you meet code? Explain.

2. If $a = 55$ feet and $b = 75$ feet, do you meet code? Explain.

3. In calculating the square root of $a^2 + b^2$, is your answer the same as $a + b$? Explain.

4. If the distance between the septic tank and the well is exactly 100 feet and b is 80 feet, what is a?

EXERCISES

Use the context of this activity to answer the following questions.

1. If $a = 60$ feet and $b = 80$ feet, do you meet code? Explain.

2. If $a = 70$ feet and $b = 40$ feet, do you meet code? Explain.

3. If $c = 130$ feet and $a = 50$ feet, determine b.

4. If $c = 260$ feet and $b = 240$ feet, determine a.

ACTIVITY 1.26

Basketballs, Soup Cans, Boxes, and Ice Cream Cones

Topic: *Volume of Three-Dimensional Objects*

Three-dimensional objects appear everywhere. One important measure associated with these figures is their *volume*—the amount of "space" inside the objects, measured in unit cubes. The following table contains formulas for finding volumes.

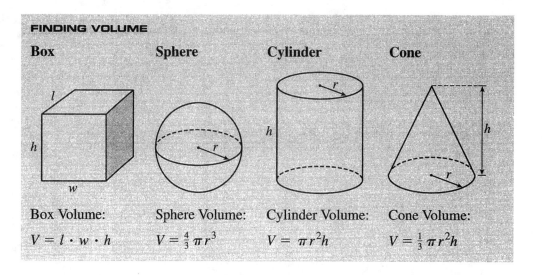

FINDING VOLUME

Box	Sphere	Cylinder	Cone
Box Volume:	Sphere Volume:	Cylinder Volume:	Cone Volume:
$V = l \cdot w \cdot h$	$V = \frac{4}{3}\pi r^3$	$V = \pi r^2 h$	$V = \frac{1}{3}\pi r^2 h$

For example, the volume of a standard basketball with radius 11 centimeters is given by

$$V = \frac{4}{3}\pi r^3 = \frac{4}{3}\pi \left(11 \text{ cm}\right)^3 = \frac{5324}{3}\pi \text{ cm}^3 \approx 5575.28 \text{ cm}^3.$$

1. Measure the dimensions of a typical soup can and use these measurements to determine its volume in cubic centimeters.

2. You buy a can of soda and notice that the label reads 12 ounces. You decide to check on the accuracy of the label. You measure the height of the can and find that it is approximately 4.5 inches, and the can's diameter is 2.5 inches. You check a math table and find that 1 oz $= 1.8$ in^3. Is the label accurate? Explain.

3. Which one of the following containers encloses the greatest volume? Explain.

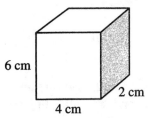

6 cm

4 cm   2 cm

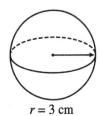

$r = 3$ cm

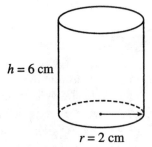

$h = 6$ cm

$r = 2$ cm

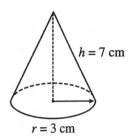

$h = 7$ cm

$r = 3$ cm

EXERCISES

1. You are assistant manager of the Tastee Ice Cream Shop in your hometown. Your manager has purchased a new cone size—the super deluxe. You have been asked to determine a price for soft ice cream cones made using the new cones.

a. Calculate the total volume of ice cream that fills the super deluxe cone in the accompanying diagram.

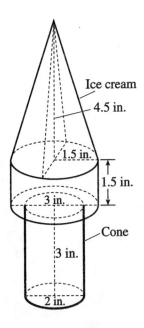

Ice cream

4.5 in.

1.5 in.

1.5 in.

3 in.

Cone

3 in.

2 in.

Exercise numbers appearing in color are answered in the Selected Answers section of this book.

b. The average cost per cubic inch of ice cream is 3 cents. If each cone costs 2 cents, calculate the cost of the ice cream and the cone.

c. The price charged for this ice cream cone is set at double the cost of the ice cream and the cone. Calculate this price.

EXPLORING NUMERACY

If you could put a rope firmly around the equator and then loosen the rope by 1 inch, do you think you could slip a piece of paper through the space between the rope and the globe? A penny? If you put a rope around a basketball and then loosen the rope by 1 inch, how thick an object do you think you can slip through the space between the rope and the basketball? Explain.

Another New Pool

Topics: *Measurement, Scale Drawing, Volume*

A friend of yours is so excited by your new pool (see Activity 1.23) that she decides to buy a new in-ground swimming pool with the dimensions given by the following scale drawing.

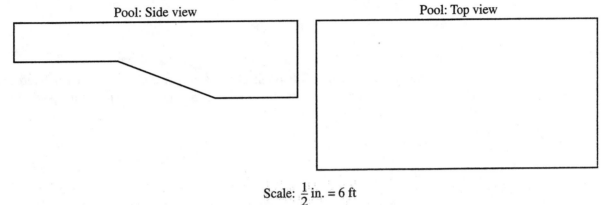

Scale: $\frac{1}{2}$ in. = 6 ft

1. Measure the scale drawing and use the measurements to determine the dimensions (in feet) of your friend's new pool.

2. Calculate the area of the top surface of water in her pool.

3. **a.** Calculate the area of the side of the pool (shown in the figure).

   b. Calculate the total volume of the pool. (*Hint:* What is the distance between the two sides?)

4. If the pool is to be filled with water to 6 inches from the top, calculate the amount of water, in cubic feet, needed to fill the pool.

5. Determine the number of gallons of water needed to fill the pool. (There are 7.48 gallons in 1 cubic foot of water.)

6. A garden hose can fill the pool at the rate of 4.5 gallons per minute. How many minutes will it take to fill the pool with the garden hose? How many hours? How many days?

7. A company that fills pools charges 3¢ per gallon for water delivered in a big tanker truck. How much will this company charge to fill the pool?

8. Because of the soil conditions in your area, your friend needs to know the weight of the water in the pool. Water weighs 62.4 pounds per cubic foot. Calculate the weight of the water in the pool to the nearest pound. Compare it with the weight of an average car.

9. The pool liner is guaranteed for five years. A new pool liner sells for $6.19 per square yard. How much will a new liner for your friend's pool cost? (Note that the liner covers all surfaces, the sides and bottom.)

10. To prevent accidents, state law requires that all pools be enclosed by a fence. How many feet of fencing are needed if a fence will be placed around the pool 4 feet from each side?

What Have I Learned?

In the Cluster 5 activities, you solved problems involving geometry. Review what you have learned by responding to the following questions.

1. Approximate the area of this irregular shape. Carefully explain your approach.

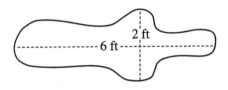

2. Measurement seldom produces the exact answer produced by the geometric formulas. Why do you think this is true?

3. You have a friend who has always had problems distinguishing perimeter from area. In language that your friend can understand, explain the difference. Expand your explanation to include the concept of volume. Include units in your explanation.

4. Why do you think so many shapes in the natural world are described by the formulas you investigated in these activities?

5. Geometry is one of the oldest areas of mathematics, with many important results dating back to the Greeks over 2000 years ago. Investigate some of this history by researching such names as Euclid or Archimedes. They and others may be found in history of mathematics books written by P. Beckmann, E. T. Bell, C. Boyer, F. Cajori, V. Katz, M. Kline, and D. Struick. The Internet is another good source of information. Write a summary of what you learn.

How Can I Practice?

1. Calculate the area of each of the following figures.

   a.

   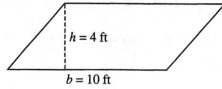

   $h = 4$ ft

   $b = 10$ ft

   b.

   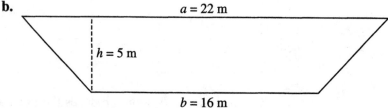

   $a = 22$ m

   $h = 5$ m

   $b = 16$ m

   c.

   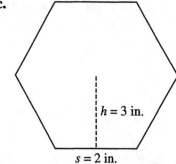

   $h = 3$ in.

   $s = 2$ in.

2. Calculate the area of each of the following figures.

   a. Rectangle topped by a semicircle

   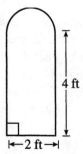

   4 ft

   ⊢—2 ft—⊣

b. Rectangle topped by a right triangle

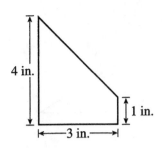

3. Determine the perimeter of each of the following.

   a. A parallelogram with a pair of parallel sides of 14 inches and 5 inches.

b.
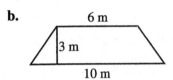

c.
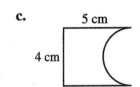

4. Determine the area of the *shaded region* in each of the following.

a.
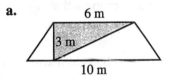

b.
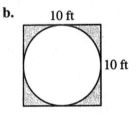

5. Determine the volume of each of the following.

a.
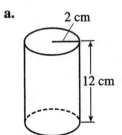

b.
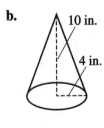

6. Consider the right triangle with dimensions as shown.

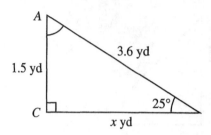

a. Determine the length x of the unknown side, rounded to the nearest thousandth.

b. Determine the measure of angle A.

c. Determine the area of the triangle.

7. You are remodeling your house. In one room, you want to put in a Norman window, which is a rectangle with a semicircle on top. The width of the window is 30 inches, and the total height of the window is 60 inches.

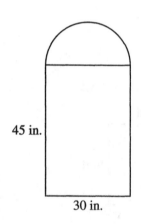

a. Determine the total area of the window, rounded to the nearest hundredth. Label the result appropriately.

b. Determine the total outside perimeter of the window, rounded to the nearest hundredth. Label the result appropriately.

8. In addition to a Norman window, you also intend to put in a 4-foot-wide concrete walkway along two sides of your house, as shown.

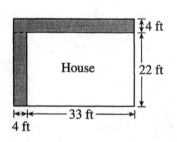

a. Determine the area covered by the walkway only.

b. If the walkway is to be 4 inches thick, then determine the volume of concrete needed to build it, rounded to the nearest hundredth. Label the result appropriately.

SKILLS CHECK 2

1. Which number is greater, 1.0001 or 1.001?

2. Multiply: $32.09 \cdot 0.0006$

3. Evaluate 27^0.

4. Evaluate $|-9|$.

5. Determine the length of the hypotenuse of a right triangle if each of the legs has a length of 6 meters.

6. Evaluate $|9|$.

7. Write 203,000,000 in scientific notation.

8. How many quarts are there in 8.3 liters?

9. Write 2.76×10^{-6} in standard form.

10. How many ounces are there in a box of crackers that weighs 283 grams?

11. Determine the area of a U.S. one-dollar bill.

12. Determine the circumference of a quarter.

13. Determine the area of a triangle with base 14 inches and height 18 inches.

14. Twenty-five percent of the students in your history class scored between 70 and 80 on the last exam. In a class of 32 students, how many students does this include?

15. You have decided to accept typing jobs to earn some extra money. Your first job is to type a 420-page thesis. If you can type 12 pages per hour, how long will it take you to finish the job?

16. If you make 10 mistakes in typing 8 pages, how many mistakes will you make typing a 420-page thesis?

Exercise numbers appearing in color are answered in the Selected Answers section of this book.

17. How many pieces of string 1.6 yards long can be cut from a length of string 9 yards long?

18. Reduce $\frac{16}{36}$ to lowest terms.

19. Change $\frac{16}{7}$ to a mixed number.

20. Change $4\frac{6}{7}$ to an improper fraction.

21. Add: $\frac{2}{9} + \frac{3}{5}$

22. Subtract: $4\frac{2}{5} - 2\frac{7}{10}$

23. Multiply: $\frac{4}{21} \cdot \frac{14}{9}$

24. Divide: $1\frac{3}{4} \div \frac{7}{12}$

25. You mix $2\frac{1}{3}$ cups of flour, $\frac{3}{4}$ cup of sugar, $\frac{3}{4}$ cup of mashed bananas, $\frac{1}{2}$ cup of walnuts, and $\frac{1}{2}$ cup of milk to make banana bread. How many cups of mixture do you have?

$$\frac{45}{6}$$

26. Your stock starts the day at $30\frac{1}{2}$ points and goes down $\frac{7}{8}$ of a point during the day. What is its value at the end of the day?

27. You have just opened a container of orange juice that has 64 fluid ounces. You have three people in your household who drink one 8-ounce serving of orange juice per day. In how many days will you need a new container?

28. You want to serve $\frac{1}{4}$-pound hamburgers at your barbecue. There will be seven adults and three children at the party, and you estimate that each adult will eat two hamburgers and each child will eat one. How much hamburger meat should you buy?

29. Your friend tells you that her height is 1.67 meters and her weight is 58 kilograms. Convert her height and weight to feet and pounds, respectively.

30. Convert the following units:

10 mi = _____ ft

3 qt = _____ oz

5 pt = _____ oz

6 gal = _____ oz

3 lb = _____ oz

31. The following table lists the minimum distance of each listed planet from Earth, in millions of miles. Convert each distance into scientific notation.

PLANET	DISTANCE (IN MILLIONS OF MILES)	DISTANCE (IN SCIENTIFIC NOTATION)
Mercury	50	
Venus	25	
Mars	35	
Jupiter	368	
Saturn	745	
Uranus	1606	
Neptune	2674	
Pluto	2658	

32. A recipe you obtained on the Internet indicates that you need to melt 650 grams of chocolate in $\frac{1}{5}$ liter of milk to prepare icing for a cake. How many pounds of chocolate and how many ounces of milk do you need?

33. You ask your friend if you may borrow his eraser. He replies that he has only a tiny piece of eraser—2.5×10^{-5} kilometers long. Does he really have such a tiny piece that he cannot share it with you?

34. $\left(3\frac{2}{3} + 4\frac{1}{2}\right) \div 2 =$

35. $18 \div 6 \cdot 3 =$

36. $18 \div (6 \cdot 3) =$

37. $\left(3\frac{3}{4} - 2\frac{1}{3}\right)^2 + 7\frac{1}{2} =$

38. $\left(5\frac{1}{2}\right)^2 - 8\frac{1}{3} \cdot 2 =$

39. $6^2 \div 3 \cdot 2 + 6 \div (-3 \cdot 2)^2 =$

40. $6^2 \div 3 \cdot -2 + 6 \div 3 \cdot 2^2 =$

41. $-4 \cdot 9 + -9 \cdot -8 =$

42. $-6/3 - 3 + 5^0 - 14 \cdot -2 =$

CHAPTER 1

Gateway Review

1. Write the number 2.0202 in words.

2. Write the number fourteen and three thousandths in standard form.

3. What is the place value of the 4 in the number 3.06704?

4. Add: $3.02 + 0.5 + 7 + 0.004$

5. Subtract 9.04 from 21.2.

6. Multiply: $6.003 \cdot 0.05$

7. Divide 0.0063 by 0.9.

8. Round 2.045 to the nearest hundredth.

9. Change 4.5 to a percent.

10. Change 0.3% to a decimal.

11. Change 7.3 to a fraction.

12. Change $\frac{3}{5}$ to a percent.

13. Write the numbers in order from largest to smallest:
    $1.001 \qquad 1.1 \qquad 1.01 \qquad 1\frac{1}{8}$

14. Evaluate 3^3.

15. Evaluate 6^0.

16. Evaluate 4^{-2}.

17. Evaluate $\sqrt{36}$.

18. Evaluate $\sqrt{\frac{4}{100}}$.

19. The square root of 18 falls between what two whole numbers?

20. Evaluate $|-12|$.

Exercise numbers appearing in color are answered in the Selected Answers section of this book.

21. Write 0.0000543 in scientific notation.

22. Write 3.7×10^4 in standard form.

23. Determine the average of your exam scores: 25 out of 30, 85 out of 100, and 60 out of 70. Assume that each exam counts equally.

24. Change $\frac{9}{2}$ to a mixed number.

25. Change $5\frac{3}{4}$ to an improper fraction.

26. Reduce $\frac{15}{25}$ to lowest terms.

27. Add: $\frac{1}{6} + \frac{5}{8}$

28. Subtract: $5\frac{1}{4} - 3\frac{3}{4}$

29. Multiply: $\frac{2}{9} \cdot 3\frac{3}{8}$

30. Divide $\frac{6}{11}$ by $\frac{8}{22}$.

31. Multiply: $2\frac{5}{8} \cdot 2\frac{2}{7}$

32. Solve the proportion for x:

$$\frac{x}{8} = \frac{9}{4}$$

33. What is 20% of 80?

34. Twenty-five percent of what number is 50?

35. Thirty is what percent of 60?

36. Find the length of one side of a right triangle when the other side is 7 centimeters and the hypotenuse is 12 centimeters. Write your answer rounded to the nearest whole number.

37. Find the circumference of a circle whose radius is 3 inches.

38. Determine the perimeter of the following figure.

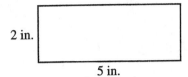

2 in.

5 in.

39. Find the area of a triangle with a base of 5 feet and a height of 7 feet.

40. Find the area of a circle whose radius is 1 inch. Round your answer to the nearest tenth.

41. Find the volume of a road cone with a radius of 10 centimeters and a height of 20 centimeters. Round your answer to the nearest whole number.

42. The number of ice-cream stands in your town decreased from 10 to 7 in one summer. What is the percent decrease in the number of stands?

43. A campus survey reveals that 30% of the students are in favor of the proposal for no smoking in the cafeteria. If 540 students responded to the survey, how many students are in favor of the proposal?

44. You read 15 pages of your psychology text in 90 minutes. At this rate, how many pages can you read in 4 hours?

45. The scale at a grocery store registered 0.62 kilogram. Convert this weight to pounds (1 kg = 2.2 lb). Round your answer to the nearest pound.

46. Your turtle walks at the rate of 2 centimeters per minute. What is the turtle's rate in inches per second (1 in. = 2.54 cm)?

47. Use the formula $C = \frac{5}{9}(F - 32)$ to determine the Celsius temperature when the Fahrenheit temperature is 50°.

48. $-5 + 4 =$

49. $2(-7) =$

50. $-3 - 4 - 6 =$

51. $-12 \div (-4) =$

52. $-5^2 =$

53. $(-1)(-1)(-1) =$

54. $-5 - (-7) =$

55. $-3 + 2 - (-3) - 4 - 9 =$

56. $3 - 10 + 7 =$

57. $\left(-\frac{1}{6}\right)\left(-\frac{3}{5}\right) =$

58. $7 \cdot 3 - \frac{4}{2} =$

59. $4(6 + 7 \cdot 2) =$

60. $3 \cdot 4^3 - \frac{6}{2} \cdot 3 =$

61. $5(7 - 3) =$

62. A deep-sea diver dives from the surface to 133 feet below the surface. If the diver swims down another 27 feet, determine his depth.

63. You lose $200 on each of three consecutive days in the stock market. Represent your total loss as a product of signed numbers, and write the result.

64. You have $85 in your checking account. You write a check for $53, make a deposit of $25, and then write another check for $120. How much is left in your account?

65. A poll is conducted asking 120 students about their preference for soft drinks. The results are given in the following table.

DRINK	Pepsi	Coke	7-Up	Dr. Pepper	Mountain Dew	Other	Total
FREQ.	37	33	12	10	9	19	120

    a. Draw a bar graph to represent these data.

    b. What percent of students prefer Dr. Pepper?

66. The mass of the hydrogen atom is about 0.00000000000000000000002 gram. If 1 gram is equal to 0.0022 pound, determine the mass of a hydrogen atom in pounds. Express the result in scientific notation.

Selected Answers

Chapter 1

Activity 1.3 **Exercises:** **1.** 3.143; **2.** 2.590; **3. b.** 2.542.

Activity 1.4 **Exercises:** **3. a.** $53.58; **b.** $3.75; **c.** $8.04; **d.** $65.37; **e.** $21.79; **4 a.** $55.92; **b.** $417.56; **c.** No, short $17.56.

Activity 1.5 **Exercises:** **1. b.** 4.134×10^{-5}; **c.** 5.551405×10^{14}; **2. a.** 453,200,000,000; **d.** 0.0000004532; **3. a.** 30; **d.** 12; **e.** 390625; **g.** .2; **4. b.** Approximately 89,740,000,000 or eighty-nine billion seven hundred forty million acres.

What Have I Learned? **1. b.** The total bill, including tax, is $105.07, so $100 will not cover your purchases.

How Can I Practice? **3. b.** 13; **d.** $5.\overline{81}$; **6.** approximately 8555; **7. a.** 1.7501 E 15 km; **b.** 5.83 E 9 seconds $\approx$ 185 years.

Activity 1.8 **Exercises:** **1.** $27.50; **4.** $\frac{11}{30}$; **6. a.** $2\frac{7}{9}$; **6. b.** $\frac{17}{28}$; **6. c.** $\frac{1}{6}$.

Activity 1.9 **Exercises:** **1.** 434; **3.** $\frac{5}{12}$; **5.** 22; **6. a.** $2\frac{17}{21}$; **c.** $9\frac{3}{4}$; **f.** $1\frac{13}{50}$.

Activity 1.10 **Exercises:** **2.** $1\frac{1}{6}$ cups.

How Can I Practice? **1.** $2\frac{7}{8}$ in.; **2.** $4\frac{9}{10}$; **4.** $1\frac{3}{4}$ ft; **6. d.** $1\frac{19}{30}$; **g.** $\frac{13}{36}$; **m.** 9; **p.** 16; **t.** $1\frac{23}{26}$; **v.** $5\frac{1}{4}$.

Activity 1.11 **Exercises:** **2. a.** $\frac{31}{55}$; **b.** $.56\overline{36}$; **c.** $\approx$ 56%; **5.** Test 1; **6.** 0.23%; **8.** 60.5%.

Activity 1.12 **Exercises:** **1. b.** 250; **e.** 15; **g.** 6; **h.** 180; **2. a.** 12; **c.** 45; **3.** fifty; **4.** $36.90; **6.** 35; **8.** 180; **10.** 770; **12.** $9; **13.** $125; **17.** $420,000.

Activity 1.13 **Exercises:** **1.** 15; **3.** $119,600; **5.** 1:36 P.M.

Activity 1.14 **Exercises:** **1.** Approximately

1.94×10^9 acres; **3.** 338,400 sq ft; **5.** 149,572,640 km; **9.** 2.12 quarts; **10.** Approximately 7900 miles.

Activity 1.15 **Exercises:** **1. a.** $125,000; **b.** Approximately 71.4%; **3.** 12.5%; **6.** 1760; **9.** $68.04.

What Have I Learned? **Exercises:** **5. a.** Growth: 35% increase; **b.** Growth: 7% increase; **d.** Decay: 14% decrease.

How Can I Practice? **Exercises:** **3.** $\approx$ 64%; **5.** $21; **8.** $\approx$ 77.35%; **10. a.** 432; **b.** $29.\overline{45}$ hr; **c.** $162; **12.** $8.\overline{18}$ kg, $\approx$ 2.83 ℓ; **16.** $\approx$ 29%; **17. a.** $\approx$ 6%; **20.** $\approx$ 84.62.

Skills Check 1 **Exercises:** **1.** 219; **2.** 5372; **3.** Sixteen and seven hundred nine ten-thousandths; **4.** 3402.029; **5.** 567.05; **6.** 2.599; **7.** 87.913; **8.** 28.82; **9.** 0.72108; **10.** 95.7; **11.** 12%; **12.** 300%; **13.** 0.065; **14.** 3.6; **15.** $0.1\overline{3}$; **16.** $\approx$ 42.9%; **17.** $\frac{1}{8}$; **18.** 3.0027, 3.0207, 3.027, 3.27; **19.** $\approx$ 41; **20.** $\approx$ 52% preferred Coke. **21.** $\approx$ $8.67 total cost of cap; **22.** $\approx$ 32% of monthly income is spent of food; **23.** 10,023 students are expected this year. **24.** 37.5% decrease; **25.** = 36,540,000,000 acres. **26. a.** No, the percent reductions are based on the price at the time of the specific reduction; **b.** $450 before Thanksgiving, $270 in December, and $135 in January; **c.** final price in January would be $135, the same as before. Before Thanksgiving $250; December $150; **27.** 74% of the pre-1980 scores; **28.** little over $7 million; **29.** approximately $1166.

Activity 1.17 **Exercises:** **3.** 43-yard gain; **6.** -11°C; **8.** 35°C.

Activity 1.18 **Exercises:** **4.** $125; **6.** total loss of $36.

Activity 1.19 **Exercises:** **2. a.** 3; **b.** -19; **d.** -14.4; **f.** 9; **g.** -1; **j.** $-30,000$; **k.** ≈ -11.538; **4. a.** 8.8×10^{-4} lb = .00088 lb.

How Can I Practice? **37.** 6 pounds;
38. 2616 feet apart; **39. b.** $-19°C$; **d.** $9°C$ drop;
e. $8°$ rise; **40. a.** -9; **c.** -12.625; **e.** 17; **g.** -9.

Activity 1.20 **Exercises: 2.** 13.5 cm, 4.225 sq cm;
4. 17.2 cm, 12.25 sq cm; **6.** 12.3 cm, 7.11 sq cm;
7. 15.75 sq cm, 15 cm.

Activity 1.21 **Exercises: 2.** ≈ 27.8 sq ft;
3. 66 sq ft; **5.** 1152 sq in.

Activity 1.23 **Exercises: 1.** ≈ 6.28 in.;
2. ≈ 26.283 sq ft.

Activity 1.25 **Exercises: 2.** No, since $80.6 < 100$,
you do not meet code. **3.** 120 ft.

Activity 1.26 **Exercises: 1. a.** 30.62 cu in.;
b. $\approx \$.94$; **c.** \$1.88.

How Can I Practice? **1. a.** 40 sq ft; **b.** 95 sq m;
c. 18 sq in.; **2. b.** 7.5 sq in.; **4.** $a \approx 21.46$ sq ft;
5. $b \approx 150.8$ cu cm; **7. a.** ≈ 1703.43 sq in.; **b.** 167.12 in.

Skills Check 2 **1.** 1.001; **2.** 0.019254; **3.** 1; **4.** 9;
5. ≈ 8.49 m; **6.** 9; **7.** 2.03×10^8; **8.** ≈ 8.8 quarts;
9. 0.00000276; **10.** ≈ 9.9 ounces; **11.** 16.1 sq in.;
12. ≈ 2.95 in.; **13.** 126 sq in.; **14.** 8 students; **15.** 35
hours; **16.** 525 mistakes; **17.** 5 pieces; **18.** $\frac{4}{9}$; **19.** $2\frac{2}{7}$;
20. $\frac{34}{7}$; **21.** $\frac{37}{45}$; **22.** $1\frac{7}{10}$; **23.** $\frac{8}{27}$; **24.** 3; **25.** $4\frac{5}{6}$ cups;
26. $29\frac{5}{8}$; **27.** $2.\overline{6}$ days; **28.** $4\frac{1}{4}$ lb; **29.** 128.2; **30.** 52,800
ft; 96 oz; 80 oz; 768 oz; 48 oz; **31.** 5×10^7; 2.5×10^7;
3.5×10^7; 3.68×10^8; 7.45×10^8; 1.606×10^9;
2.674×10^9; 2.658×10^9; **32.** 1.43 lb chocolate; ≈ 6.78
oz milk; **33.** a 1-inch eraser is big enough to share;
34. $4\frac{1}{12}$; **35.** 9; **36.** 1; **37.** $9\frac{73}{144}$; **38.** $13\frac{7}{12}$; **39.** $24\frac{1}{6}$;
40. -16; **41.** 36; **42.** 24.

Gateway Review **1.** two and two hundred two
ten-thousandths; **2.** 14.003; **3.** hundred thousandths;
4. 10.524; **5.** 12.16; **6.** 0.30015; **7.** 0.007; **8.** 2.05;
9. 450%; **10.** 0.003; **11.** $7\frac{3}{10}$ or $\frac{73}{10}$; **12.** 60%; **13.** $1\frac{1}{8}$, 1.1,
1.01, 1.001; **14.** 27; **15.** 1; **16.** $\frac{1}{4^2} = \frac{1}{16}$; **17.** 6; **18.** $\frac{2}{10} = \frac{1}{5}$;
19. $4 < \sqrt{18} < 5$; **20.** 12; **21.** 5.43×10^{-5};
22. 37,000; **23.** $\frac{25}{30} + \frac{85}{100} + \frac{60}{70} = 84.68\%$; **24.** $4\frac{1}{2}$; **25.** $\frac{23}{4}$;
26. $\frac{3}{5}$; **27.** $\frac{4}{24} + \frac{15}{24} = \frac{19}{24}$; **28.** $\frac{21}{4} - \frac{15}{4} = \frac{6}{4} = \frac{3}{2}$;

29. $\frac{\cancel{2}}{\cancel{8}} \cdot \frac{\overset{3}{\cancel{27}}}{\cancel{8}} = \frac{3}{4}$; **30.** $\frac{\overset{3}{\cancel{6}}}{\cancel{21}} \cdot \frac{\overset{2}{\cancel{22}}}{\cancel{8}} = \frac{6}{4} = \frac{3}{2} = 1\frac{1}{2}$; **31.** $\frac{\overset{3}{\cancel{21}}}{\cancel{8}} \cdot \frac{\overset{2}{\cancel{16}}}{\cancel{7}} = 6$;

32. $\frac{x}{8} = \frac{9}{4}$; $x = \frac{9 \cdot 8}{4} = 18$; **33.** $.2(80) = 16$;
34. $.25x = 50$, $\frac{25x}{100} = 50$, $x = \frac{5000}{25} = 200$; **35.** 50%;
36. ≈ 10 cm; **37.** ≈ 18.84 in.; **38.** $= 14$ in.; **39.** 17.5 sq
ft; **40.** ≈ 3.1 sq in.; **41.** $2.093.\overline{3} \approx 2.093$ cu cm;
42. 30% decrease; **43.** 162 students; **44.** 40 pages;
45. 1.364 lb; **46.** 0.013 in./sec; **47.** $10°C$; **48.** -1;
49. -14; **50.** -13; **51.** 3; **52.** -25; **53.** -1; **54.** 2;
55. -11; **56.** 0; **57.** $\frac{1}{10}$; **58.** 19; **59.** 80; **60.** 183; **61.** 20;
62. 160 feet below surface; **63.** $-\$600$, representing a
loss of \$600 in stocks; **64.** $-\$63$, meaning you are over-
drawn and are \$63 in debt; **65. b.** $\frac{10}{120} \approx 8.\overline{3}\%$; **66.** mass
of hydrogen atom $\approx 4.4 \times 10^{-27}$ lb.

Chapter 2

8 Pythagorean Theorem

OBJECTIVES

1 Find square roots using the square root key on a calculator.

2 Find the unknown length in a right triangle.

3 Solve application problems involving right triangles.

Recall the formula for area of a square, $A = s^2$. The square on the left has an area of 25 cm².

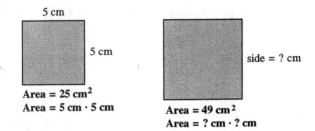

5 cm

5 cm

Area = 25 cm²
Area = 5 cm · 5 cm

side = ? cm

Area = 49 cm²
Area = ? cm · ? cm

The square on the right has an area of 49 cm². To find the length of a side, ask yourself, "What number can be multiplied by itself to give 49?" Because 7 • 7 = 49, the length of each side is 7 cm.

Remember: 7 • 7 = 49, so 7 is the **square root** of 49, or $\sqrt{49} = 7$. Also, $\sqrt{81} = 9$, since 9 • 9 = 81.

WORK PROBLEM I AT THE SIDE. ▶▶

A number that has a whole number as its square root is called a *perfect square.* For example, 9 is a perfect square because $\sqrt{9} = 3$, and 3 is a whole number.

The first few perfect squares are listed here.

$\sqrt{1} = 1$	$\sqrt{16} = 4$	$\sqrt{49} = 7$	$\sqrt{100} = 10$
$\sqrt{4} = 2$	$\sqrt{25} = 5$	$\sqrt{64} = 8$	$\sqrt{121} = 11$
$\sqrt{9} = 3$	$\sqrt{36} = 6$	$\sqrt{81} = 9$	$\sqrt{144} = 12$

OBJECTIVE 1 If a number is not a perfect square, then you can find its approximate square root by using a calculator with a square root key.

Calculator Tip: To find a square root, use the $\boxed{\sqrt{\ }}$ key on a standard calculator or the $\boxed{\sqrt{x}}$ key on a scientific calculator. In either case, you do *not* need to use the $\boxed{=}$ key. Try these. Jot down your answers.

To find $\sqrt{16}$ press: 16 $\boxed{\sqrt{x}}$ Answer is 4.
To find $\sqrt{7}$ press: 7 $\boxed{\sqrt{x}}$

For $\sqrt{7}$, your calculator shows 2.645751311 which is an *approximate* answer. We will be rounding to the nearest thousandth so $\sqrt{7} \approx 2.646$. To check, multiply 2.646 times 2.646. Do you get 7 as the result? No, but 7.001316 is very close to 7. The difference is due to rounding.

─ **E X A M P L E   I   Finding the Square Root of a Number**

Use a calculator to find each square root. Round your answers to the nearest thousandth.

(a) $\sqrt{35}$ Calculator shows 5.916079783; round to 5.916

(b) $\sqrt{124}$ Calculator shows 11.13552873; round to 11.136

(c) $\sqrt{200}$ Calculator shows 14.14213562; round to 14.142

1. Find each square root.

(a) $\sqrt{36}$

(b) $\sqrt{25}$

(c) $\sqrt{9}$

(d) $\sqrt{100}$

(e) $\sqrt{121}$

182

2. Use a calculator with a square root key to find each square root. Round to the nearest thousandth if necessary.

(a) $\sqrt{11}$

(b) $\sqrt{40}$

(c) $\sqrt{56}$

(d) $\sqrt{196}$

(e) $\sqrt{147}$

◀◀ **WORK PROBLEM 2 AT THE SIDE.**

OBJECTIVE 2 One place you will use square roots is when working with the *Pythagorean Theorem.* This theorem applies only to *right* triangles (triangles with a 90° angle). The longest side of a right triangle is called the **hypotenuse** (hy-POT-en-oos). It is opposite the right angle. The other two sides are called *legs.* The legs form the right angle.

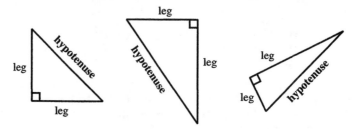

Examples of right triangles

Pythagorean Theorem

$$(\text{hypotenuse})^2 = (\text{leg})^2 + (\text{leg})^2$$

In other words, square the length of each side. After you have squared all the sides, the sum of the squares of the two legs will equal the square of the hypotenuse.

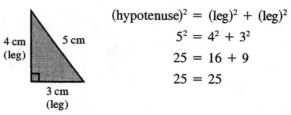

$$(\text{hypotenuse})^2 = (\text{leg})^2 + (\text{leg})^2$$
$$5^2 = 4^2 + 3^2$$
$$25 = 16 + 9$$
$$25 = 25$$

The theorem is named after Pythagoras, a Greek mathematician who lived about 2500 years ago. He and his followers may have used floor tiles to prove the theorem, as shown here.

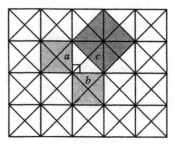

The right triangle in the center of the drawing has sides a, b, and c. The square drawn on side a contains four triangles. The square on side b contains four triangles. The square on side c contains eight triangles. The number of triangles in the square on side c equals the sum of the number of triangles in the squares on sides a and b, that is, 8 triangles = 4 triangles + 4 triangles. As a result, you often see the Pythagorean Theorem written as $c^2 = a^2 + b^2$.

ANSWERS

2. (a) ≈3.317 **(b)** ≈6.325
(c) ≈7.483 **(d)** 14
(e) ≈12.124

If you know the lengths of any two sides in a right triangle, you can use the Pythagorean Theorem to find the length of the third side.

Using the Pythagorean Theorem

To find the hypotenuse, use this formula:

$$\text{hypotenuse} = \sqrt{(\text{leg})^2 + (\text{leg})^2}$$

To find a leg, use this formula:

$$\text{leg} = \sqrt{(\text{hypotenuse})^2 - (\text{leg})^2}$$

Note

Remember: A small square drawn in one angle of a triangle indicates a right angle. You can use the Pythagorean Theorem *only* on triangles that have a right angle.

E X A M P L E   2   Finding the Unknown Length in a Right Triangle

Find the unknown length in each right triangle.

(a)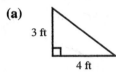

The length of the side opposite the right angle is unknown. That side is the hypotenuse, so use this formula.

$$\text{hypotenuse} = \sqrt{(\text{leg})^2 + (\text{leg})^2} \quad \text{Find the hypotenuse.}$$
$$\text{hypotenuse} = \sqrt{(3)^2 + (4)^2} \quad \text{Legs are 3 and 4.}$$
$$= \sqrt{9 + 16} \quad 3 \cdot 3 \text{ is 9} \quad \text{and} \quad 4 \cdot 4 \text{ is 16}$$
$$= \sqrt{25}$$
$$= 5$$

The hypotenuse is 5 ft long.

(b)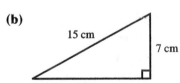

You *do* know the length of the hypotenuse (15 cm), so it is the length of one of the legs that is unknown. Use this formula.

$$\text{leg} = \sqrt{(\text{hypotenuse})^2 - (\text{leg})^2} \quad \text{Find a leg.}$$
$$\text{leg} = \sqrt{(15)^2 - (7)^2} \quad \text{Hypotenuse is 15, one leg is 7.}$$
$$= \sqrt{225 - 49} \quad 15 \cdot 15 \text{ is 225} \quad \text{and} \quad 7 \cdot 7 \text{ is 49}$$
$$= \sqrt{176} \quad \text{Use calculator to find } \sqrt{176}.$$
$$\approx 13.266 \quad \text{Round 13.26649916 to 13.266.}$$

The length of the leg is approximately 13.266 cm.

Note

You use the Pythagorean Theorem to find the *length* of one side, *not* the area of the triangle. Your answer will be in linear units, such as ft, yd, cm, m, and so on (*not* ft², cm², m²).

WORK PROBLEM 3 AT THE SIDE. ▶▶

---

3. Find the unknown length in each right triangle. Round your answers to the nearest thousandth, if necessary.

(a)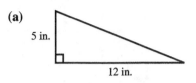

(b)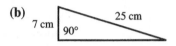

📱 **(c)**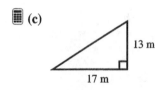

📱 **(d)**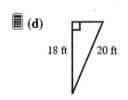

📱 **(e)**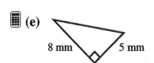

ANSWERS

3. (a) 13 in. **(b)** 24 cm
(c) ≈21.401 m **(d)** ≈8.718 ft
(e) ≈9.434 mm

184

4. These problems show ladders leaning against buildings. Find the unknown lengths. Round to the nearest thousandth of a foot, if necessary.

(a)

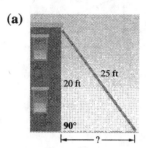

How far away from the building is the bottom of the ladder?

(b)

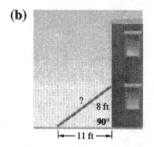

How long is the ladder?

(c) A 17-foot ladder is leaning against a building. The bottom of the ladder is 10 ft from the building. How high up on the building will the ladder reach? (*Hint:* Start by drawing the building and the ladder.)

OBJECTIVE 3 The next example shows an application of the Pythagorean Theorem.

EXAMPLE 3   Using the Pythagorean Theorem

A television antenna is on the roof of a house, as shown. Find the length of the support wire.

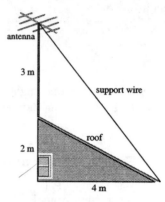

A right triangle is formed. The total length of the side at the left is 3 m + 2 m = 5 m.

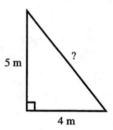

The support wire is the hypotenuse of the right triangle.

$\text{hypotenuse} = \sqrt{(\text{leg})^2 + (\text{leg})^2}$	Find the hypotenuse.
$\text{hypotenuse} = \sqrt{(5)^2 + (4)^2}$	Legs are 5 and 4.
$= \sqrt{25 + 16}$	5^2 is 25 and 4^2 is 16.
$= \sqrt{41}$	Use $\sqrt{x}$ key on a calculator.
≈ 6.403	Round 6.403124237 to 6.403.

The length of the support wire is ≈ 6.403 m.

◀◀ WORK PROBLEM 4 AT THE SIDE.

ANSWERS

4. (a) $\sqrt{225} = 15$ ft
   (b) $\sqrt{185} \approx 13.601$ ft
   (c) $\sqrt{189} \approx 13.748$ ft

8   Exercises

Find each square root. Starting with Exercise 5, use the square root key on a calculator.
Round your answers to the nearest thousandth, when necessary.

1. $\sqrt{16}$ **2.** $\sqrt{4}$ **3.** $\sqrt{64}$ **4.** $\sqrt{81}$

5. $\sqrt{11}$ **6.** $\sqrt{23}$ **7.** $\sqrt{5}$ **8.** $\sqrt{2}$

9. $\sqrt{73}$ **10.** $\sqrt{80}$ **11.** $\sqrt{101}$ **12.** $\sqrt{125}$

13. $\sqrt{190}$ **14.** $\sqrt{160}$ **15.** $\sqrt{1000}$ **16.** $\sqrt{2000}$

Find the areas of the squares on the sides of the right triangles in Exercises 17 and 18. Check
to see if the Pythagorean Theorem holds true.

17.
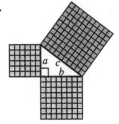

18.
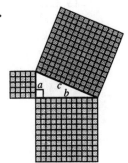

Find the unknown length in each right triangle. Use a calculator to find square roots. Round
your answers to the nearest thousandth, if necessary.

19.
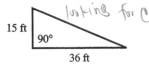
looking for c
15 ft
90°
36 ft

20.
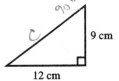
90°
c
9 cm
12 cm

21.
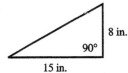
8 in.
90°
15 in.

a–b interchangeable

22.
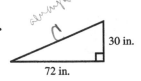
answr
c
30 in.
72 in.

23.

16 mm
20 mm

24.
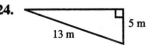
5 m
13 m

25.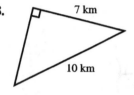
3 in.
8 in.

26.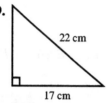
5 cm
11 cm

27.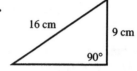
7 yd
90°
4 yd

28.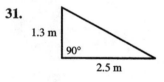
7 km
10 km

29.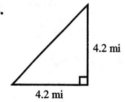
22 cm
17 cm

30.
16 cm
9 cm
90°

31.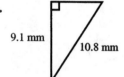
1.3 m
90°
2.5 m

32.
4.2 mi
4.2 mi

33.
11.5 cm
8.2 cm

34.
9.1 mm
10.8 mm

35.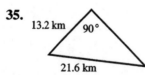
13.2 km
90°
21.6 km

36.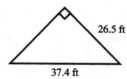
26.5 ft
37.4 ft

▦ *Solve each application problem. Round your answers to the nearest tenth when necessary.*

37. Find the length of this loading ramp.

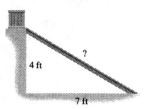

4 ft

?

7 ft

38. Find the unknown length in this roof plan.

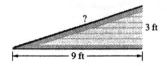

?

3 ft

9 ft

39. How high is the airplane above the ground?

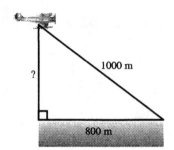

?

1000 m

800 m

40. Find the height of this farm silo.

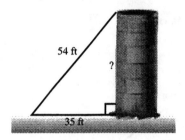

54 ft

?

35 ft

41. To reach his lady-love, a knight placed a 12-foot ladder against the castle wall. If the base of the ladder is 3 feet from the building, how high on the castle will the top of the ladder reach? Draw a sketch of the castle and ladder and solve the problem.

42. William drove his car 15 miles north, then made a right turn and drove 7 miles east. How far is he, in a straight line, from his starting point? Draw a sketch to illustrate the problem and solve it.

43. You know that $\sqrt{25} = 5$ and $\sqrt{36} = 6$. Using just that information (no calculator), describe how you could estimate $\sqrt{30}$. How would you estimate $\sqrt{26}$ or $\sqrt{35}$? Now check your estimates using a calculator.

44. Describe the two errors made by a student in solving this problem. Also find the correct answer. Round to the nearest tenth.

$$? = \sqrt{(13)^2 + (20)^2}$$
$$= \sqrt{169 + 400}$$
$$= \sqrt{569} \approx 23.9 \text{ m}^2$$

45. Find the lengths of $\overline{BC}$ and $\overline{BD}$.

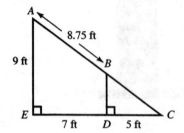

46. Find the lengths of $\overline{CD}$ and $\overline{DB}$. Round your answers to the nearest tenth.

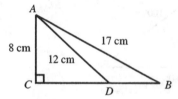

Review and Prepare

Find the missing number in each of the following proportions.

47. $\dfrac{2}{9} = \dfrac{x}{36}$

48. $\dfrac{7}{x} = \dfrac{21}{24}$

49. $\dfrac{x}{9.2} = \dfrac{15.6}{7.8}$

50. $\dfrac{0.8}{5} = \dfrac{12.4}{x}$

Basic Algebra 9

1 Signed Numbers

All the numbers you have studied so far in this book have been either 0 or greater than 0. Numbers greater than 0 are called *positive numbers*. For example, you have worked with these positive numbers:

salary of $800

temperature of 98.6°F

length of $3\frac{1}{2}$ feet.

OBJECTIVE 1 Not all numbers are positive. For example, "15 degrees below 0" or "a loss of $500" is expressed with a number less than 0. Numbers less than 0 are called **negative** (NEG-uh-tiv) **numbers.** Zero is neither positive nor negative.

Writing Negative Numbers

Write negative numbers with a *negative sign,* −.

For example, "15 degrees below 0" is written with a negative sign, as −15°. And "a loss of $500" is written −$500.

WORK PROBLEM I AT THE SIDE. ▶▶

OBJECTIVE 2 Earlier you graphed positive numbers on a number line. Negative numbers can also be shown on a number line. Zero separates the positive numbers from the negative numbers on the number line. The number −5 is read "negative five."

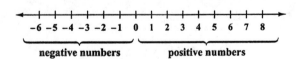

Note
For every positive number on a number line, there is a corresponding negative number on the opposite side of 0.

When you work with both positive and negative numbers (and zero) we say you are working with **signed numbers.**

OBJECTIVES
1 Write negative numbers.
2 Use number lines.
3 Graph numbers.
4 Use the < and > symbols.
5 Find absolute value.
6 Find the opposite of a number.

1. Write each number.

   (a) A temperature at the North Pole of 70 degrees below 0.

   (b) Your checking account is overdrawn by 15 dollars.

   (c) The altitude of a place 284 feet below sea level.

ANSWERS
1. (a) −70° (b) −$15 (c) −284 ft

2. Write *positive, negative,* or *neither* for each number.

(a) −8

(b) −$\frac{3}{4}$

(c) 1

(d) 0

3. Graph each list of numbers.

(a) −1, 1, −3, 3

−4 −3 −2 −1 0 1 2 3 4

(b) −2, 4, 0, −1, −4

−4 −3 −2 −1 0 1 2 3 4

Writing Positive Numbers

Positive numbers can be written in two ways:

1. Use a "+" sign. For example, +2 is "positive two."
2. Do not write any sign. For example, 3 is assumed to be "positive three."

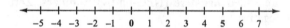 **WORK PROBLEM 2 AT THE SIDE.**

OBJECTIVE 3 The next example shows you how to graph signed numbers.

E X A M P L E 1   Graphing Signed Numbers

Graph **(a)** −4   **(b)** 3   **(c)** −1   **(d)** 0   **(e)** $1\frac{1}{4}$

Place a dot at the correct location for each number.

```
        (a)           (c) (d) (e)      (b)
    ←————●———+———+———●——●——●—+———●———+——→
       −4  −3  −2  −1  0   1   2   3   4
```

■

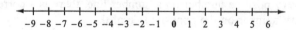 **WORK PROBLEM 3 AT THE SIDE.**

OBJECTIVE 4 As shown on the following number line, 3 is to the left of 5.

```
    ←—+——+——+——+——+——+——+——+——+——+——+——+——+——→
     −5 −4 −3 −2 −1  0  1  2  3  4  5  6  7
```

Also, 3 is *less than* 5.

Recall the following symbols for comparing two numbers.

< means **"is less than"**

> means **"is greater than"**

Use these symbols to write "3 is less than 5" as follows.

$$3 \quad < \quad 5$$
$$\downarrow \quad \downarrow \quad \downarrow$$
3 is less than 5

As this example suggests,

The lesser of two numbers is the one farther to the *left* on a number line.

E X A M P L E 2   Using the Symbols < and >

Use this number line and > or < to make true statements.

```
    ←—+——+——+——+——+——+——+——+——+——+——+——+——+——+——+——→
     −9 −8 −7 −6 −5 −4 −3 −2 −1  0  1  2  3  4  5  6
```

CONTINUED ON NEXT PAGE

ANSWERS

2. (a) negative **(b)** negative **(c)** positive
(d) neither

3. (a)

−4 −3 −2 −1 0 1 2 3 4

(b)

−4 −3 −2 −1 0 1 2 3 4

(a) $2 < 6$ (read "2 is less than 6") because 2 is to the *left* of 6 on the number line.

(b) $-9 < -4$ because -9 is to the *left* of -4.

(c) $2 > -1$ because 2 is to the *right* of -1.

(d) $-4 < 0$ because -4 is to the *left* of 0.

Note

When using $>$ and $<$, the *small* pointed end of the symbol points to the *smaller* (lesser) number.

> **WORK PROBLEM 4 AT THE SIDE.** ▶▶

OBJECTIVE 5 ▶ In order to graph a number on the number line, you need to know two things:

1. Which *direction* it is from 0. It can be in a *positive* direction or a *negative* direction. You can tell the direction by looking for a positive or negative sign.

2. How *far* it is from zero. The *distance* from zero is the **absolute** (ab-soh-LOOT) **value** of a number.

Absolute value is indicated by two vertical bars. For example, $|6|$ is read "the **absolute value** of 6."

Note

Absolute value is never negative, because it is a distance and distance is never negative.

E X A M P L E 3   Finding Absolute Value

Find each of the following.

(a) $|8|$ The distance from 0 to 8 is 8, so $|8| = 8$.

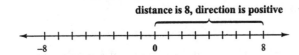

distance is 8, direction is positive

(b) $|-8|$ The distance from 0 to -8 is also 8, so $|-8| = 8$.

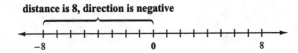

distance is 8, direction is negative

(c) $|0| = 0$

(d) $-|-3|$ First, $|-3|$ is 3. But there is also a negative sign outside the absolute value bars. So, -3 is the solution.

Note

A negative sign *outside* the absolute value bars is *not* affected by the absolute value bars. Therefore, your final answer is negative, as in Example 3(d) above.

> **WORK PROBLEM 5 AT THE SIDE.** ▶▶

4. Write $<$ or $>$ in each blank to make a true statement.

(a) $4 \underline{>} 0$

(b) $-1 \underline{\phantom{<}<} 0$

(c) $-3 \underline{\phantom{<}<} -1$

(d) $-8 \underline{>} -9$

(e) $0 \underline{>} -3$

5. Find each of the following.

(a) $|5|$ 5

(b) $|-5|$ 5

(c) $|-17|$ 17

(d) $-|-9|$ -9

(e) $-|2|$ -2

6. Find the opposite of each number.

(a) 4

(b) 10

(c) 49

(d) $\frac{2}{5}$

7. Find the opposite of each number.

(a) −4

(b) −10

(c) −25

(d) −1.9

(e) −0.85

(f) $-\frac{3}{4}$

OBJECTIVE 6 Two numbers that are the same distance from 0 on a number line, but on opposite sides of 0, are called **opposites** of each other. As this number line shows, −3 and 3 are opposites of each other.

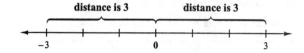

To indicate the opposite of a number, write a negative sign in front of the number.

E X A M P L E 4 Finding Opposites

Find the opposite of each number.

Number	Opposite
5	−(5) = −5 ←—— Write a negative sign.
9	−(9) = −9
$\frac{4}{5}$	$-\left(\frac{4}{5}\right) = -\frac{4}{5}$
0	−(0) = 0 ←—— No negative sign.

The opposite of 0 is 0. Zero is neither positive nor negative.

◀◀ **WORK PROBLEM 6 AT THE SIDE.**

Some numbers have two negative signs, such as

$$-(-3).$$

The negative sign in front of −3 means the *opposite* of −3. The opposite of −3 is 3, so

$$-(-3) = 3.$$

Use the following rule to find the opposite of a negative number.

Double Negative Rule

$$-(-x) = x$$

The opposite of a negative number is positive.

E X A M P L E 5 Finding Opposites

Find the opposite of each number.

Number	Opposite	
−2	−(−2) = 2	By double negative rule
−9	−(−9) = 9	
$-\frac{1}{2}$	$-\left(-\frac{1}{2}\right) = \frac{1}{2}$	

◀◀ **WORK PROBLEM 7 AT THE SIDE.**

1 *Exercises*

Write a signed number for each of the following.

1. Water freezes at 32 degrees above zero on the Fahrenheit temperature scale.

2. She made a profit of $920.

3. The price of the stock fell $12.

4. His checking account is overdrawn by $30.

5. The river is 20 feet above flood stage.

6. The team lost 6 yards on that play.

Write positive, negative, *or* neither *for each of the following numbers.*

7. 24

8. -8

9. $-\dfrac{7}{10}$

10. $2\dfrac{1}{3}$

11. 0

12. $+6$

13. -6.3

14. -0.25

Graph each of the following lists of numbers.

Example: $-3, -\dfrac{2}{3}, -5, 1, 2, \dfrac{3}{4}$ **Solution:** Place a dot on a number line for each number.

15. $4, -1, 2, 3, 0, -2$

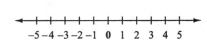

16. $-5, -3, 1, 4, 0$

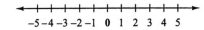

17. $-\dfrac{1}{2}, -3, -5, \dfrac{1}{2}, 1\dfrac{3}{4}, 3$

18. $-4, -\dfrac{3}{4}, -2, 4, 1, 2\dfrac{1}{2}$

19. $-2, -4, -3\frac{1}{5}, -\frac{5}{8}, 1, 2$

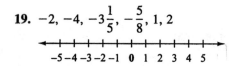

20. $-5, -3, -2, -4\frac{2}{3}, -1\frac{1}{2}, 0, 1$

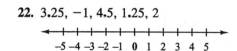

21. $3, 4.5, -1.5, 2.2, 0.1$

22. $3.25, -1, 4.5, 1.25, 2$

23. $-14, -11, -10.5, -13, -7.3$

24. $-10, -7, -14.8, -9.25, -13.75$

Write < or > in each blank to make a true statement.

Examples: -4 _____ 2 -5 _____ -9

Solutions: Because -4 is to the *left* of 2 on a number line, -4 is less than 2.

$-4 < 2$

Because -5 is to the *right* of -9 on a number line, -5 is greater than -9.

$-5 > -9$

25. 9 _____ 14

26. 6 _____ 11

27. 0 _____ -2

28. 0 _____ 2

29. -6 _____ 3

30. -4 _____ 7

31. 1 _____ 0

32. -1 _____ 0

33. -11 _____ -2

34. -5 _____ -1

35. -75 _____ -72

36. -50 _____ -60

37. 2 _____ -1

38. 4 _____ -9

39. -115 _____ -120

40. -205 _____ -210

Name _____

Find the absolute value of the following.

> **Examples:** $|8|$ $|-7|$ $-|-2|$
>
> **Solutions:** $|8| = 8$ $|-7| = 7$ $-|-2| = -2$

41. $|5|$ **42.** $|12|$ **43.** $|-5|$ **44.** $|-16|$ **45.** $|-1|$

46. $|-14|$ **47.** $|251|$ **48.** $|397|$ **49.** $|0|$ **50.** $|-199|$

51. $\left|-\dfrac{1}{2}\right|$ **52.** $\left|-\dfrac{9}{5}\right|$ **53.** $|-9.5|$ **54.** $|-0.72|$ **55.** $|0.618|$

56. $|4.7|$ **57.** $-|-10|$ **58.** $-|-8|$ **59.** $-\left|-\dfrac{5}{2}\right|$ **60.** $-\left|-\dfrac{1}{3}\right|$

61. $-|-7.6|$ **62.** $-|-1.03|$ **63.** $-|4|$ **64.** $-|20|$

Find the opposite of each number.

> **Examples:**   **Solutions:**
>
> | Number | Opposite |
> |--------|----------|
> | 8 | $-(8) = -8$ |
> | -5 | $-(-5) = 5$ |
> | 0 | $-(0) = 0$ |

65. 2   **66.** 7   **67.** -54 **68.** -75

69. -11 **70.** -24 **71.** 163   **72.** 502

73. 0   **74.** $\frac{5}{8}$ **75.** $-4\frac{1}{2}$ **76.** $-1\frac{2}{3}$

77. 5.2   **78.** 3.7   **79.** -1.4 **80.** -0.65

81. In your own words, explain opposite numbers. Include an example of opposite numbers and draw a number line to illustrate your example.

82. Explain why the opposite of zero is zero.

83. Describe three different situations at home, work, or school where you have used negative numbers.

84. Explain in your own words why absolute value is never negative.

Write true *or* false *for each statement.*

85. $|-5| > 0$ True   **86.** $|-12| > |-15|$ False   **87.** $0 < -(-6)$ True

88. $-9 < -(-6)$ True   **89.** $-|-4| < -|-7|$ False   **90.** $-|-0| > 0$

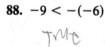 *Review and Prepare*

Add or subtract the following numbers.

91. $\frac{3}{4} + \frac{1}{5}$ **92.** $\frac{3}{10} + \frac{3}{8}$

93. $\frac{5}{6} - \frac{1}{4}$ **94.** $\frac{2}{3} - \frac{5}{9}$

2 | Addition and Subtraction of Signed Numbers

You can show a positive number on a number line by drawing an arrow pointing to the right. In the following examples both arrows represent positive 4 units.

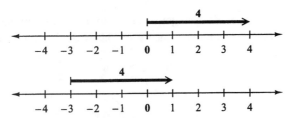

Draw arrows pointing to the left to show negative numbers. Both of the following arrows represent −3 units.

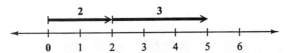

WORK PROBLEM 1 AT THE SIDE. ▶▶

OBJECTIVE 1 You can use a number line to add signed numbers. For example, the next number line shows how to add 2 and 3.

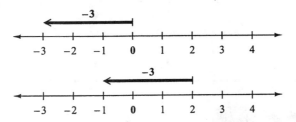

Add 2 and 3 by starting at zero and drawing an arrow 2 units to the right. From the end of this arrow, draw another arrow 3 units to the right. This second arrow ends at 5, showing that

$$2 + 3 = 5.$$

─**E X A M P L E   1**   **Adding Signed Numbers by Using a Number Line**

Add by using a number line.

(a) 4 + (−1)

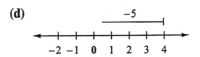

Start at zero and draw an arrow 4 units to the right. From the end of this arrow, draw an arrow 1 unit to the *left*. (Remember to go to the left for a negative number.) This second arrow ends at 3, so

$$4 + (−1) = 3.$$

Note
Always start at 0 when adding on the number line.

CONTINUED ON NEXT PAGE

CONTINUED ON NEXT PAGE

OBJECTIVES

1 ▶ Add signed numbers by using a number line.

2 ▶ Add signed numbers without using a number line.

3 ▶ Find the additive inverse of a number.

4 ▶ Subtract signed numbers.

5 ▶ Add or subtract a series of signed numbers.

1. Complete each arrow so it represents the indicated number of units.

(a)

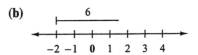

(b)

(c)

(d)

ANSWERS

1. (a)

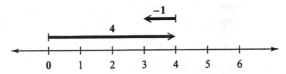

(b)

(c)

(d)

199

2. Draw arrows to find each of the following.

(a) 3 + (−2)

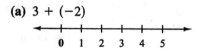

(b) −4 + 1

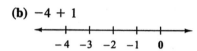

(c) −3 + 7

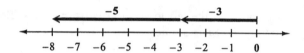

(d) −1 + (−4)

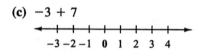

2. (a) 3 + (−2) = 1

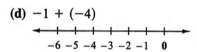

(b) −4 + 1 = −3

(c) −3 + 7 = 4

(d) −1 + (−4) = −5

(b) −6 + 2

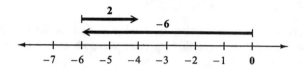

Draw an arrow from zero going 6 units to the left. From the end of this arrow, draw an arrow 2 units to the right. This second arrow ends at −4, so

$$-6 + 2 = -4.$$

(c) −3 + (−5)

As the arrows along the number line show,

$$-3 + (-5) = -8.$$

◀◀ **WORK PROBLEM 2 AT THE SIDE.**

OBJECTIVE 2 ▶ After working with number lines for awhile, you will see ways to add signed numbers without drawing arrows. You already know how to add two positive number. Here are the steps for adding two negative numbers.

Adding Negative Numbers

Step 1 Add the absolute values of the numbers.

Step 2 Write a negative sign in front of the sum.

E X A M P L E 2 Adding Negative Numbers

Add (without number lines).

(a) −4 + (−12)

The absolute value of −4 is **4**.
The absolute value of −12 is **12**.

Add the absolute values.

$$4 + 12 = 16$$

Write a negative sign in front of the sum.

$$-4 + (-12) = -16 \quad \text{Write a negative sign in front of 16.}$$

(b) −5 + (−25) = −30 ← Sum of absolute values, with a negative sign written in front of 30.

(c) −11 + (−46) = −57

CONTINUED ON NEXT PAGE ───

(d) $-\dfrac{3}{4} + \left(-\dfrac{1}{2}\right)$

The absolute value of $-\frac{3}{4}$ is $\frac{3}{4}$, and the absolute value of $-\frac{1}{2}$ is $\frac{1}{2}$. Add the absolute values. Check that the answer is in lowest terms.

$$\frac{3}{4} + \frac{1}{2} = \frac{3}{4} + \frac{2}{4} = \frac{5}{4} \quad \leftarrow \text{ Lowest terms.}$$

Write a negative sign in front of the sum.

$$-\frac{3}{4} + \left(-\frac{1}{2}\right) = -\frac{5}{4} \quad \text{Write a negative sign.}$$

Note

In algebra we always write fractions in lowest terms, but usually do *not* change improper fractions to mixed numbers because improper fractions are easier to work with. In Example 2(d) above, we checked that $-\frac{5}{4}$ was in lowest terms but did *not* rewrite it as $-1\frac{1}{4}$.

WORK PROBLEM 3 AT THE SIDE. ▶▶

Use the following steps to add two numbers with *different* signs.

Adding Two Numbers with Different Signs

Step 1 Subtract the smaller absolute value from the larger absolute value.

Step 2 Write the sign of the number with the *larger* absolute value in front of the answer.

E X A M P L E 3   Adding Two Numbers with Different Signs

Add.

(a) $8 + (-3)$

Find this sum with a number line as follows.

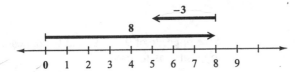

Because the top arrow ends at 5,

$$8 + (-3) = 5.$$

Find the sum by using the rule as follows. First, find the absolute value of each number.

$$|8| = 8 \qquad |-3| = 3$$

Subtract the absolute value of the smaller number from the larger number.

$$8 - 3 = 5$$

Here the positive number 8 has the larger absolute value, so the answer is positive.

$$8 + (-3) = 5 \quad \leftarrow \text{ Positive answer}$$

CONTINUED ON NEXT PAGE

3. Add.

(a) $-4 + (-4)$

(b) $-3 + (-20)$

(c) $-31 + (-5)$

(d) $-10 + (-8)$

(e) $-\dfrac{9}{10} + \left(-\dfrac{3}{5}\right)$

$$-\frac{3}{2\cancel{10}} - \frac{\cancel{6}}{\cancel{5}1} = \frac{-3}{2}$$

Answers

3. (a) -8 (b) -23 (c) -36 (d) -18
   (e) $-\dfrac{3}{2}$

4. Add.

(a) $10 + (-2)$

(b) $-7 + 8$

(c) $-11 + 11$

(d) $23 + (-32)$

(e) $-\dfrac{7}{8} + \dfrac{1}{4}$

(b) $-12 + 4$

First, find absolute values.

$$|-12| = \mathbf{12} \qquad |4| = \mathbf{4}$$

Subtract:

$$\mathbf{12 - 4} = 8$$

The negative number -12 has the larger absolute value, so the answer is negative.

$$-12 + 4 = \underset{\uparrow}{-8}$$

Write negative sign in front of the answer because -12 has the larger absolute value.

(c) $15 + (-21) = \underset{\uparrow}{-6}$

Write negative sign in front of the answer because -21 has the larger absolute value.

(d) $13 + (-9) = 4 \leftarrow$ Positive answer because the positive number 13 has the larger absolute value.

(e) $-\dfrac{1}{2} + \dfrac{2}{3}$

The absolute value of $-\frac{1}{2}$ is $\frac{1}{2}$, and the absolute value of $\frac{2}{3}$ is $\frac{2}{3}$. Subtract the absolute value of the smaller number from the larger.

$$\frac{2}{3} - \frac{1}{2} = \frac{4}{6} - \frac{3}{6} = \frac{1}{6}$$

Because the positive number $\frac{2}{3}$ has the larger absolute value, the answer is positive.

$$-\frac{1}{2} + \frac{2}{3} = \frac{1}{6} \leftarrow \text{Positive answer}$$

◀◀ **WORK PROBLEM 4 AT THE SIDE.**

OBJECTIVE 3▶ Recall that the opposite of 9 is -9, and the opposite of -4 is $-(-4)$, or 4. Add these opposites as follows.

$$9 + (-9) = 0 \quad and \quad -4 + 4 = 0$$

The sum of a number and its opposite is always 0. For this reason, opposites are also called **additive** (ADD-ih-tiv) **inverses** of each other.

Additive Inverse

The opposite of a number is called its **additive inverse**. The sum of a number and its opposite is zero.

ANSWERS

4. (a) 8 **(b)** 1 **(c)** 0 **(d)** -9 **(e)** $-\dfrac{5}{8}$

EXAMPLE 4   Finding the Additive Inverse

This chart shows you several numbers and the additive inverse of each.

Number	Additive Inverse	Sum of Number and Inverse
6	−6	$6 + (−6) = 0$
−8	$−(−8)$ or 8	$(−8) + 8 = 0$
4	−4	$4 + (−4) = 0$
−3	$−(−3)$ or 3	$−3 + 3 = 0$
$\dfrac{5}{8}$	$−\dfrac{5}{8}$	$\dfrac{5}{8} + \left(−\dfrac{5}{8}\right) = 0$
0	0	$0 + 0 = 0$

WORK PROBLEM 5 AT THE SIDE. ▶▶

OBJECTIVE 4 You may have noticed that negative numbers are often written with parentheses, like $(−8)$. This is especially helpful when subtracting because the $−$ sign is used both to indicate a **negative number** and to indicate **subtraction**.

Example	How to Say It
$(−5)$	**negative five**
8	positive eight
$−3 − 2$	**negative three minus** positive two
$6 − (−4)$	positive six **minus negative four**
$−7 − (−1)$	**negative seven minus negative one**
$8 − 3$	positive eight **minus** positive three

Note
Be sure you understand when the "$−$" sign means "subtract," and when it means "negative number."

WORK PROBLEM 6 AT THE SIDE. ▶▶

When working with signed numbers, it is helpful to write a subtraction problem as an addition problem. For example, you know that $6 − 4 = 2$. But you get the same result by *adding* 6 and the *opposite* of 4, that is, $6 + (−4)$.

$$\left.\begin{array}{l} 6 − 4 = 2 \\ 6 + (−4) = 2 \end{array}\right\} \text{Same result}$$

This suggests the following definition of subtraction.

Defining Subtraction

The difference of two numbers, a and b, is

$$a − b = a + (−b).$$

Subtract two numbers by adding the first number and the opposite (additive inverse) of the second.

---

5. Give the additive inverse of each number. Then find the sum of the number and its inverse.

(a) 12

(b) −9

(c) 3.5

(d) $−\dfrac{7}{10}$

(e) 0

6. Write each example in words.

(a) $−7 − 2$

(b) $−10$

(c) $3 − (−5)$

(d) 4

(e) $−8 − (−6)$ _−2_

(f) $2 − 9$ _−7_

ANSWERS

5. (a) $−12$; $12 + (−12) = 0$
   (b) 9; $−9 + 9 = 0$
   (c) $−3.5$; $3.5 + (−3.5) = 0$
   (d) $\dfrac{7}{10}$; $−\dfrac{7}{10} + \dfrac{7}{10} = 0$
   (e) 0; $0 + 0 = 0$
6. (a) negative seven minus positive two
   (b) negative ten
   (c) positive three minus negative five
   (d) positive four
   (e) negative eight minus negative six
   (f) positive two minus positive nine

204

7. Subtract.

(a) $-6 - 5$

(b) $3 - (-10)$

(c) $-8 - (-2)$

(d) $4 - 9$

(e) $-7 - (-15)$

(f) $-\dfrac{2}{3} - \left(-\dfrac{5}{12}\right)$

Subtracting Signed Numbers

To subtract two signed numbers, add the opposite of the second number to the first number. Use these steps.

Step 1 Change the subtraction sign to addition.

Step 2 Change the sign of the second number to its opposite.

Step 3 Proceed as in addition.

Note

The pattern in a subtraction problem is:

$$\underset{\text{number}}{\text{1st}} - \underset{\text{number}}{\text{2nd}} = \underset{\text{number}}{\text{1st}} + \underset{\text{2nd number}}{\text{opposite of}}$$

E X A M P L E 5   Subtracting Signed Numbers

Subtract.

(a) $8 - 11$

The first number, 8, stays the same. Change the subtraction sign to addition. Change the sign of the second number to its opposite.

$$\begin{array}{ccc} \text{Positive 8} & 8 - \quad 11 & \text{Positive 11 changed to} \\ \text{stays} & \downarrow \quad \downarrow & \text{its opposite } -11 \\ \text{the same} & 8 + (-11) & \end{array}$$

Subtraction changed to addition

Now add.

$$8 + (-11) = -3$$
$$\text{So } 8 - \quad 11 = -3 \quad \text{also.}$$

(b) $\begin{array}{cc} -9 - & 15 \\ \downarrow & \downarrow \\ \end{array}$ Positive 15 is changed to its opposite (-15).
$$-9 + (-15) = -24$$

(c) $\begin{array}{cc} -5 - & (-7) \\ \downarrow & \downarrow \\ \end{array}$ Negative 7 is changed to its opposite $(+7)$.
$$-5 + (+7) = 2$$

(d) $\begin{array}{cc} 7.6 - & (-8.3) \\ \downarrow & \downarrow \\ \end{array}$ Negative 8.3 is changed to its opposite $(+8.3)$.
$$7.6 + (+8.3) = 15.9$$

(e) $\begin{array}{cc} \dfrac{5}{8} - & \left(-\dfrac{1}{2}\right) \\ \downarrow & \downarrow \\ \end{array}$
$$\frac{5}{8} + \left(+\frac{1}{2}\right) = \frac{5}{8} + \left(+\frac{4}{8}\right) = \frac{9}{8}$$

◄◄ WORK PROBLEM 7 AT THE SIDE.

ANSWERS

7. (a) -11 **(b)** 13 **(c)** -6 **(d)** -5 **(e)** 8
(f) $-\dfrac{1}{4}$

Objective 5 If a problem involves both addition and subtraction, use the order of operations and work from left to right.

┌─ **E X A M P L E 6** **Combining Addition and Subtraction of Signed Numbers**

Perform the addition and subtraction from left to right.

(a) $\underbrace{-6 + (-11)}_{-17} - 5$

$\quad\quad -17 \quad - \quad 5 \quad$ Change subtraction to addition;
$\quad\quad\quad\quad\quad\downarrow\quad\quad\downarrow\quad$ change positive 5 to its opposite (−5)

$\quad\quad \underbrace{-17 \quad + \quad (-5)}_{-22}$

(b) $4 - (-3) + (-9) \quad$ Change subtraction to addition;
$\quad\quad\downarrow\quad\downarrow\quad\quad\quad$ change −3 to its opposite (+3).

$\quad \underbrace{4 + (+3)}_{7} + (-9)$

$\quad\quad \underbrace{7 \quad\quad + (-9)}_{-2}$

WORK PROBLEM 8 AT THE SIDE. ▶▶

┌─ **E X A M P L E 7** **Using the Order of Operations to Combine More than Two Numbers**

Find each sum.

(a) $\underbrace{-7 + 12}_{5} + (-3)$

$\quad \underbrace{5 \quad + (-3)}_{2}$

(b) $\underbrace{14 + (-9)}_{5} - (-8) + 10$

$\quad\quad 5 \quad - (-8) + 10 \quad$ Change subtraction to addition;
$\quad\quad\quad\downarrow\quad\downarrow\quad\quad\quad$ change −8 to its opposite (+8).

$\quad \underbrace{5 \quad + (+8)}_{13} + 10$

$\quad\quad \underbrace{13 \quad\quad + 10}_{23}$

(c) −6.3
$\quad\quad$ −14.9
$\quad\quad$ 8.5
$\quad\quad$ −7.4
$\quad\quad$ 5.2

Start at the top.

$\begin{array}{c} \left.\begin{array}{r}-6.3\\-14.9\end{array}\right\} \rightarrow \left.\begin{array}{r}-21.2\\8.5\end{array}\right\} \rightarrow \left.\begin{array}{r}-12.7\\-7.4\end{array}\right\} \rightarrow \begin{array}{r}-20.1\\5.2\\\hline -14.9\end{array} \\ \begin{array}{r}8.5\\-7.4\\5.2\end{array} \quad \begin{array}{r}-7.4\\5.2\end{array} \quad \begin{array}{r}5.2\end{array} \end{array}$

WORK PROBLEM 9 AT THE SIDE. ▶▶

8. Perform the addition and subtraction from left to right.

(a) $6 - 7 + (-3)$

(b) $-2 + (-3) - (-5)$

(c) $-3 - (-9) - (-5)$

(d) $8 - (-2) + (-6)$

9. Add.

(a) $-1 - 2 + 3 - 4$

(b) $7 - 6 - 5 + (-4)$

(c) $-6 + (-15) - (-19)$
$\quad\quad + (-25)$

(d) −19.2
$\quad\quad$ −6.7
$\quad\quad$ 15.8
$\quad\quad$ 17.1
$\quad\quad$ −5.4

ANSWERS
8. (a) −4 **(b)** 0 **(c)** 11 **(d)** 4
9. (a) −4 **(b)** −8 **(c)** −27 **(d)** 1.6

2   *Exercises*

Add by using the number line.

1. −2 + 5

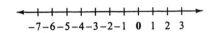
−7 −6 −5 −4 −3 −2 −1 0 1 2 3

2. −3 + 4

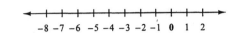
−8 −7 −6 −5 −4 −3 −2 −1 0 1 2

3. −5 + (−2)

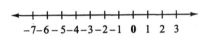
−7 −6 − 5 −4 −3 −2 −1 0 1 2 3

4. −2 + (−2)

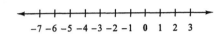
−7 −6 −5 −4 −3 −2 −1 0 1 2 3

5. 3 + (−4)

−7 −6 − 5 −4 −3 −2 −1 0 1 2 3

6. 5 + (−1)

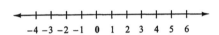
−4 −3 −2 −1 0 1 2 3 4 5 6

Add.

Example: −4 + (−11)   **Solution:** Add absolute values.

$$|-4| = 4 \qquad |-11| = 11 \qquad 4 + 11 = 15$$

Write a negative sign in front of the sum,
because both numbers are negative.   −4 + (−11) = **−15**

7. −8 + 5

8. −3 + 2

9. −1 + 8

10. −4 + 10

11. −2 + (−5)

12. −7 + (−3)

13. 6 + (−5)

14. 11 + (−3)

15. 4 + (−12)

16. 9 + (−10)

17. −10 + (−10)

18. −5 + (−20)

Write and solve an addition problem for each situation.

19. The football team gained 13 yards on the first play and lost 17 yards on the second play.

20. At penguin breeding grounds on Antarctic islands, winter temperatures routinely drop to −15°C; but at the interior of the continent, temperatures may easily drop another 60° below that.

21. Nicole's checking account was overdrawn by $52.50. She deposited $50 in the account.

22. $48.40 was stolen from Jay's car. He got $30 of it back.

Add.

23. $7.8 + (-14.6)$

24. $4.9 + (-8.1)$

25. $-\dfrac{1}{2} + \dfrac{3}{4}$

26. $-\dfrac{2}{3} + \dfrac{5}{6}$

27. $-\dfrac{7}{10} + \dfrac{2}{5}$

28. $-\dfrac{3}{4} + \dfrac{3}{8}$

29. $-\dfrac{7}{3} + \left(-\dfrac{5}{9}\right)$

30. $-\dfrac{8}{5} + \left(-\dfrac{3}{10}\right)$

31. Explain in your own words how to add two numbers with different signs. Include two examples in your explanation, one that has a positive answer and one that has a negative answer.

32. Work these two examples:
    (a) $-5 + 3$ (b) $3 + (-5)$
    Explain why the answers are the same.

Give the additive inverse of each number.

Number	Additive Inverse		Number	Additive Inverse		Number	Additive Inverse		Number	Additive Inverse
33. 3		34.	4		35.	-9		36.	-14	
37. $\dfrac{1}{2}$		38.	$\dfrac{7}{8}$		39.	-6.2		40.	-0.5	

Subtract by changing subtraction to addition.

Examples: $-8 - (-2)$
$7 - 11$

Solutions:
Change subtraction to addition. Change the sign of the second number to its opposite.

$\begin{array}{cc} -8 - (-2) & 7 - \quad 11 \\ \downarrow \quad \downarrow & \downarrow \quad \downarrow \\ -8 + (+2) = -6 & 7 + (-11) = -4 \end{array}$

41. $19 - 5$

42. $24 - 11$

43. $10 - 12$

44. $1 - 8$

45. $7 - 19$

46. $2 - 17$

47. $-15 - 10$

48. $-10 - 4$

Name _____

49. $-9 - 14$ **50.** $-3 - 11$ **51.** $-3 - (-8)$ **52.** $-1 - (-4)$

53. $6 - (-14)$ **54.** $8 - (-1)$ **55.** $1 - (-10)$ **56.** $6 - (-1)$

57. $-30 - 30$ **58.** $-25 - 25$ **59.** $-16 - (-16)$ **60.** $-20 - (-20)$

61. $-\dfrac{7}{10} - \dfrac{4}{5}$ **62.** $-\dfrac{8}{15} - \dfrac{3}{10}$ **63.** $\dfrac{1}{2} - \dfrac{9}{10}$

64. $\dfrac{2}{3} - \dfrac{11}{12}$ **65.** $-8.3 - (-9)$ **66.** $-2 - (-3.9)$

67. Explain the purpose of the "$-$" sign in each of these examples.
   (a) $6 - 9$ **(b)** (-9) **(c)** $-(-2)$

68. Solve these two examples.
   (a) $8 - 3$ **(b)** $3 - 8$
   How are the answers similar? How are they different? Write a rule that explains what happens when you switch the order of the numbers in a subtraction problem.

Follow the order of operations to work each problem.

Example: $\underbrace{-6 + (-9)}_{} - (-10)$ Add and subtract from left to right.

Solution: $-15 \quad - (-10)$ Change subtraction to addition;
   $\qquad\qquad \downarrow \qquad \downarrow$ change -10 to its opposite $(+10)$.
   $\underbrace{-15 \quad + (+10)}_{-5}$

69. $-2 + (-11) - (-3)$ **70.** $-5 - (-2) + (-6)$ **71.** $4 - (-13) + (-5)$

72. $6 - (-1) + (-10)$ **73.** $-12 - (-3) - (-2)$ **74.** $-1 - (-7) - (-4)$

75. $4 - (-4) - 3$

76. $5 - (-2) - 8$

77. $\frac{1}{2} - \frac{2}{3} + \left(-\frac{5}{6}\right)$

78. $\frac{2}{5} - \frac{7}{10} + \left(-\frac{3}{2}\right)$

79. $-5.7 - (-9.4) - 8.1$

80. $-6.5 - (-11.2) - 1.4$

Add or subtract the following.

81. $-2 + (-11) + |-2|$

82. $|-7 + 2| + (-2) + 4$

83. $-3 - (-2 + 4) + (-5)$
(*Hint:* Work inside parentheses first.)

84. $5 - 8 - (6 - 7) + 1$

85. $2\frac{1}{2} + 3\frac{1}{4} - \left(-1\frac{3}{8}\right) - 2\frac{3}{8}$

86. $\frac{5}{8} - \left(-\frac{1}{2} - \frac{3}{4}\right)$

Review and Prepare

Multiply or divide the following.

87. $23 \cdot 46$

88. $\frac{8}{11} \cdot \frac{3}{5}$

89. $71.20 \cdot 21.25$

90. $2\frac{2}{3} \cdot 2\frac{3}{4}$

91. $1235 \div 5$

92. $1\frac{2}{3} \div 2\frac{7}{9}$

93. $\frac{7}{9} \div \frac{14}{27}$

3 Multiplication and Division of Signed Numbers

How do you multiply two numbers with different signs? Look for a pattern in the following list of products.

$$4 \cdot 2 = 8$$
$$3 \cdot 2 = 6$$
$$2 \cdot 2 = 4$$
$$1 \cdot 2 = 2$$
$$0 \cdot 2 = 0$$
$$-1 \cdot 2 = ?$$

As the numbers in blue decrease by 1, the numbers in red decrease by 2. You can continue the pattern by replacing **?** with a number 2 *less than* 0, which is **−2**. Therefore:

$$-1 \cdot 2 = -2$$

OBJECTIVE 1 The pattern above suggests a rule for multiplying numbers with different signs.

> **Multiplying Numbers with Different Signs**
> The product of two numbers with *different* signs is *negative*.

1. Multiply.

(a) $5 \cdot (-4)$

(b) $-9 \cdot (15)$

E X A M P L E I   **Multiplying Numbers with Different Signs**

Multiply.

(a) $-8 \cdot 4 = -32$ ← The product is negative.

(b) $6 \cdot (-3) = -18$

(c) $-5 \cdot (11) = -55$

(d) $12 \cdot (-7) = -84$

WORK PROBLEM I AT THE SIDE. ▶▶

(c) $12 \cdot (-1)$

For two numbers with the same signs, look at this pattern.

$$4 \cdot (-2) = -8$$
$$3 \cdot (-2) = -6$$
$$2 \cdot (-2) = -4$$
$$1 \cdot (-2) = -2$$
$$0 \cdot (-2) = 0$$
$$-1 \cdot (-2) = ?$$

This time, as the numbers in blue decrease by 1, the products increase by 2. You can continue the pattern by replacing **?** with a number 2 *greater than* 0, which is positive 2. Therefore:

$$-1 \cdot (-2) = 2$$

OBJECTIVE 2 In the pattern above, a negative number times a negative number gave a positive result.

(d) $-6 \cdot (6)$

(e) $\left(-\dfrac{7}{8}\right)\left(\dfrac{4}{3}\right)$

211

2. Multiply.

(a) $(-5) \cdot (-5)$

(b) $(-14)(-1)$

(c) $-7 \cdot (-8)$

(d) $3 \cdot 12$

(e) $\left(-\dfrac{2}{3}\right)\left(-\dfrac{6}{5}\right)$

3. Divide.

(a) $\dfrac{-20}{4}$

(b) $\dfrac{-50}{-5}$

(c) $\dfrac{44}{2}$

(d) $\dfrac{6}{-6}$

(e) $\dfrac{-15}{-1}$

(f) $\dfrac{-\dfrac{3}{5}}{\dfrac{9}{10}}$

(g) $\dfrac{-35}{0}$

ANSWERS

2. (a) 25 **(b)** 14 **(c)** 56 **(d)** 36 **(e)** $\dfrac{4}{5}$

3. (a) -5 **(b)** 10 **(c)** 22 **(d)** -1 **(e)** 15

   (f) $-\dfrac{2}{3}$ **(g)** undefined

Multiplying Numbers with the Same Sign

The product of two numbers with the *same* sign is *positive*.

E X A M P L E   2   Multiplying Two Numbers with the Same Sign

Multiply.

(a) $(-9)(-2)$ The numbers have the same sign (both are negative).

   $(-9)(-2) = 18$ ← The product is positive.

(b) $-7 \cdot (-4) = 28$ **(c)** $(-6)(-2) = 12$

(d) $(-10)(-5) = 50$ **(e)** $7 \cdot 5 = 35$

◀◀ **WORK PROBLEM 2 AT THE SIDE.**

You can use the same rules for dividing signed numbers as you use for multiplying signed numbers.

Dividing Signed Numbers

When two nonzero numbers with *different* signs are divided, the result is *negative*.

When two nonzero numbers with the *same* sign are divided, the result is *positive*.

Division with zero works the same as it did for whole numbers. Division by zero cannot be done. We say it is undefined. Zero divided by any other number is zero.

E X A M P L E   3   Dividing Signed Numbers

Divide.

(a) $\dfrac{-15}{5}$ ← Numbers have different signs so the answer is negative. $\dfrac{-15}{5} = -3$

(b) $\dfrac{-8}{-4}$ ← Numbers have same sign (both negative) so answer is positive. $\dfrac{-8}{-4} = 2$

(c) $\dfrac{-75}{-25} = 3$ **(d)** $\dfrac{-6}{0}$ is undefined   Division by zero cannot be done.

(e) $\dfrac{0}{-5} = 0$ **(f)** $\dfrac{90}{-9} = -10$

(g) $\dfrac{-\dfrac{2}{3}}{-\dfrac{5}{9}} = -\dfrac{2}{3} \cdot \left(-\dfrac{9}{5}\right)$ Invert the divisor: $-\dfrac{5}{9}$ becomes $-\dfrac{9}{5}$.

   $= -\dfrac{2}{\underset{1}{\cancel{3}}} \cdot \left(-\dfrac{\overset{3}{\cancel{9}}}{5}\right)$ Cancel when possible. Then multiply.

   $= \dfrac{6}{5}$ Both numbers were negative so answer is positive.

◀◀ **WORK PROBLEM 3 AT THE SIDE.**

3 Exercises

Multiply.

Examples: $-6 \cdot 5$ $(-4)(-3)$ $-\dfrac{3}{4} \cdot \left(-\dfrac{2}{3}\right)$

Solutions: $-6 \cdot 5 = -30$ $(-4)(-3) = 12$ $-\dfrac{\overset{1}{\cancel{3}}}{\underset{2}{\cancel{4}}} \cdot \left(-\dfrac{\overset{1}{\cancel{2}}}{\underset{1}{\cancel{3}}}\right) = \dfrac{1}{2}$

1. $-5 \cdot 7$ **2.** $-10 \cdot 2$ **3.** $(-5)(9)$ **4.** $(-9)(4)$

5. $3 \cdot (-6)$ **6.** $8 \cdot (-6)$ **7.** $10 \cdot (-5)$ **8.** $5 \cdot (-11)$

9. $(-1)(40)$ **10.** $(75)(-1)$ **11.** $-8 \cdot (-4)$ **12.** $-3 \cdot (-9)$

13. $11 \cdot 7$ **14.** $4 \cdot 25$ **15.** $-19 \cdot (-7)$ **16.** $-21 \cdot (-3)$

17. $-13 \cdot (-1)$ **18.** $-1 \cdot (-31)$ **19.** $(0)(-25)$ **20.** $(-50)(0)$

21. $-\dfrac{1}{2} \cdot (-8)$ **22.** $\dfrac{1}{3} \cdot (-15)$ **23.** $-10 \cdot \left(\dfrac{2}{5}\right)$ **24.** $-25 \cdot \left(-\dfrac{7}{10}\right)$

25. $\left(\dfrac{3}{5}\right)\left(-\dfrac{1}{6}\right)$ **26.** $\left(-\dfrac{7}{9}\right)\left(-\dfrac{3}{4}\right)$ **27.** $-\dfrac{7}{5} \cdot \left(-\dfrac{10}{3}\right)$ **28.** $-\dfrac{9}{10} \cdot \dfrac{5}{4}$

29. $-\dfrac{7}{15} \cdot \dfrac{25}{14}$ **30.** $-\dfrac{5}{9} \cdot \dfrac{18}{25}$ **31.** $-\dfrac{5}{2} \cdot \left(-\dfrac{7}{10}\right)$ **32.** $-\dfrac{8}{5} \cdot \left(-\dfrac{15}{16}\right)$

33. $9 \cdot (-4.7)$ **34.** $15 \cdot (-6.3)$ **35.** $(-0.5)(-12)$ **36.** $(-3.15)(-5)$

37. $-6.2 \cdot (5.1)$ **38.** $-4.3 \cdot (9.7)$ **39.** $-1.25 \cdot (-3.6)$ **40.** $6.33 \cdot 0.2$

41. $(-8.23)(-1)$ **42.** $(-1)(-0.69)$ **43.** $0 \cdot (-58.6)$ **44.** $-91.3 \cdot 0$

Divide.

Examples: $\dfrac{-10}{2}$ $\qquad$ $\dfrac{32}{-8}$ $\qquad$ $\dfrac{-21}{-3}$ $\qquad$ $\dfrac{-8}{0}$

Solutions: $\dfrac{-10}{2} = -5$ $\qquad$ $\dfrac{32}{-8} = -4$ $\qquad$ $\dfrac{-21}{-3} = 7$ $\qquad$ Division by zero is undefined.

45. $\dfrac{-14}{7}$ **46.** $\dfrac{-8}{2}$ **47.** $\dfrac{30}{-6}$ **48.** $\dfrac{21}{-7}$

49. $\dfrac{-28}{0}$ **50.** $\dfrac{-40}{0}$ **51.** $\dfrac{14}{-1}$ **52.** $\dfrac{25}{-1}$

53. $\dfrac{-20}{-2}$ **54.** $\dfrac{-80}{-4}$ **55.** $\dfrac{-48}{-12}$ **56.** $\dfrac{-30}{-15}$

Name _____

57. $\dfrac{-18}{18}$

58. $\dfrac{50}{-50}$

59. $\dfrac{-573}{-3}$

60. $\dfrac{-580}{-5}$

61. $\dfrac{0}{-9}$

62. $\dfrac{0}{-4}$

63. $\dfrac{-30}{-30}$

64. $\dfrac{-25}{-25}$

65. $\dfrac{-\frac{5}{7}}{-\frac{15}{14}}$

66. $\dfrac{-\frac{3}{4}}{-\frac{9}{16}}$

67. $-\dfrac{2}{3} \div (-2)$

68. $-\dfrac{3}{4} \div (-9)$

69. $5 \div \left(-\dfrac{5}{8}\right)$

70. $7 \div \left(-\dfrac{14}{15}\right)$

71. $-\dfrac{7}{5} \div \dfrac{3}{10}$

72. $-\dfrac{4}{9} \div \dfrac{8}{3}$

73. $\dfrac{-18.92}{-4}$

74. $\dfrac{-22.75}{-7}$

75. $\dfrac{-7.05}{1.5}$

76. $\dfrac{-17.02}{7.4}$

77. $\dfrac{45.58}{-8.6}$

78. $\dfrac{6.27}{-0.3}$

Following the order of operations, work from left to right in each of the following.

79. $(-4) \cdot (-6) \cdot \dfrac{1}{2}$

80. $(-9) \cdot (-3) \cdot \dfrac{2}{3}$

81. $(-0.6)(-0.2)(-3)$

82. $(-4)(-1.2)(-0.7)$

83. $\left(-\dfrac{1}{2}\right) \cdot \left(\dfrac{2}{5}\right) \cdot \left(\dfrac{7}{8}\right)$

84. $\left(\dfrac{3}{4}\right) \cdot \left(-\dfrac{5}{6}\right) \cdot \left(\dfrac{2}{3}\right)$

85. Write three examples for each of these situations:
(a) a positive number multiplied by −1
(b) a negative number multiplied by −1
Now write a rule that explains what happens when you multiply a signed number by −1.

86. Write three examples for each of these situations:
(a) a negative number divided by −1
(b) a positive number divided by −1
(c) a negative number divided by itself
Now write a rule that explains what happens when you divide a signed number by −1. Write another rule for a negative number divided by itself.

87. Explain what is different and what is similar between multiplying and dividing signed numbers.

88. Explain why $\frac{0}{-3}$ and $\frac{-3}{0}$ do **not** give the same result.

Simplify the following.

89. $-36 \div (-2) \div (-3) \div (-3) \div (-1)$

90. $-48 \div (-8) \cdot (-4) \div (-4) \div (-3)$

91. $|-8| \div (-4) \cdot |-5|$

92. $-6 \cdot |-3| \div |9| \cdot (-2)$

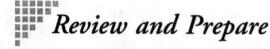 *Review and Prepare*

Simplify the following.

93. $8 + 4 \cdot 2 \div 8$

94. $16 \div 2 \cdot 4 + (15 - 2 \cdot 3)$

95. $7 + 6 \div 2 \cdot 4 - 9$

96. $9 \div 3 + 8 \div 4 \cdot 2 - 7$

4   *Order of Operations*

You have already worked examples that mixed either addition and subtraction or multiplication and division. In those situations you worked from left to right. Here are two more examples.

WORK PROBLEM 1 AT THE SIDE.

Work additions and subtractions from left to right.

$$-8 - (-6) + (-11)$$
$$\underbrace{-2} + (-11)$$
$$-13$$

Work multiplications and divisions from left to right.

$$(-15) \div (-3) \cdot 6$$
$$\underbrace{5} \cdot 6$$
$$30$$

OBJECTIVE 1   Before working examples that mix division with addition or include parentheses, let's review the order of operations.

Order of Operations

1. Work inside **parentheses.**
2. Simplify expressions with **exponents,** and find any **square roots.**
3. Multiply or divide from **left to right.**
4. Add or subtract from **left to right.**

EXAMPLE 1   Using the Order of Operations

Use the order of operations to simplify the following.

$4 - 10 \div 2 + 7$ Check for parentheses: none. Check for exponents and square roots: none. Move from left to right, checking for multiplying and dividing.

$4 - \underbrace{10 \div 2} + 7$ Yes, here is dividing. Use the number on either side of the ÷ sign. $10 \div 2$ is 5. Bring down the other numbers and signs you haven't used.

$4 - 5 + 7$

Move from left to right, checking for adding and subtracting. Yes, here is subtracting.

$4 - 5 + 7$ Change subtraction to addition; change 5 to its opposite (−5).

$\underbrace{4 + (-5)} + 7$ Add $4 + (-5)$ to get −1.

$\underbrace{-1 + 7}$ Add $-1 + 7$ to get 6.

6

WORK PROBLEM 2 AT THE SIDE.

OBJECTIVES

1. Use the order of operations.
2. Use the order of operations with exponents.
3. Use the order of operations with fraction bars.

1. Simplify.

(a) $-9 + (-15) + (-3)$

(b) $-8 - (-2) + (-6)$

(c) $-2 - (-7) - (-4)$

(d) $3 \cdot (-4) \div (-6)$

(e) $-18 \div 9 \cdot (-4)$

2. Use the order of operations to simplify each of the following.

(a) $10 + 8 \div 2$

(b) $4 - 6 \cdot (-2)$

(c) $-3 + (-5) \cdot 2 - 1$

(d) $-6 \div 2 + 3 \cdot (-2)$

(e) $7 - 6 \cdot 2 \div (-3)$

ANSWERS

1. (a) −27 (b) −12 (c) 9 (d) 2 (e) 8
2. (a) 14 (b) 16 (c) −14 (d) −9 (e) 11

218

3. Simplify each of the following.

(a) $2 + 40 \div (-5 + 3)$

(b) $-5 \cdot 5 - (15 + 5)$

(c) $(-24 \div 2) + (15 - 3)$

(d) $-3 \cdot (2 - 8) - 5 \cdot (4 - 3)$

(e) $3 \cdot 3 - (10 \cdot 3) \div 5$

$9 - (30) \div 5$

21

(f) $6 - (2 + 7) \div (-4 + 1)$

ANSWERS

3. (a) -18 **(b)** -45 **(c)** 0 **(d)** 13
  (e) 3 **(f)** 9

E X A M P L E   2   Parentheses and Order of Operations

Use the order of operations to simplify each of the following.

(a) $-8 \cdot (7 - 5) - 9$ Check for parentheses first. Yes; so do whatever you can inside the parentheses.

$-8 \cdot 2 - 9$ Bring down the other numbers and signs you haven't used yet. Check for exponents and square roots: none.

$-8 \cdot 2 - 9$ Move from left to right, checking for multiplying and dividing. Yes, multiplying.

$-16 - 9$ Change subtraction to addition.

$-16 + (-9)$ Add $-16 + (-9)$ to get -25.

-25

(b) $3 + 2 \cdot (6 - 8) \cdot (15 \div 3)$ Work inside first set of parentheses; change $6 - 8$ to $6 + (-8)$ to get (-2).

$3 + 2 \cdot (-2) \cdot (15 \div 3)$ Work inside second set of parentheses.

$3 + 2 \cdot (-2) \cdot 5$ Multiply from left to right; first multiply $2 \cdot (-2)$ to get -4.

$3 + -4 \cdot 5$ Then multiply $-4 \cdot 5$ to get -20.

$3 + -20$ Add last. $3 + (-20)$ gives -17.

-17

◀◀ WORK PROBLEM 3 AT THE SIDE.

OBJECTIVE 2 Remember that 2^3 means 2 is used as a factor 3 times:

$$2^3 = 2 \cdot 2 \cdot 2 = 8.$$

The 3 is called an *exponent*. Exponents are also used with signed numbers. For example:

$$(-3)^2 = (-3) \cdot (-3) = 9$$

$$(-4)^3 = (-4) \cdot (-4) \cdot (-4)$$ Be careful! Multiply two numbers at a time. Watch the signs.
$$= 16 \cdot (-4)$$
$$= -64$$

$$\left(-\frac{1}{2}\right)^4 = \left(-\frac{1}{2}\right) \cdot \left(-\frac{1}{2}\right) \cdot \left(-\frac{1}{2}\right) \cdot \left(-\frac{1}{2}\right)$$
$$= \frac{1}{4} \cdot \left(-\frac{1}{2}\right) \cdot \left(-\frac{1}{2}\right)$$
$$= -\frac{1}{8} \cdot \left(-\frac{1}{2}\right)$$
$$= \frac{1}{16}$$

Be very careful with exponents and signed numbers. For example:

$$(-3)^2 = (-3) \cdot (-3) = 9. \leftarrow \text{Positive 9}$$

But the expression -3^2, with *no parentheses,* is different.

$$-3^2 = -(3 \cdot 3) = -9 \leftarrow \text{Negative 9}$$

Note

$(-3)^2$ is **not** the same as -3^2.

$$(-3)^2 = (-3) \cdot (-3) = 9 \quad but \quad -3^2 = -(3 \cdot 3) = -9$$

You will need this information as you take more algebra classes.

E X A M P L E 3 Using Exponents and Order of Operations

Simplify each of the following.

(a) $\underbrace{4^2 - \underbrace{(-3)^2}}$

$\underbrace{16 \overset{\downarrow}{-} 9}$

7

There are parentheses around (-3) but no work can be done inside these parentheses.
Work with the exponents: $4^2 = 4 \cdot 4 = 16$ and $(-3)^2 = (-3)(-3) = 9$
Subtract: $16 - 9 = 7$

(b) $(-5)^2 - \underbrace{(4 - 6)^2} \cdot (-3)$ Work inside parentheses first.

$\underbrace{(-5)^2} - \underbrace{(-2)^2} \cdot (-3)$ Use the exponents next.

$25 \quad - \quad 4 \quad \cdot (-3)$ Multiply.

$25 \quad - \quad (-12)$ Change subtraction to addition.

$\downarrow \qquad \qquad \downarrow$

$\underbrace{25 \quad + \quad (+12)}$ Add.

37

(c) $\left(\dfrac{2}{3} - \dfrac{1}{6}\right)^2 \div \left(-\dfrac{3}{8}\right)$ Inside parentheses: $\frac{2}{3} - \frac{1}{6} = \frac{4}{6} - \frac{1}{6} = \frac{3}{6} = \frac{1}{2}$

$\underbrace{\left(\dfrac{1}{2}\right)^2} \div \left(-\dfrac{3}{8}\right)$ Use the exponent: $(\frac{1}{2})^2 = \frac{1}{2} \cdot \frac{1}{2} = \frac{1}{4}$

$\dfrac{1}{4} \div \left(-\dfrac{3}{8}\right)$ Invert the divisor: $-\frac{3}{8}$ becomes $-\frac{8}{3}$

$\underbrace{\dfrac{1}{4} \cdot \left(-\dfrac{8}{3}\right)}$ Cancel and multiply: $\frac{1}{\cancel{4}} \cdot -\frac{\overset{2}{\cancel{8}}}{3} = -\frac{2}{3}$

$-\dfrac{2}{3}$

WORK PROBLEM 4 AT THE SIDE. ▶▶

Note

Parentheses can be used in several different ways:

To indicate multiplication.	$(4)(-3) = -12$
To separate a negative number from a minus sign.	$8 - (-2) = 10$
To indicate which operation to do first.	$35 + \underbrace{(6 - 2)}$ $\underbrace{35 + \quad 4}$ 39

---

4. Simplify each of the following.

(a) $2^3 - 3^2$

$8 - 9 = -1$

(b) $4^2 - 3^2 \cdot (5 - 2)$

$16 - 9 \cdot (3)$

$7 \cdot 3 = 21$

(c) $-18 \div (-3) \cdot 2^3$

$-18 - 6 \cdot 8 = 48$

(d) $(-3)^3 + (3 - 8)^2$

$-27 + (5)^2$

$-27 - 25 = -2$

(e) $\dfrac{3}{8} + \left(-\dfrac{1}{2}\right)^2 \div \dfrac{1}{4}$

$\frac{3}{8} + \left(-\frac{1}{4}\right) \div \frac{1}{4}$

$\frac{3}{8} - \frac{27}{4} = \frac{3}{8} - \frac{4}{8} = \frac{21}{8} \cdot \frac{4}{1} = 8$

ANSWERS

4. (a) -1 **(b)** -11 **(c)** 48
(d) -2 **(e)** $\dfrac{11}{8}$

220

5. Simplify each of the following.

(a) $\dfrac{-3 \cdot 2^3}{-10 - 6 + 8}$

$\dfrac{-3 \cdot 8}{-10-6+8} = \dfrac{-24}{-16+8}$

$\dfrac{-24}{-8} = 3$

(b) $\dfrac{(-10)(-5)}{-6 \div 3 \cdot 5}$

$\dfrac{50}{-2 \cdot 5} = \dfrac{50}{-10} = -5$

(c) $\dfrac{6 + 18 \div (-2)}{(1 - 10) \div 3}$

$\dfrac{6-9}{-9 \div 3} = \dfrac{-3}{-3} = 1$

(d) $\dfrac{6^2 - 3^2 \cdot 4}{5 + (3 - 7)^2}$

$\dfrac{36 - 9 \cdot 4}{5 + (4)^2} = \dfrac{36 - 36}{5 + 16} = \dfrac{10}{21} = 0$

OBJECTIVE 3 A fraction bar indicates division, as in $\frac{-6}{2}$ which means $-6 \div 2$. In an example like the one below

$$\frac{-5 + 3^2}{16 - 7 \cdot 2}$$

the fraction bar also tells us to do the work in the numerator, then the work in the denominator. The last step is to divide the results.

$$\frac{-5 + 3^2}{16 - 7 \cdot 2} \rightarrow \frac{-5 + 9}{16 - 14} \rightarrow \frac{4}{2} \rightarrow \text{Now divide.} \quad 4 \div 2 = 2$$

The final result is 2.

E X A M P L E   4   Fraction Bars and Order of Operations

Simplify the following.

$$\frac{-8 + (4 - 6) \cdot 5}{4 - 4^2 \div 8}$$

First do the work in the numerator.

$$-8 + \underline{(4 - 6)} \cdot 5 \qquad \text{Work inside parentheses.}$$
$$-8 + \underline{-2 \cdot 5} \qquad \text{Multiply.}$$
$$\underline{-8 + (-10)} \qquad \text{Add.}$$
$$\text{Numerator} \rightarrow -18$$

Now do the work in the denominator.

$$4 - \underline{4^2} \div 8 \qquad \text{No parentheses; use exponent.}$$
$$4 - \underline{16 \div 8} \qquad \text{Divide.}$$
$$\underline{4 - 2} \qquad \text{Subtract.}$$
$$\text{Denominator} \rightarrow 2$$

The last step is the division.

$$\frac{\text{Numerator} \rightarrow -18}{\text{Denominator} \rightarrow 2} = -9$$

◄◄ WORK PROBLEM 5 AT THE SIDE.

$\dfrac{-8 + (4-6) \cdot 5}{4 - 4^2 \div 8} = \dfrac{-8 + (-2) \cdot 5}{4 - 16 \div 8}$

$\dfrac{-8 - 2 \cdot 5}{4 - 16 \div 8}$

$\dfrac{-8 - 10}{4 - 2} = \dfrac{-18}{2} = -9$

4   Exercises

Simplify each of the following.

Examples: $-6 - \underbrace{3^2}$ $\quad 4 \cdot \underbrace{(6 - 11)^2} - (-8)$

Solutions: $-6 - \underset{\downarrow}{9}$ $\quad 4 \cdot \underbrace{(-5)^2} - (-8)$

$\underbrace{-6 + (-9)}$ $\quad \underbrace{4 \cdot \quad 25} \quad - (-8)$

$\underset{-15}{}$ $\quad 100 \quad - (-8)$

$\quad\quad\quad \underbrace{100 \quad + (+8)}$

$\quad\quad\quad\quad\quad 108$

1. $6 + 3 \cdot (-4)$

2. $10 - 30 \div 2$

3. $-1 + 15 + (-7) \cdot 2$

4. $9 + (-5) + 2 \cdot (-2)$

5. $6^2 + 4^2$

6. $3^2 + 8^2$

7. $10 - 7^2$

8. $5 - 5^2$

9. $(-2)^5 + 2$

10. $(-2)^4 - 7$

11. $4^2 + 3^2 + (-8)$

12. $5^2 + 2^2 + (-12)$

13. $2 - (-5) + 3^2$

14. $6 - (-9) + 2^3$

15. $(-4)^2 + (-3)^2 + 5$

16. $(-5)^2 + (-6)^2 + 12$

17. $3 + 5 \cdot (6 - 2)$

18. $4 + 3 \cdot (8 - 3)$

19. $-7 + 6 \cdot (8 - 14)$

20. $-3 + 5 \cdot (9 - 12)$

21. $-6 + (-5) \cdot (9 - 14)$

22. $-5 + (-3) \cdot (6 - 7)$

23. $(-5) \cdot (7 - 13) \div (-10)$

24. $(-4) \cdot (9 - 17) \div (-8)$

25. $9 \div (-3)^2 + (-1)$

26. $-48 \div (-4)^2 + 3$

27. $2 - (-5) \cdot (-3)^2$

28. $1 - (-10) \cdot (-2)^3$

29. $(-2) \cdot (-7) + 3 \cdot 9$

30. $4 \cdot (-2) + (-3) \cdot (-5)$

31. $30 \div (-5) - 36 \div (-9)$

32. $8 \div (-4) - 42 \div (-7)$

33. $2 \cdot 5 - 3 \cdot 4 + 5 \cdot 3$

34. $9 \cdot 3 - 6 \cdot 4 + 3 \cdot 7$

35. $4 \cdot 3^2 + 7 \cdot (3 + 9) - (-6)$

36. $5 \cdot 4^2 - 6 \cdot (1 + 4) - (-3)$

37. $\dfrac{-1 + 5^2 - (-3)}{-6 - 9 + 12}$

38. $\dfrac{-6 + 3^2 - (-7)}{7 - 9 - 3}$

39. $\dfrac{-2 \cdot 4^2 - 4 \cdot (6 - 2)}{-4 \cdot (8 - 13) \div (-5)}$

40. $\dfrac{3 \cdot 3^2 - 5 \cdot (9 - 2)}{8 \cdot (6 - 9) \div (-3)}$

41. $\dfrac{2^3 \cdot (-2 - 5) + 4 \cdot (-1)}{4 + 5 \cdot (-6 \cdot 2) + (5 \cdot 11)}$

42. $\dfrac{3^3 + (-1 - 2) \cdot 4 - 25}{-4 + 4 \cdot (3 \cdot 5) + (-6 \cdot 9)}$

Name _____

43. $(-4)^2 \cdot (7 - 9)^2 \div 2^3$

44. $(-5)^2 \cdot (9 - 17)^2 \div (-10)^2$

45. $(-0.3)^2 + (-0.5)^2 + 0.9$

46. $(0.2)^3 - (-0.4)^2 + 3.02$

47. $(-0.75) \cdot (3.6 - 5)^2$

48. $(-0.3) \cdot (4 - 6.8)^2$

49. $(0.5)^2 \cdot (-8) - (0.31)$

50. $(0.3)^3 \cdot (-5) - (-2.8)$

51. $\dfrac{2}{3} \div \left(-\dfrac{5}{6}\right) - \dfrac{1}{2}$

52. $\dfrac{5}{8} \div \left(-\dfrac{10}{3}\right) - \dfrac{3}{4}$

53. $\left(-\dfrac{1}{2}\right)^2 - \left(\dfrac{3}{4} - \dfrac{7}{4}\right)$

54. $\left(-\dfrac{2}{3}\right)^2 - \left(\dfrac{1}{6} - \dfrac{11}{6}\right)$

55. $\dfrac{3}{5} \cdot \left(-\dfrac{7}{6}\right) - \left(\dfrac{1}{6} - \dfrac{5}{3}\right)$

56. $\dfrac{2}{7} \cdot \left(-\dfrac{14}{5}\right) - \left(\dfrac{4}{3} - \dfrac{13}{9}\right)$

57. $5^2 \cdot (9 - 11) \cdot (-3) \cdot (-2)^3$

58. $4^2 \cdot (13 - 17) \cdot (-2) \cdot (-3)^2$

59. $1.6 \cdot (-0.8) \div (-0.32) \div 2^2$

60. $6.5 \cdot (-4.8) \div (-0.3) \div (-2)^3$

61. Solve this series of examples.

$$(-2)^2 = \qquad (-2)^6 =$$
$$(-2)^3 = \qquad (-2)^7 =$$
$$(-2)^4 = \qquad (-2)^8 =$$
$$(-2)^5 = \qquad (-2)^9 =$$

What pattern do you see in the sign of the answers?

62. Explain the difference between -5^2 and $(-5)^2$.

Simplify each of the following.

63. $\dfrac{-9 + 18 \div (-3) \cdot (-6)}{5 - 4 \cdot 12 \div 3 \cdot 2}$

64. $\dfrac{-20 - 15 \cdot (-4) - (-40)}{4 + 27 \div 3 \cdot (-2) - 6}$

65. $-7 \cdot \left(6 - \dfrac{5}{8} \cdot 24 + 3 \cdot \dfrac{8}{3} \right)$

66. $(-0.3)^2 \cdot (-5 \cdot 3) + (6 \div 2 \cdot 0.4)$

67. $|-12| \div 4 + 2 \cdot 3^2 \div 6$

68. $6 - (2 - 3 \cdot 4) + 5^2 \div \left(-2 \cdot \dfrac{5}{2} \right) + (2)^2$

Review and Prepare

Evaluate the following.

69. $\dfrac{6}{7} \cdot \dfrac{14}{9}$

70. $\dfrac{17}{15} \div \dfrac{34}{5}$

71. $\dfrac{5}{3} - \dfrac{3}{8} \cdot \dfrac{4}{9}$

72. $\dfrac{7}{12} \div \dfrac{21}{10} \cdot \dfrac{4}{5}$

5   *Evaluating Expressions and Formulas*

OBJECTIVES

1 Define variable and expression.

2 Find the value of an expression when values of the variables are given.

In formulas you have seen that numbers can be represented by letters. For example, you used this formula for finding simple interest.

$$I = p \cdot r \cdot t$$

In this formula, p (principal) represents the amount of money borrowed, r is the rate of interest, and t is the time in years. In algebra, we often write multiplication without the multiplication dots. If there is no operation sign written between two letters, or between a letter and a number, you assume it is multiplication.

Showing Multiplication in Algebra

If there is no operation sign, it is understood to be multiplication. Here are some examples.

$I = p \cdot r \cdot t$	is written	$I = prt$
$2 \cdot r$	is written	$2r$
$3 \cdot x + 4 \cdot y$	is written	$3x + 4y$

OBJECTIVE 1 Letters (such as the I, p, r, or t used above) that represent numbers are called **variables** (VAIR-ee-uh-buls). A combination of letters and numbers is an **expression** (eks-PRESH-un). Three examples of expressions are shown here.

$$9 + p \qquad\qquad 8r \qquad\qquad 7k - 2m$$

OBJECTIVE 2 The value of an expression changes depending upon the value of each variable. To find the value of an expression, replace the variables with their values. It is helpful to write each value inside parentheses when multiplication is involved.

E X A M P L E   1   Finding the Value of an Expression

Find the value of $5x - 3y$, if $x = 2$ and $y = 7$.

Replace x with 2. Replace y with 7.

Using the order of operations, multiply first.

$$
\begin{array}{cc}
5x & -3y \\
\downarrow\downarrow & \downarrow\downarrow \\
5(2) & -3(7) \\
\hline
10 & -21 \\
\end{array}
$$
$$-11$$

WORK PROBLEM 1 AT THE SIDE. ▶▶

E X A M P L E   2   Finding the Value of an Expression

Find the value of $7m - 8n + p$, if $m = -2$, $n = 4$, and $p = 3$.

Replace m with -2, n with 4, and p with 3.

$$
\begin{array}{cccc}
7m & -8n & +p \\
\downarrow\downarrow & \downarrow\downarrow & \downarrow \\
7(-2) & -8(4) & +3 \\
\hline
-14 & -32 & +3 \\
\hline
& -46 & +3 \\
\end{array}
$$
$$-43$$

Multiply from left to right.

Add and subtract from left to right.

WORK PROBLEMS 2 AND 3 AT THE SIDE. ▶▶

---

1. Find the value of $5x - 3y$ if

   (a) $x = 1, y = 2$.

   (b) $x = 3, y = -4$.

   (c) $x = 0, y = 6$.

2. Find the value of $7m - 8n + p$ if

   (a) $m = 1, n = 2, p = 5$.

   (b) $m = -4, n = -3, p = -7$.

   (c) $m = -5, n = 0, p = -1$.

3. Find the value of $x + 6y$ if

   (a) $x = 9, y = -3$.

   (b) $x = -2, y = 1$.

   (c) $x = 6, y = -1$.

ANSWERS

1. (a) -1 (b) 27 (c) -18
2. (a) -4 (b) -11 (c) -36
3. (a) -9 (b) 4 (c) 0

226

4. Find the value of $\dfrac{3k + r}{2s}$ if

(a) $k = 1, r = 1, s = 2$.

(b) $k = 8, r = -2,$
$s = -4$.

(c) $k = -3, r = 1,$
$s = -2$.

5. Find the value of A, P, d, and C in these formulas.

(a) $A = \dfrac{1}{2}bh$; $b = 6$ yd,
$h = 12$ yd

(b) $P = 2l + 2w$; $l = 10,$
$w = 8$

(c) $d = rt$; $r = 4,$
$t = 80$

(d) $C = 2\pi r$; $\pi \approx 3.14,$
$r = 6$

ANSWERS

4. (a) $\dfrac{4}{4} = 1$ (b) $\dfrac{22}{-8} = -\dfrac{11}{4}$ (c) $\dfrac{-8}{-4} = 2$
5. (a) $A = 36$ yd² (b) $P = 36$
(c) $d = 32$ (d) $C \approx 37.68$

E X A M P L E 3   Finding the Value of an Expression

Find the value of $5x - y$, if $x = 2$ and $y = -3$.

Replace x with 2. $5\,x\ -\ y$ Replace y with -3.

$$5(2) - (-3)$$
$$10\ +\ (+3)$$
$$13$$

E X A M P L E 4   Finding the Value of an Expression

What is the value of $\dfrac{6k + 2r}{5s}$, if $k = -2, r = 5$, and $s = -1$?

Replace k with -2, r with 5, and s with -1.

$$\frac{6k + 2r}{5s} = \frac{6(-2) + 2(5)}{5(-1)}$$

$$= \frac{-12 + 10}{-5} \quad \text{Multiply.}$$

$$= \frac{-2}{-5} \quad \text{Add in numerator.}$$

$$= \frac{2}{5} \quad \text{Dividing two numbers with the same sign gives a positive answer.}$$

◀◀ **WORK PROBLEM 4 AT THE SIDE.**

E X A M P L E 5   Evaluating a Formula

The formula you used previously for the area of a triangle can now be written without the multiplication dots.

$$A = \frac{1}{2} \cdot b \cdot h \quad \text{is written} \quad A = \frac{1}{2}bh$$

In this formula, b is the length of the base and h is the height. What is the area if $b = 9$ cm and $h = 24$ cm?

$A = \dfrac{1}{2}\ b\ \ h$ Replace b with 9 cm and h with 24 cm.

$A = \dfrac{1}{2}(9\text{ cm})(24\text{ cm})$

$A = \dfrac{1}{2}(9\text{ cm})(\overset{12}{24}\text{ cm})$ Cancel if possible.

$A = 108$ cm²

The area of the triangle is 108 cm².

Note
Area is measured in square units. The short way to write square centimeters is cm².

◀◀ **WORK PROBLEM 5 AT THE SIDE.**

5 Exercises

Find the value of the expression 2r + 4s for each of the following values of r and s.

Example: $r = 3, s = -5$

Solution:
Replace r with 3.
Replace s with -5.
Using the order of operations, multiply first, then add.

$$2\,r\ + 4\ s$$
$$\downarrow\downarrow\ \ \ \downarrow\ \downarrow$$
$$\underbrace{2(3)}\ +\ \underbrace{4(-5)}$$
$$\underbrace{6\ \ +\ (-20)}$$
$$-14$$

1. $r = 2, s = 6$

2. $r = 6, s = 1$

3. $r = 1, s = -3$

4. $r = 7, s = -2$

5. $r = -4, s = 4$

6. $r = -3, s = 5$

7. $r = -1, s = -7$

8. $r = -3, s = -5$

9. $r = 0, s = -2$

10. $r = -7, s = 0$

Use the given values of the variables to find the value of each expression.

11. $8x - y; x = 1, y = 8$

12. $a - 5b; a = 10, b = 2$

13. $6k + 2s; k = 1, s = -2$

14. $7p + 7q; p = -4, q = 1$

15. $\dfrac{-m + 5n}{2s + 2}$; $m = 4, n = -8, s = 0$

16. $\dfrac{2y - z}{x - 2}$; $y = 0, z = 5, x = 1$

17. $-m - 3n$; $m = \dfrac{1}{2}, n = \dfrac{3}{8}$

18. $7k - 3r$; $k = \dfrac{2}{3}, r = -\dfrac{1}{3}$

Be careful when an expression has a negative sign and the value of the variable is also negative. Use the given values to find the value of each expression.

Example: Find the value of $-c - 5b$ when $c = -2$ and $b = -3$

Solution: Replace c with -2.
Replace b with -3.
$-(-2)$ is the opposite
of (-2) which is $(+2)$.

$$
\begin{array}{cc}
-\ c & -\ 5\ b \\
\downarrow\ \downarrow & \downarrow\ \downarrow \\
\underline{-(-2)} - \underline{5(-3)} & \text{Multiply } 5 \cdot (-3) \\
+2 \quad -\ (-15) & \text{Change subtraction} \\
\downarrow \quad\quad \downarrow & \text{to addition.} \\
\underbrace{2 \quad +\ (+15)} & \\
17 &
\end{array}
$$

19. $-c - 5b$; $c = -8, b = -4$

20. $-c - 5b$; $c = -1, b = -2$

21. $-4x - y$; $x = 5, y = -15$

22. $-4x - y$; $x = 3, y = -8$

23. $-k - m - 8n$; $k = 6, m = -9, n = 0$

24. $-k - m - 8n$; $k = 0, m = -7, n = -1$

25. $\dfrac{-3s - t - 4}{-s + 6 + t}$; $s = -1, t = -13$

26. $\dfrac{-3s - t - 4}{-s - 20 - t}$; $s = -3, t = -6$

Name _____

In each of the following, use the given formula and values of the variables to find the value of the remaining variable.

Example: $P = 2l + 2w$; $l = 33$, $w = 16$

Solution: Replace l with 33 and w with 16.

$$P = 2 \quad l \quad + 2 \quad w$$
$$P = \underbrace{2 \cdot (33)} + \underbrace{2 \cdot (16)}$$
$$P = \quad 66 \quad + \quad 32$$
$$P = \mathbf{98}$$

27. $P = 4s$; $s = 7.5$

28. $P = 4s$; $s = 0.8$

29. $P = 2l + 2w$; $l = 9$, $w = 5$

30. $P = 2l + 2w$; $l = 12$, $w = 2$

31. $A = \pi r^2$; $\pi \approx 3.14$, $r = 5$

32. $A = \pi r^2$; $\pi \approx 3.14$, $r = 10$

33. $A = \dfrac{1}{2}bh$; $b = 15$, $h = 3$

34. $A = \dfrac{1}{2}bh$; $b = 5$, $h = 11$

35. $V = \dfrac{1}{3}Bh$; $B = 30$, $h = 60$

36. $V = \dfrac{1}{3}Bh$; $B = 105$, $h = 5$

37. $d = rt$; $r = 53$, $t = 6$

38. $d = rt$; $r = 180$, $t = 5$

39. $C = 2\pi r$; $\pi \approx 3.14$, $r = 4$

40. $C = 2\pi r$; $\pi \approx 3.14$, $r = 18$

41. Find and correct the error made by the student who solved this example:

Find the value of $-x - 4y$ if $x = -3$ and $y = -1$.

$$-x - 4y$$
$$-3 - 4(-1)$$
$$-3 - (-4)$$
$$-3 + (+4)$$
$$1$$

Also write a sentence next to each step, explaining what is being done in that step.

42. Go back and look up one of the formulas listed below. Pick values for the variables indicated and find the value of A or V. Then pick different values for the variables and again find the value of A or V.

Area of a trapezoid: pick values for h, a, and b.

Volume of a rectangular solid: pick values for l, w, and h.

Use the given formula and values of the variables to find the value of the remaining variable. Write a sentence telling when you would use each formula.

43. $F = \dfrac{9C}{5} + 32$; $C = -40$

44. $C = \dfrac{5(F - 32)}{9}$; $F = -4$

45. $V = \dfrac{4\pi r^3}{3}$; $\pi \approx 3.14$, $r = 3$

46. $c^2 = a^2 + b^2$; $a = 3$, $b = 4$

47. $A = \dfrac{1}{2}h(b + B)$; $h = 7$, $b = 4$, $B = 12$

48. $V = \dfrac{\pi r^2 h}{3}$; $\pi \approx 3.14$, $r = 6$, $h = 10$

Review and Prepare

Simplify the following.

49. $-\dfrac{1}{9} \cdot 9$

50. $4 \cdot \left(-\dfrac{3}{2}\right)$

51. $-\dfrac{4}{3} \cdot \left(-\dfrac{3}{4}\right)$

52. $-\dfrac{2}{5} \cdot \left(-\dfrac{5}{2}\right)$

6 *Solving Equations*

OBJECTIVES

1 ▶ Tell whether a number is a solution of an equation.

2 ▶ Solve equations using the addition property of equations.

3 ▶ Solve equations using the multiplication property of equations.

An **equation** (ee-KWAY-zhuhn) is a statement that says two expressions are equal. Examples of equations are shown here.

$$x + 1 = 9 \qquad 20 = 5k \qquad 6r - 1 = 17$$

The **equal sign** in an equation divides the equation into two parts, the *left side* and the *right side*. In $6r - 1 = 17$, the left side is $6r - 1$, and the right side is 17.

$$\boxed{6r - 1} = \boxed{17}$$
Left side   Right side

You solve an equation by finding all numbers that can be substituted for the variable to make the equation true. These numbers are called **solutions** of the equation.

OBJECTIVE 1 ▶ To tell whether a number is a solution of the equation, substitute the number in the equation to see whether the result is true.

┌─ **E X A M P L E I   Determining If a Number Is a Solution of an Equation**

Is 7 a solution of the following equations?

(a) $12 = x + 5$

Replace x with 7.

$$12 = x + 5$$
$$12 = 7 + 5 \qquad \text{Replace } x \text{ with 7.}$$
$$12 = 12 \qquad \text{True}$$

Because the statement is true, 7 is a solution of $12 = x + 5$.

(b) $2y + 1 = 16$

Replace y with 7.

$$2y + 1 = 16$$
$$2(7) + 1 = 16$$
$$14 + 1 = 16$$
$$15 = 16 \qquad \text{False}$$

The false statement shows that 7 is *not* a solution of $2y + 1 = 16$.
└─

WORK PROBLEM I AT THE SIDE. ▶▶

OBJECTIVE 2 ▶ If the equation $a = b$ is true, and if a number c is added to both a and b, the new equation is also true. This rule is called the **addition property of equations**. It means that you can add the same number to both sides of an equation and still have a true equation.

> **Addition Property of Equations**
>
> If $a = b$, then $a + c = b + c$. In other words, you may add the same number to both sides of an equation.

You can use the addition property to solve equations. The idea is to get the variable (the letter) by itself on one side of the equal sign and a number by itself on the other side.

1. Decide if the given number is a solution of the equation.

(a) $p + 1 = 8; \quad 7$

(b) $30 = 5r; \quad 6$

(c) $3k - 2 = 4; \quad 3$

(d) $23 = 4y + 3; \quad 5$

ANSWERS

1. **(a)** solution **(b)** solution **(c)** not a solution **(d)** solution

2. Solve each equation. Check each solution.

(a) $n - 5 = 8$

(b) $5 = r - 10$

(c) $3 = z + 1$

(d) $k + 9 = 0$

(e) $-2 = y + 9$

(f) $x - 2 = -6$

E X A M P L E 2   Solving an Equation by Using the Addition Property

Solve each equation.

(a) $k - 4 = 6$

To get k by itself on the left side, add 4 to the left side, because $k - 4 + 4$ gives $k + 0$. You must then add 4 to the right side also.

$$k - 4 = 6 \qquad \leftarrow \text{Original equation}$$
$$k \underbrace{- 4 + 4}_{} = 6 + 4 \qquad \text{Add 4 to both sides.}$$
$$k + 0 = 10$$
$$k = 10$$

The solution is 10. Check by replacing k with 10 in the original equation.

$$k - 4 = 6$$
$$10 - 4 = 6 \qquad \text{Replace } k \text{ with 10.}$$
$$6 = 6 \qquad \text{True}$$

This result is true, so 10 is the solution.

(b) $2 = z + 8$

To get z by itself on the right side, add -8 to both sides.

$$2 = z + 8 \qquad \leftarrow \text{Original equation}$$
$$2 + (-8) = z + 8 + (-8) \qquad \text{Add } (-8) \text{ to both sides.}$$
$$-6 = z + 0$$
$$-6 = z$$

Check the solution by replacing z with -6 in the original equation.

$$2 = z + 8$$
$$2 = -6 + 8$$
$$2 = 2 \qquad \text{True, so } -6 \text{ is the solution}$$

Notice that we *added* -8 to both sides to get z by itself. We can accomplish the same thing by *subtracting* 8 from both sides. Recall that subtraction is defined in terms of addition. On the left side of the equation above

$$2 - 8 \text{ gives the same result as } 2 + (-8).$$

Note
You may add *or subtract* the same number on both sides of an equation.

◄◄ WORK PROBLEM 2 AT THE SIDE.

OBJECTIVE 3 ▶ Here is a summary of the rules you can use to solve equations using the addition property. In these rules, x is the variable and a and b are numbers.

Solving Equations Using the Addition Property

Solve $x - a = b$ or $b = x - a$ by adding a to both sides.

Solve $x + a = b$ or $b = x + a$ by subtracting a from both sides.

ANSWERS

2. (a) 13 (b) 15 (c) 2 (d) -9 (e) -11
   (f) -4

Multiplication Property of Equations

If $a = b$ and c does not equal 0, then

$$a \cdot c = b \cdot c \quad \text{and} \quad \frac{a}{c} = \frac{b}{c}.$$

In other words, you can multiply or divide both sides of an equation by the same number. (The only exception is you cannot divide by zero.)

3. Solve each equation. Check each solution.

(a) $2y = 14$

E X A M P L E   3   Solving an Equation by Using the Multiplication Property

Solve each equation.

(a) $9p = 63$

You want to get the variable, p, by itself on the left side. The expression $9p$ means $9 \cdot p$. To get p by itself, *divide* both sides by 9.

$$9p = 63$$

$$\frac{\overset{1}{\cancel{9}} \cdot p}{\underset{1}{\cancel{9}}} = \frac{63}{9} \qquad \text{Divide both sides by 9.}$$

$$p = 7$$

Check.

$$9p = 63$$
$$9 \cdot 7 = 63 \qquad \text{Replace } p \text{ with 7.}$$
$$63 = 63 \qquad \text{True}$$

The result is true, so 7 is the solution.

(b) $-4r = 24$

Divide both sides by -4 to get r by itself on the left.

$$\frac{\overset{1}{\cancel{-4}} \cdot r}{\underset{1}{\cancel{-4}}} = \frac{24}{-4} \qquad \text{Divide both sides by } -4.$$

$$r = -6$$

Check this solution: $-4 \cdot (-6) = 24$ is true.

(c) $-55 = -11m$

Divide both sides by -11 to get m by itself on the right.

$$\frac{-55}{-11} = \frac{\overset{1}{\cancel{-11}} \cdot m}{\underset{1}{\cancel{-11}}}$$

$$5 = m$$

Check this solution: $-55 = -11 \cdot (5)$ is true, so 5 is the solution.

(b) $42 = 7p$

(c) $-8a = 32$

(d) $-3r = -15$

(e) $-60 = -6k$

(f) $10x = 0$

WORK PROBLEM 3 AT THE SIDE. ▶▶

ANSWERS

3. **(a)** 7 **(b)** 6 **(c)** -4 **(d)** 5 **(e)** 10 **(f)** 0

4. Solve each equation. Check each solution.

(a) $\dfrac{a}{4} = 2$

(b) $\dfrac{y}{7} = -3$

(c) $-8 = \dfrac{k}{6}$

(d) $8 = -\dfrac{4}{5}z$

(e) $-\dfrac{5}{8}p = -10$

EXAMPLE 4   Solving an Equation by Using the Multiplication Property

Solve each equation.

(a) $\dfrac{x}{2} = 9$

Replace $\dfrac{x}{2}$ with $\dfrac{1}{2}x$ because dividing by 2 is the same as multiplying by $\dfrac{1}{2}$. Then, to get x by itself, multiply both sides by $\dfrac{2}{1}$ (because $\dfrac{1}{2}$ times $\dfrac{2}{1}$ is 1).

$$\dfrac{1}{2}x = 9$$

$$\dfrac{\overset{1}{\cancel{2}}}{1} \cdot \dfrac{1}{\underset{1}{\cancel{2}}}x = 2 \cdot 9 \qquad \text{Multiply both sides by } \dfrac{2}{1} \text{ (which equals 2)}$$

$$1x = 18$$
$$x = 18$$

Check.
$$\dfrac{x}{2} = 9$$

$$\dfrac{18}{2} = 9 \qquad \text{Replace } x \text{ with 18.}$$

$$9 = 9 \qquad \text{True}$$

18 is the correct solution.

(b) $-\dfrac{2}{3}r = 4$

Multiply both sides by $-\dfrac{3}{2}$ (because the product of $-\dfrac{3}{2}$ and $-\dfrac{2}{3}$ is 1).

$$-\dfrac{2}{3}r = 4$$

$$-\dfrac{\overset{1}{\cancel{3}}}{\underset{1}{\cancel{2}}} \cdot \left(-\dfrac{\overset{1}{\cancel{2}}}{\underset{1}{\cancel{3}}}r\right) = -\dfrac{3}{\underset{1}{\cancel{2}}} \cdot \dfrac{\overset{2}{\cancel{4}}}{1}$$

$$r = -6$$

Check by replacing r with -6. Write -6 as $\dfrac{-6}{1}$.

$$-\dfrac{2}{\underset{1}{\cancel{3}}} \cdot \dfrac{\overset{-2}{\cancel{-6}}}{1} = 4$$

$$4 = 4 \qquad \text{True, so } -6 \text{ is the solution.}$$

◀◀ WORK PROBLEM 4 AT THE SIDE.

Here is a summary of the rules for using the multiplication property. In these rules, x is the variable and a, b, and c are numbers.

Solving Equations Using the Multiplication Property

Solve the equation $ax = b$ by dividing both sides by a.

Solve the equation $\dfrac{a}{b}x = c$ by multiplying both sides by $\dfrac{b}{a}$.

ANSWERS

4. (a) 8 (b) -21 (c) -48 (d) -10 (e) 16

6   Exercises

Decide whether the given number is a solution of the equation.

1. $x + 7 = 11$;   4

2. $k - 2 = 7$;   9

3. $4y = 28$;   7

4. $5p = 30$;   6

5. $2z - 1 = -15$; -8

6. $6r - 3 = -14$; -2

Solve each equation by using the addition property. Check each solution.

Example: $m - 2 = 7$	**Solution:**	**Check:**
	Add 2 to both sides.	$m - 2 = 7$
	$m - 2 + 2 = 7 + 2$	$9 - 2 = 7$ Replace m with 9.
	$m = 9$	$7 = 7$ True
		The solution is 9.

7. $p + 5 = 9$

8. $a + 3 = 12$

9. $k + 15 = 0$

10. $y + 6 = 0$

11. $z - 5 = 3$

12. $x - 9 = 4$

13. $8 = r - 2$

14. $3 = b - 5$

15. $-5 = n + 3$

16. $-1 = a + 8$

17. $7 = r + 13$

18. $12 = z + 7$

19. $-4 + k = 14$

20. $-9 + y = 7$

21. $-12 + x = -1$

22. $-3 + m = -9$

23. $-5 = -2 + r$

24. $-1 = -10 + y$

25. $d + \dfrac{2}{3} = 3$

26. $x + \dfrac{1}{2} = 4$

27. $z - \dfrac{7}{8} = 10$

28. $m - \dfrac{3}{4} = 6$

29. $\dfrac{1}{2} = k - 2$

30. $\dfrac{3}{5} = t - 1$

31. $m - \dfrac{7}{5} = \dfrac{11}{4}$

32. $z - \dfrac{7}{3} = \dfrac{32}{9}$

33. $x - 0.8 = 5.07$

34. $a - 3.82 = 7.9$

35. $3.25 = 4.76 + r$

36. $8.9 = 10.5 + b$

Solve each equation. Check each solution.

Example: $5k = 60$	Solution:	Check:
	Divide both sides by 5.	$5k = 60$
	$\dfrac{\overset{1}{\cancel{5}} \cdot k}{\underset{1}{\cancel{5}}} = \dfrac{60}{5}$	$5(12) = 60$
		$60 = 60 \qquad$ True
	$k = \mathbf{12}$	The solution is 12.

37. $6z = 12$

38. $8k = 24$

39. $48 = 12r$

40. $99 = 11m$

41. $3y = 0$

42. $5a = 0$

43. $-6k = 36$

44. $-7y = 70$

Name _____

45. $-36 = -4p$

46. $-54 = -9r$

47. $-1.2m = 8.4$

48. $-5.4z = 27$

49. $-8.4p = -9.24$

50. $-3.2y = -16.64$

Solve each equation. Check each solution.

Example: $\dfrac{p}{4} = -3$

Solution:

Replace $\dfrac{p}{4}$ with $\dfrac{1}{4}p$.

Multiply both sides by 4.

$$\dfrac{\overset{1}{\cancel{4}}}{1} \cdot \dfrac{1}{\underset{1}{\cancel{4}}}p = 4 \cdot (-3)$$

$$p = -12$$

Check:

$$\dfrac{p}{4} = -3$$

$$\dfrac{-12}{4} = -3$$

$$-3 = -3 \quad \text{True}$$

The solution is -12.

51. $\dfrac{k}{2} = 17$

52. $\dfrac{y}{3} = 5$

53. $11 = \dfrac{a}{6}$

54. $5 = \dfrac{m}{8}$

55. $\dfrac{r}{3} = -12$

56. $\dfrac{z}{9} = -3$

57. $-\dfrac{2}{5}p = 8$

58. $-\dfrac{5}{6}k = 15$

59. $-\dfrac{3}{4}m = -3$

60. $-\dfrac{9}{10}b = -18$

61. $6 = \dfrac{3}{8}x$

62. $4 = \dfrac{2}{3}a$

63. $\dfrac{y}{2.6} = 0.5$

64. $\dfrac{k}{0.7} = 3.2$

65. $\dfrac{z}{-3.8} = 1.3$

66. $\dfrac{m}{-5.2} = 2.1$

67. Explain the addition property of equations. Then show an example of an equation where you would use the addition property to solve it. Make the equation so it has -3 as the solution.

68. Explain the multiplication property of equations. Then show an example of an equation where you would use the multiplication property to solve it. Make the equation so it has $+6$ as the solution.

Solve the following equations.

69. $x - 17 = 5 - 3$

70. $y + 4 = 10 - 9$

71. $3 = x + 9 - 15$

72. $-1 = y + 7 - 9$

73. $\dfrac{7}{2}x = \dfrac{4}{3}$

74. $\dfrac{3}{4}x = \dfrac{5}{3}$

Review and Prepare

Use the order of operations to simplify the following.

75. $2\dfrac{1}{5} \div \left(3\dfrac{1}{3} - 4\dfrac{1}{5}\right)$

76. $\dfrac{2}{3} + \dfrac{5}{6} \cdot \left(-\dfrac{3}{4}\right)$

$$\frac{4}{6} + \frac{5}{6} = 9$$

77. $\dfrac{1}{2} + \dfrac{3}{4} \cdot \dfrac{8}{9} - \dfrac{1}{6}$

78. $2 - \left(3 \cdot \dfrac{1}{2} \div \dfrac{2}{3}\right) - \dfrac{7}{4}$

7 Solving Equations with Several Steps

OBJECTIVES

1. Solve equations with several steps.
2. Use the distributive property.
3. Combine like terms.
4. Solve more difficult equations.

You cannot solve the equation $5m + 1 = 16$ by just adding the same number to both sides, nor by just dividing both sides by the same number.

OBJECTIVE 1 Instead, you will use a combination of both operations. Here are the steps.

> **Solving Equations Using the Addition and Multiplication Properties**
>
> *Step 1* Add or subtract the same amount on both sides of the equation so that the variable term ends up by itself on one side.
>
> *Step 2* Multiply or divide both sides by the same number to find the solution.
>
> *Step 3* Check the solution.

E X A M P L E 1   Solving Equations with Several Steps

Solve $5m + 1 = 16$.

First subtract 1 from both sides so that $5m$ will be by itself on the left side.

$$5m + 1 - 1 = 16 - 1$$
$$5m = 15$$

Next, divide both sides by 5.

$$\frac{\overset{1}{\cancel{5}} \cdot m}{\underset{1}{\cancel{5}}} = \frac{15}{5}$$

$$m = 3$$

Check.

$$5m + 1 = 16$$
$$5\,(3) + 1 = 16 \qquad \text{Replace } m \text{ with 3.}$$
$$15 + 1 = 16$$
$$16 = 16 \qquad \text{True}$$

The solution is 3.

WORK PROBLEM 1 AT THE SIDE. ▶▶

OBJECTIVE 2 We can use the order of operations to simplify these two expressions:

$$\underset{\underset{28}{2(14)}}{2(\underbrace{6 + 8})} \qquad \text{and} \qquad \underset{\underset{28}{12 \ + \ 16}}{\underbrace{2 \cdot 6} + \underbrace{2 \cdot 8}}$$

Because both answers are the same, the two expressions are equivalent.

$$2(6 + 8) = 2 \cdot 6 + 2 \cdot 8$$

This is an example of the **distributive** (dis-TRIB-yoo-tiv) **property.**

> **Distributive Property**
>
> $$a(b + c) = ab + ac$$

1. Solve each equation. Check each solution.

   (a) $2r + 7 = 13$

   (b) $20 = 6y - 4$

   (c) $7m + 9 = 9$

   (d) $-2 = 4p + 10$

   (e) $-10z - 9 = 11$

ANSWERS

1. (a) 3 (b) 4 (c) 0 (d) -3 (e) -2

239

2. Use the distributive property.

(a) $3(2 + 6)$

$6 + 18 = 24$

(b) $8(k - 3)$

$8k - 24$

(c) $-6(r + 5)$

$-6r - 30$

(d) $-9(s - 8)$

$-9s + 72$

3. Combine like terms.

(a) $5y + 11y$

$16y$

(b) $10a - 28a$

$18a$

(c) $3x + 3x - 9x$

$6x - 9x = -3x$

(d) $k + k$

$2k$

(e) $6b - b - 7b$

$5b - 7b = 2b$

EXAMPLE 2 Using the Distributive Property

Simplify each expression by using the distributive property.

(a) $9(4 + 2) = 9 \cdot 4 + 9 \cdot 2 = 36 + 18 = 54$

The 9 on the outside of the parentheses is *distributed* over the 4 and the 2 on the inside of the parentheses. That means that each number inside the parentheses is multiplied by 9.

(b) $-3(k + 9) = -3 \cdot k + (-3) \cdot 9 = -3k + (-27) = -3k - 27$

(c) $6(y - 5) = 6 \cdot y - 6 \cdot 5 = 6y - 30$

(d) $-2(x - 3) = -2 \cdot x - (-2) \cdot 3 = -2x - (-6) = -2x + 6$

◀◀ WORK PROBLEM 2 AT THE SIDE.

OBJECTIVE 3 ▶ A single letter or number, or the product of a variable and a number, makes up a *term*. Here are six examples of terms.

$$3y \qquad 5 \qquad -9 \qquad 8r \qquad 10r^2 \qquad x$$

*Terms with exactly the same variable and the same exponent are called **like terms**.*

$5x$	and	$3x$	like terms
$5x$	and	$3m$	not like terms; variables are different
$5x^2$	and	$5x^3$	not like terms; exponents are different
$5x^4$	and	$3x^4$	like terms

The distributive property can be used to simplify a sum of like terms such as $6r + 3r$.

$$6r + 3r = (6 + 3)r = 9r$$

This process is called *combining like terms*.

EXAMPLE 3 Combining Like Terms

Use the distributive property to combine like terms.

(a) $5k + 11k = (5 + 11)k = 16k$

(b) $10m - 14m + 2m = (10 - 14 + 2)m = -2m$

(c) $-5x + x$ can be written $-5x + 1x = (-5 + 1)x = -4x$

◀◀ WORK PROBLEM 3 AT THE SIDE.

OBJECTIVE ▶4▶ The next examples show you how to solve more difficult equations using the addition, multiplication, and distributive properties.

┌ E X A M P L E 4   **Solving Equations**

Solve each equation.

(a) $6r + 3r = 36$

You can combine $6r$ and $3r$ because they are like terms.
$6r + 3r$ is $9r$, so the equation becomes:

$$9r = 36$$

Next, divide both sides by 9.

$$\frac{\overset{1}{\cancel{9}} \cdot r}{\underset{1}{\cancel{9}}} = \frac{36}{9}$$

$$r = 4$$

Check.

$$6r + 3r = 36$$
$$6(4) + 3(4) = 36 \qquad \text{Replace } r \text{ with 4.}$$
$$24 + 12 = 36$$
$$36 = 36 \qquad \text{True}$$

The solution is 4.

(b) $2k - 2 = 5k - 11$

First, to get the variable term on one side, subtract $5k$ from both sides.

$$2k - 2 - \mathbf{5k} = 5k - 11 - \mathbf{5k}$$
$$2k - 5k - 2 = 5k - 5k - 11$$
$$-3k - 2 = -11$$

Next, add 2 to both sides.

$$-3k - 2 + \mathbf{2} = -11 + \mathbf{2}$$
$$-3k = -9$$

Finally, divide both sides by -3.

$$\frac{\overset{1}{\cancel{-3}} \cdot k}{\underset{1}{\cancel{-3}}} = \frac{-9}{-3}$$

$$k = 3$$

Check.

$$2k - 2 = 5k - 11$$
$$2(3) - 2 = 5(3) - 11 \qquad \text{Replace } k \text{ with 3.}$$
$$6 - 2 = 15 - 11$$
$$4 = 4 \qquad \text{True}$$

The solution is 3.

WORK PROBLEM 4 AT THE SIDE. ▶▶

4. Solve each equation. Check each solution.

(a) $3y - 1 = 2y + 7$

(b) $5a + 7 = 3a - 9$

(c) $3p - 2 = p - 6$

242

5. Solve each equation. Check each solution.

(a) $-12 = 4(y - 1)$

$$-12 = 4y - 4$$
$$\underline{+4 \qquad +4}$$
$$\frac{-8}{4} = \frac{4y}{4}$$
$$y = {}^-2$$

(b) $5(m + 4) = 20$

$$5m + 20 = 20$$
$$\underline{-20 \quad -20}$$
$$5m = 0$$

(c) $6(t - 2) = 18$

$$6t - 12 = 18$$
$$\underline{+12 \quad +12}$$
$$\frac{6t}{6} = \frac{30}{6}$$
$$t = 5$$

Now that you know about the distributive property and combining like terms, here is a summary of all the steps you can use to solve an equation.

> **Solving Equations**
>
> *Step 1* If possible, use the **distributive property** to remove parentheses.
>
> *Step 2* **Combine** any like terms on the left side of the equation. Combine any like terms on the right side of the equation.
>
> *Step 3* **Add or subtract** the same amount on both sides of the equation so that the variable term ends up by itself on one side.
>
> *Step 4* **Multiply or divide** both sides by the same number to find the solution.
>
> *Step 5* **Check** your solution by going back to the original equation. Replace the variable with your solution. Follow the order of operations to complete the calculations. If the two sides of the equation are equal, your solution is correct.

EXAMPLE 5 Solving Equations Using the Distributive Property

Solve $-6 = 3(y - 2)$

Step 1 Use the distributive property on the right side of the equation.

$$3(y - 2) \text{ becomes } 3 \cdot y - 3 \cdot 2 \text{ or } 3y - 6$$

Now the equation looks like this.

$$-6 = 3y - 6$$

Step 2 Combine like terms. Check the left side of the equation. There are no like terms. Check the right side. No like terms there either, so go on to Step 3.

Step 3 Add 6 to both sides in order to get the variable term by itself on the right side.

$$-6 + 6 = 3y - 6 + 6$$
$$0 = 3y$$

Step 4 Divide both sides by 3.

$$\frac{0}{3} = \frac{\overset{1}{\cancel{3}} \cdot y}{\underset{1}{\cancel{3}}}$$
$$0 = y$$

Step 5 Check. Go back to the original equation.

$$-6 = 3(y - 2)$$
$$-6 = 3(0 - 2) \qquad \text{Replace } y \text{ with } 0.$$
$$-6 = 3(-2)$$
$$-6 = -6 \qquad \text{True}$$

The solution is 0.

◀◀ **WORK PROBLEM 5 AT THE SIDE.**

7   *Exercises*

Solve each equation. Check each solution.

Examples:

$9p - 7 = 11$ $-3m + 2 = 8$

Solutions:

Add 7 to both sides.   Subtract 2 from both sides.

$9p - 7 + 7 = 11 + 7$ $-3m + 2 - 2 = 8 - 2$

$\qquad 9p = 18$ $\qquad -3m = 6$

Divide both sides by 9.   Divide both sides by -3.

$$\frac{\overset{1}{\cancel{9}} \cdot p}{\underset{1}{\cancel{9}}} = \frac{18}{9}$$ $$\frac{\overset{1}{\cancel{-3}} \cdot m}{\underset{1}{\cancel{-3}}} = \frac{6}{-3}$$

$\qquad p = 2$ $\qquad m = -2$

Check: Replace p with 2.   Check: Replace m with -2.

$\qquad 9(2) - 7 = 11$ $\qquad -3(-2) + 2 = 8$

$\qquad 18 - 7 = 11$ $\qquad 6 + 2 = 8$

$\qquad 11 = 11$ True $\qquad 8 = 8$ True

The solution is **2**.   The solution is **-2**.

1. $7p + 5 = 12$

$\qquad \underline{-5 \quad -5}$

$\qquad \dfrac{7p}{7} = \dfrac{7}{7} = 1$

2. $6k + 3 = 15$

3. $2 = 8y - 6$

4. $10 = 11p - 12$

5. $-3m + 1 = 1$

6. $-4k + 5 = 5$

7. $28 = -9a + 10$

8. $5 = -10p + 25$

9. $-5x - 4 = 16$

10. $-12a - 3 = 21$

11. $-\dfrac{1}{2}z + 2 = -1$

12. $-\dfrac{5}{8}r + 4 = -6$

Use the distributive property to simplify.

13. $6(x + 4)$

14. $8(k + 5)$

15. $7(p - 8)$

16. $9(t - 4)$

17. $-3(m + 6)$

18. $-5(a + 2)$

19. $-2(y - 3)$

20. $-4(r - 7)$

21. $-5(z - 9)$

Combine like terms.

22. $11r + 6r$

23. $2m + 5m$

24. $8z + 7z$

25. $10x - 2x$

26. $9y - 3y$

27. $-10a + a$

28. $-4t + t$

29. $3y - y - 4y$

30. $7p - 9p - p$

Solve each equation. Check each solution.

31. $4k + 6k = 50$

32. $3a + 2a = 15$

33. $54 = 10m - m$

34. $28 = x + 6x$

35. $2b - 6b = 24$

36. $3r - 9r = 18$

37. $-12 = 6y - 18y$

38. $-5 = 10z - 15z$

39. $6p - 2 = 4p + 6$

Name _____

40. $5y - 5 = 2y + 10$

41. $9 + 7z = 9z + 13$

42. $8 + 4a = 2a + 2$

43. $-2y + 6 = 6y - 10$

44. $5x - 4 = -3x + 4$

45. $b + 3.05 = 2$

46. $t + 0.8 = -1.7$

47. $2.5r + 9 = -1$

48. $0.5x - 6 = 2$

49. $-10 = 2(y + 4)$

50. $-3 = 3(x + 6)$

51. $-4(t + 2) = 12$

52. $-5(k + 3) = 25$

53. $6(x - 5) = -30$

54. $7(r - 5) = -35$

55. Solve $-2t - 10 = 3t + 5$. Show each step you take in solving it. Next to each step, write a sentence that explains what you did in that step. Be sure to tell when you used the addition property of equations and when you used the multiplication property of equations.

56. Here is one student's solution to an equation.

$$3(2x + 5) = -7$$
$$6x + 5 = -7$$
$$6x + 5 - 5 = -7 - 5$$
$$6x = -12$$
$$x = -2$$

Show how to check the solution. If the solution does not check, find and correct the error.

Solve each equation.

57. $30 - 40 = -2x + 7x - 4x$

58. $-6 - 5 + 14 = -50a + 51a$

59. $0 = -2(y - 2)$

60. $0 = -9(b - 1)$

61. $\dfrac{y}{2} - 2 = \dfrac{y}{4} + 3$

62. $\dfrac{z}{3} + 1 = \dfrac{z}{2} - 3$

Review and Prepare

Solve each word problem.

63. A chip and dip set is on sale after Christmas at 60% off the regular price. How much will Beyanjeru pay for a set regularly priced at $28?

64. A "going out of business" sale at the Great Goods store promises 75% off on all items. Gel-pack batteries for electric wheelchairs are regularly priced at $99. Find the amount that Will paid for a battery during the sale.

65. If the sales tax rate is 6% and a refrigerator costs $420, what is the amount of sales tax?

66. A VCR sells for $450 plus 4% sales tax. Find the price of the VCR including sales tax.

8 *Applications*

It is rare for an application problem to be presented as an equation. Usually, the problem is given in words. You need to *translate* these words into an equation that you can solve.

OBJECTIVES

1. Translate word phrases by using variables.

2. Solve application problems.

OBJECTIVE 1 The following examples show you how to translate word phrases into algebra.

┌─ **E X A M P L E 1** **Translating Word Phrases by Using Variables**

Write in symbols by using x as the variable.

Words	*Algebra*
a number **plus** 2	$x + 2$ or $2 + x$
the **sum** of 8 and a number	$8 + x$ or $x + 8$
5 **more than** a number	$x + 5$ or $5 + x$
-35 **added to** a number	$-35 + x$ or $x + (-35)$
a number **increased by** 6	$x + 6$ or $6 + x$
9 **less than** a number	$x - 9$
a number **subtracted from** 3	$3 - x$
a number **decreased by** 4	$x - 4$
10 **minus** a number	$10 - x$

Note
Recall that addition can be done in any order, so $x + 2$ gives the same result as $2 + x$. This is *not* true in subtraction, so be careful. $10 - x$ does *not* give the same result as $x - 10$.

WORK PROBLEM 1 AT THE SIDE. ▶▶

┌─ **E X A M P L E 2** **Translating Word Phrases by Using Variables**

Write in symbols by using x as the variable.

Words	*Algebra*
8 **times** a number	$8x$
the **product** of 12 and a number	$12x$
double a number (meaning "2 times")	$2x$
the **quotient** of 6 and a number	$\dfrac{6}{x}$
a number **divided by** 10	$\dfrac{x}{10}$
one-third of a number	$\dfrac{1}{3}x$ or $\dfrac{x}{3}$
the result **is**	$=$

WORK PROBLEM 2 AT THE SIDE. ▶▶

OBJECTIVE 2 The next examples show you how to solve application problems. Notice that you begin each solution by selecting a variable to represent the unknown.

1. Write in symbols by using x as the variable.

   (a) 15 less than a number

   (b) 12 more than a number

   (c) a number increased by 13

   (d) a number minus 8

   (e) -10 plus a number

   (f) 6 minus a number

2. Write in symbols by using x as the variable.

   (a) double a number

   (b) the product of -8 and a number

   (c) the quotient of 15 and a number

   (d) one-half of a number

ANSWERS

1. (a) $x - 15$ (b) $x + 12$ or $12 + x$
   (c) $x + 13$ or $13 + x$ (d) $x - 8$
   (e) $-10 + x$ or $x + (-10)$ (f) $6 - x$

2. (a) $2x$ (b) $-8x$ (c) $\dfrac{15}{x}$ (d) $\dfrac{1}{2}x$ or $\dfrac{x}{2}$

3. Solve each application problem. Check your solution by going back to the words in the original problem.

(a) If 3 times a number is added to 4, the result is 19. Find the number.

$3x + 4 = 19$

(b) If -6 times a number is added to 5, the result is -13. Find the number.

(c) Susan donated $10 more than twice what LuAnn donated. If Susan donated $22, how much did LuAnn donate?

ANSWERS
3. (a) $3x + 4 = 19$
   $x = 5$
   (b) $-6x + 5 = -13$
   $x = 3$
   (c) $2x + 10 = 22$
   $x = 6$
   LuAnn donated $6.

E X A M P L E   3   Solving Application Problems

If 5 times a number is added to 11, the result is 26. Find the number.

Let x represent the unknown number.

Use the information in the problem to write an equation.

$$\underbrace{\text{5 times a number}}_{5x} \quad \underbrace{\text{added to}}_{+} \quad \underbrace{11}_{11} \quad \underbrace{\text{is}}_{=} \quad \underbrace{26.}_{26}$$

Note
The phrase "the result is" translates to "=."

Next, solve the equation. First subtract 11 from both sides.

$$5x + 11 - \mathbf{11} = 26 - \mathbf{11}$$
$$5x = 15$$
$$\frac{\overset{1}{\cancel{5}}x}{\underset{1}{\cancel{5}}} = \frac{15}{5} \qquad \text{Divide both sides by 5.}$$
$$x = 3$$

The number is 3.
To check the solution, go back to the words of the original problem.

$$\underbrace{\text{If 5 times}}_{5 \ \cdot} \quad \underbrace{\text{a number}}_{3} \quad \underbrace{\text{is added to}}_{+} \quad \underbrace{11,}_{11} \quad \underbrace{\text{the result is}}_{=} \quad \underbrace{26.}_{26}$$

Does $5 \cdot 3 + 11$ really equal 26? Yes it does. So 3 is the correct solution because it "works" when you put it back into the original problem.

E X A M P L E   4   Solving Application Problems

Michael has 5 less than three times as many lab experiments completed as David. If Michael has completed 13 experiments, how many lab experiments has David completed?

Let x represent the number of experiments David has completed.

$$\underbrace{\text{3 times David's number}}_{3x} \quad \underbrace{\text{minus}}_{-} \quad \underbrace{5}_{5} \quad \underbrace{\text{is}}_{=} \quad \underbrace{\text{Michael's number.}}_{13}$$

Next, solve the equation. First add 5 to both sides.

$$3x - 5 + \mathbf{5} = 13 + \mathbf{5}$$
$$3x = 18$$
$$\frac{\overset{1}{\cancel{3}}x}{\underset{1}{\cancel{3}}} = \frac{18}{3} \qquad \text{Divide both sides by 3.}$$
$$x = 6$$

David has completed 6 lab experiments. Check by using the words of the original problem. First take three times the solution ($3 \cdot 6$), which is 18. Then, 18 decreased by 5 is 13, which matches the 13 experiments completed by Michael. So 6 is the correct solution.

◀◀ WORK PROBLEM 3 AT THE SIDE.

The steps in solving an application problem are summarized for you here.

> **Solving Algebra Application Problems**
>
> *Step 1* Choose a variable to represent the unknown. If there are several unknowns, let the variable represent the one you know the least about.
>
> *Step 2* Use the information in the problem to write an equation that relates known information to the unknown. Make a sketch or drawing, if possible.
>
> *Step 3* Solve the equation.
>
> *Step 4* Answer the question raised in the problem.
>
> *Step 5* Check the solution with the original words of the problem.

E X A M P L E 5 Solving Application Problems

During the day, Sheila drove 72 km more than Russell. The total distance traveled by them both was 232 km. Find the distance traveled by each person.

There are two unknowns: Sheila's distance and Russell's distance.

Let x be the distance traveled by Russell, because you know less about his distance than Sheila's distance.

Since Sheila drove 72 km more than Russell, the distance she traveled is $x + 72$ km, that is, Russell's distance (x) plus 72 km.

Now write an equation and solve it.

$$\underbrace{\text{Distance for Russell}}_{} \quad \underset{\downarrow}{\text{plus}} \quad \underbrace{\text{distance for Sheila}}_{} \quad \underset{\downarrow}{\text{is}} \quad \underbrace{\text{total distance.}}_{}$$

$$x \quad + \quad x + 72 \quad = \quad 232$$

Recall that x is really $1x$, so the sum $x + x$ is $1x + 1x$ which is $2x$. The equation becomes:

$$2x + 72 = 232$$
$$2x + 72 - 72 = 232 - 72 \qquad \text{Subtract 72 from both sides.}$$
$$2x = 160 \qquad\qquad \text{Divide both sides by 2.}$$
$$x = 80$$

Russell's distance is x, so Russell traveled 80 km.
Sheila's distance is $x + 72$ so Sheila traveled $80 + 72 = 152$ km.
Check using the words of the original problem.

Sheila drove 72 km more than Russell.

Sheila's 152 km is 72 km more than Russell's 80 km, so that checks.

The total distance traveled by them both was 232 km.

Sheila's 152 km + Russell's 80 km = 232 km, so that checks.

Note

Check the solution to an application problem by putting the numbers back into the original problem. If they do *not* work, solve the problem a different way.

WORK PROBLEM 4 AT THE SIDE. ▶▶

4. (a) In a day of work, Keonda made $12 more than her daughter. Together they made $182. Find the amount made by each person. (*Hint:* Which amount do you know the least about, Keonda's, or her daughter's? Let x be that amount.)

(b) A rope is 21 m long. Marcos cut it into two pieces, so that one piece is 3 m longer than the other. Find the length of each piece.

ANSWERS

4. (a) daughter made x
Keonda made $x + 12$
$x + x + 12 = 182$
daughter made $85
Keonda made $97
(b) shorter piece is x
longer piece is $x + 3$
$x + x + 3 = 21$
shorter piece is 9 m
longer piece is 12 m

5. Make a drawing to help solve this problem. The length of Ann's rectangular garden plot is 3 m more than the width. She used 22 m of fencing around the edge. Find the length and the width of the garden.

EXAMPLE 6   Solving a Geometry Problem

The length of a rectangle is 2 cm more than the width. The perimeter is 68 cm. Find the length and width.

Let x be the width of the rectangle because you know the least about the width.

Since the length is 2 cm more than the width, the length is $x + 2$.

A drawing of the rectangle will help you see these relationships.

width $= x$
length $= x + 2$
perimeter $= 68$

Use the formula for perimeter of a rectangle, $P = 2 \cdot l + 2 \cdot w$.

$$P = 2 \cdot l \quad + 2 \cdot w$$
$$68 = 2(x + 2) + 2 \cdot x \quad \text{Use distributive property.}$$
$$68 = 2x + 4 + 2x \quad \text{Combine like terms.}$$
$$68 = 4x + 4$$
$$68 - 4 = 4x + 4 - 4 \quad \text{Subtract 4 from both sides.}$$
$$64 = 4x$$
$$\frac{64}{4} = \frac{\overset{1}{4} \cdot x}{\underset{1}{4}} \quad \text{Divide both sides by 4.}$$
$$16 = x$$

This does **not** answer the entire question in the problem, because x represents the *width* of the rectangle and the problem asks for the *length* and width.

width $= x$, so width is 16 cm

length $= x + 2$, so length is $16 + 2$ or 18 cm

Check using the words of the original problem. It says the length is 2 cm more than the width. 18 cm is 2 cm more than 16 cm, so that part checks. The original problem also says the perimeter is 68 cm. Use 18 cm and 16 cm to find the perimeter.

$$68 = 2 \cdot l + 2 \cdot w \quad \text{Let } l = 18 \text{ and } w = 16.$$
$$68 = 2 \cdot 18 + 2 \cdot 16$$
$$68 = 36 + 32$$
$$68 = 68 \quad \text{True}$$

The complete solution is width $= 16$ cm and length $= 18$ cm.

WORK PROBLEM 5 AT THE SIDE.

8   Exercises

Write in symbols by using x as the variable.

Examples:

the sum of 7 and a number
12 added to a number
a number subtracted from 57
three times a number
the sum of 15 and twice a number

Solutions:

$7 + x$ or $x + 7$
$x + 12$ or $12 + x$
$57 - x$
$3x$
$15 + 2x$ or $2x + 15$

1. 14 plus a number

$14 + x$

2. the sum of a number and -8

$x + -8$

3. -5 added to a number

$-5 + x$

4. 16 more than a number

$16 + x = x + 16$

5. 20 minus a number

$20 - x$

6. a number decreased by 25

$x - 25$

7. 9 less than a number

$9 - x$

8. a number subtracted from -7

$x - -7$

9. subtract 4 from a number

$4 - x$

10. 3 fewer than a number

$3 - x$

11. six times a number

$6x$

12. the product of -3 and a number

$-3x$

13. double a number

$2x$

14. half a number

$\dfrac{x}{2}$

15. a number divided by 2

$\dfrac{x}{2}$

16. 4 divided by a number

$\dfrac{x}{4}$

17. twice a number added to 8

$2x + 8$

18. five times a number plus 5

$5x + 5$

19. 10 fewer than seven times a number

$10 - 7x$

20. 12 less than six times a number

$12 - 6x$

21. the sum of twice a number and the number

$2x + x$

22. triple a number subtracted from the number

$3x - x$

23. In your own words, write a definition for each of these words: variable, expression, equation. Give three examples to illustrate each definition.

24. "You can use any letter to represent the unknown in an application problem." Is this statement true or false? Explain your answer.

Solve each application problem. Use the five steps for solving algebra application problems. Be sure to show your equation and the steps you use to solve the equation.

Example: If a number is multiplied by 5 and the product is added to 2, the result is -13. Find the number.

Solution:

Let x represent the unknown number.

$$\underbrace{\text{a number multiplied by 5}}_{5x} \quad \underbrace{\text{added to}}_{+} \quad \overset{\downarrow}{\underset{2}{2}} \quad \underbrace{\text{result is}}_{=} \quad \overset{\downarrow}{\underset{-13}{-13}}$$

Solve the equation.

$$5x + 2 - 2 = -13 - 2 \qquad \text{Subtract 2 from both sides.}$$
$$5x = -15 \qquad \text{Divide both sides by 5.}$$
$$x = -3$$

The number is **−3**.

Check with the words of the original problem: $-3 \cdot 5 + 2 = -13$

$$-13 = -13 \quad \text{True}$$

25. If four times a number is decreased by 2, the result is 26. Find the number.

26. The sum of 8 and five times a number is 53. Find the number.

Name_____

27. If twice a number is added to the number, the result is −15. What is the number?

28. If a number is subtracted from three times the number, the result is −8. What is the number?

29. If half a number is added to twice the number, the answer is 50. Find the number.

30. If one-third of a number is added to three times the number, the result is 30. Find the number.

31. A board is 78 cm long. Rosa cut the board into two pieces, with one piece 10 cm longer than the other. Find the length of both pieces.

32. Ed and Marge were candidates for city council. Marge won, with 93 more votes than Ed. The total number of votes cast in the election was 587. Find the number of votes received by each candidate.

33. Kerwin rented a chain saw for a one-time $9 sharpening fee plus $16 a day rental. His total bill was $89. For how many days did Kerwin rent the saw?

34. Mrs. Chao made a $50 down payment on a sofa. Her monthly payments were $158. She paid $998 in all. For how many months did she make payments?

In the next exercises, use the formula for the perimeter of a rectangle, P = 2l + 2w. Make a drawing to help you solve each problem.

35. The perimeter of a rectangle is 48 m. The width is 5 m. Find the length.

36. The length of a rectangle is 27 cm, and the perimeter is 74 cm. Find the width of the rectangle.

37. A rectangular dog pen is twice as long as it is wide. The perimeter of the pen is 36 ft. Find the length and the width of the pen.

38. A new city park is a rectangular shape. The length is triple the width. It will take 240 meters of fencing to go around the park. Find the length and width of the park.

Solve each application problem. Show your equation and the steps you use to solve the equation.

39. When 75 is subtracted from four times Tamu's age, the result is Tamu's age. How old is Tamu?

40. If three times Linda's age is decreased by 36, the result is twice Linda's age. How old is Linda?

41. A fence is 706 m long. It is to be cut into three parts. Two parts are the same length, and the third part is 25 m longer than the other two. Find the length of each part.

42. A wooden railing is 82 m long. It is to be divided into four pieces. Three pieces will be the same length, and the fourth piece will be 2 m longer than each of the other three. Find the length of each piece.

In the following exercises, use the formula for interest, $I = prt$.

43. For how long must $800 be deposited at 12% per year to earn $480 interest?

44. How much money must be deposited at 12% per year for 7 years to earn $1008 interest?

Review and Prepare

Solve the following problems.

45. 80% of $2900 is how much money?

46. What is 15% of $360?

47. Jeffrey puts 5% of his $1830 monthly salary into a retirement plan. How much goes into his plan each month?

48. Marshall College expects 9% of incoming students to need emergency loans to buy books. How many of the 2200 incoming students are expected to need loans?

CHAPTER SUMMARY

1	negative numbers	Negative numbers are numbers that are less than zero.
	signed numbers	Signed numbers are positive numbers, negative numbers, and zero.
	absolute value	Absolute value is the distance of a number from zero on a number line. Absolute value is never negative.
	opposite of a number	The opposite of a number is a number the same distance from zero on a number line as the original number but on the opposite side of zero.
2	**additive inverse**	The additive inverse is the opposite of a number. The sum of a number and its additive inverse is always 0.
5	**variables**	Variables are letters that represent numbers.
	expression	An expression is a combination of letters and numbers.
6	**equation**	An equation is a statement that says two expressions are equal.
	solution	The solution is a number that can be substituted for the variable in an equation, so that the equation is true.
	addition property of equations	The addition property of equations states that the same number can be added or subtracted on both sides of an equation.
	multiplication property of equations	The multiplication property of equations states that both sides of an equation can be multiplied or divided by the same number, except division by zero is not allowed.
7	**distributive property**	If a, b, and c are three numbers, the distributive property says that $a(b + c) = ab + ac$.
	like terms	Like terms are terms with exactly the same variable and the same exponent.

Concepts	Examples
1 Graphing Signed Numbers Place a dot at the correct location on the number line.	Graph -2, 1, 0, and $2\frac{1}{2}$. $\leftarrow\!\!+\!\!\bullet\!\!+\!\!+\!\!\bullet\!\!+\!\!\bullet\!\!+\!\!+\!\!\rightarrow$ $\quad -2\ -1\ \ 0\ \ 1\ \ 2\ \ 3$
1 Identifying the Smaller of Two Numbers Place the symbols < (less than) or > (greater than) between two numbers to make the statement true. The small pointed end of the symbol points to the smaller number.	Use the symbol < or > to make the following statements true. $2 \underline{\quad > \quad} 1$ $-3 \underline{\quad > \quad} -5$ $-6 \underline{\quad < \quad} 2$
1 Finding the Absolute Value of a Number Determine the distance from 0 to the given number on the number line.	Find each of the following. (a) $\lvert 8 \rvert$ \qquad (b) $\lvert -7 \rvert$ \qquad (c) $-\lvert -5 \rvert$ $\lvert 8 \rvert = 8$ \qquad $\lvert -7 \rvert = 7$ \qquad $\rightarrow -5$

Concepts	Examples
1 Finding the Opposite of a Number Determine the number that is the same distance from 0 as the given number, but on the opposite side of 0 on a number line.	Find the opposite of each of the following. **(a)** -6 **(b)** $+9$ $\quad -(-6) = 6$ $-(+9) = -9$

2 Adding Two Signed Numbers
Case 1: *Two positive numbers*
Add the numerical values.
 	
Case 2: *Two negative numbers*
Add the absolute values and write a negative sign in front of the sum.
 	
Case 3: *Two numbers with different signs*
Subtract the absolute values and write the sign of the number with the larger absolute value in front of the answer.
	Add the following.
	(a) $8 + 6 = 14$
	
	(b) $-8 + (-6)$
	  Find absolute values.
	$$\lvert -8 \rvert = 8 \qquad \lvert -6 \rvert = 6$$
	  Add absolute values.
	$$8 + 6 = 14$$
	  Write a negative sign: -14.
	  So, $-8 + (-6) = -14$
	(c) $5 + (-7)$
	  Find absolute values.
	$$\lvert 5 \rvert = 5 \quad \lvert -7 \rvert = 7$$
	  Subtract the smaller absolute value from the larger.
	$$7 - 5 = 2$$
	  The number with the larger absolute value is -7. Its sign is negative, so write a negative sign in front of the answer.
	$$5 + (-7) = -2$$

2 Subtracting Two Signed Numbers Follow these steps: Change the subtraction sign to addition. Change the sign of the second number to its opposite. Proceed as in addition.	Subtract. **(a)** $-6 - \quad 5$ $\quad\quad\;\downarrow\quad\downarrow$ $-6 + (-5) = -11$ **(b)** $5 - (-8)$ $\quad\quad\quad\quad\quad\quad\quad\quad\quad\quad\;\;\downarrow\quad\downarrow$ $\quad\quad\quad\quad\quad\quad\quad\quad\quad 5 + (+8) = 13$
3 Multiplying Signed Numbers Use these rules: The product of two numbers with the same sign is positive. The product of two numbers with different signs is negative.	Multiply the following. **(a)** $7 \cdot 3 = 21$ **(b)** $(-3) \cdot 4 = -12$ **(c)** $(-9) \cdot (-6) = 54$
3 Dividing Signed Numbers Use the same rules as for multiplying signed numbers: When two numbers have the same sign, the quotient is positive. When two numbers have different signs, the quotient is negative.	Divide. **(a)** $\dfrac{8}{4} = 2$ **(b)** $\dfrac{-20}{5} = -4$ **(c)** $\dfrac{50}{-5} = -10$ **(d)** $\dfrac{-12}{-6} = 2$

Concepts	Examples

4 Using the Order of Operations to Evaluate Numerical Expressions

Use the following order of operations to evaluate numerical expressions:

Work inside parentheses first.

Simplify expressions with exponents and find any square roots.

Multiply or divide from left to right.

Add or subtract from left to right.

Simplify the following.

(a) $-4 + \underbrace{6 \div (-2)}$

$\underbrace{-4 + \quad (-3)}$

-7

(b) $3^2 \cdot 4 + 3 \cdot \underbrace{(8 \div 2)}$

$\underbrace{3^2} \cdot 4 + 3 \cdot \quad 4$

$\underbrace{9 \cdot 4} + \underbrace{3 \cdot \quad 4}$

$\underbrace{36 \quad + \quad 12}$

48

---

5 Evaluating Expressions

Replace the variables in the expression with the numerical values.

Use the order of operations to evaluate.

What is the value of $6p - 5s$, if $p = -3$ and $s = -4$?

$$\begin{array}{cccc} 6 & p & - 5 & s \\ \downarrow & \downarrow & \downarrow & \downarrow \end{array}$$

$\underbrace{6(-3)} - \underbrace{5(-4)}$

$\underbrace{-18 - (-20)}$

2

---

6 Determining if a Number Is a Solution of an Equation

Substitute the number for the variable in the equation.

If the equation is true, the number is a solution.

Is the number 4 a solution of the following equation?

$$3x - 5 = 7$$

Replace x with 4.

$$3(4) - 5 = 7$$
$$12 - 5 = 7$$
$$7 = 7 \quad \text{True}$$

4 is the solution.

---

6 Using the Addition Property of Equations to Solve an Equation

Add or subtract the same number on both sides of the equation, so that you get the variable by itself on one side.

Solve each equation.

(a)
$$x - 6 = 9$$
$$x - 6 + 6 = 9 + 6 \quad \text{Add 6 to both sides.}$$
$$x + 0 = 15$$
$$x = 15$$

(b)
$$-7 = x + 9$$
$$-7 - 9 = x + 9 - 9 \quad \text{Subtract 9 from both sides.}$$
$$-16 = x + 0$$
$$-16 = x$$

Concepts	Examples
6 Using the Multiplication Property of Equations to Solve an Equation Multiply or divide both sides of the original equation by the same number so that you get the variable by itself on one side. (Do not divide by zero.)	Solve each equation. **(a)** $-54 = 6x$ **(b)** $\frac{1}{3}x = 8$ $\dfrac{-54}{6} = \dfrac{\overset{1}{\cancel{6}} \cdot x}{\underset{1}{\cancel{6}}}$ $\dfrac{\overset{1}{\cancel{3}}}{1} \cdot \dfrac{1}{\underset{1}{\cancel{3}}}x = 3 \cdot 8$ $-9 = x$ $1x = 24$ $x = 24$

7 Solving Equations with Several Steps
Use the following steps:
 	
Step 1 Add or subtract the same amount on both sides of the equation so that the variable ends up by itself on one side.
 	
Step 2 Multiply or divide both sides by the same number to find the solution.
 	
Step 3 Check the solution.
	Solve: $2p - 3 = 9$
	
	$2p - 3 + 3 = 9 + 3$ Add 3 to both sides.
	$2p = 12$
	
	$\dfrac{\overset{1}{\cancel{2}} \cdot p}{\underset{1}{\cancel{2}}} = \dfrac{12}{2}$ Divide both sides by 2.
	
	$p = 6$
	
	Check: $2p - 3 = 9$
	         $2(6) - 3 = 9$ Replace p with 6.
	         $12 - 3 = 9$
	             $9 = 9$ True
	
	The solution is 6.

7 Using the Distributive Property
To simplify expressions, use the distributive property:
 	
$$a(b + c) = ab + ac.$$
	Simplify: $-2(x + 4)$
	     $= -2 \cdot x + (-2) \cdot 4$
	     $= -2x - 8$

7 Combining Like Terms
If terms are like, combine the numbers that multiply each variable.
	Combine like terms in the following.
	(a) $6p + 7p$
	     $6p + 7p = (6 + 7)p = 13p$
	(b) $8m - 11m$
	     $8m - 11m = (8 - 11)m = -3m$

8 Translating Word Phrases by Using Variables Use x as a variable and symbolize the operations described by the words of the problem.	Write the following word phrases in symbols using x as the variable. **(a)** Two more than a number $x + 2$ or $2 + x$ **(b)** A number decreased by 8 $x - 8$ **(c)** The product of a number and 15 $15x$ **(d)** A number divided by 9 $\dfrac{x}{9}$

CHAPTER REVIEW EXERCISES

[1] *Graph the following lists of numbers.*

1. 2, −3, 4, 1, 0, −5

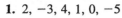

2. −2, 5, −4, −1, 3, −6

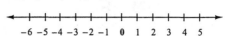

3. $-1\frac{1}{4}$, $-\frac{5}{8}$, $-3\frac{3}{4}$, $2\frac{1}{8}$, $1\frac{1}{2}$, $-2\frac{1}{8}$

4. 0, $-\frac{3}{4}$, $1\frac{1}{4}$, $-4\frac{1}{2}$, $\frac{7}{8}$, $-7\frac{2}{3}$

Place $<$ *or* $>$ *in each of the following to get a true statement.*

5. 0 _____ −2

6. −5 _____ 0

7. −1 _____ −4

8. −9 _____ −6

Find each of the following.

9. $|8|$

10. $|-19|$

11. $-|-7|$

12. $-|15|$

[2] *Add.*

13. −4 + 6

14. −10 + 3

15. −11 + (−8)

16. −9 + (−24)

17. 12 + (−11)

18. 1 + (−20)

19. $\frac{9}{10} + \left(-\frac{3}{5}\right)$

20. $-\frac{7}{8} + \frac{1}{2}$

21. −6.7 + 1.5

22. −0.8 + (−0.7)

[2] *Give the additive inverse (opposite) of each number.*

23. 6   **24.** −14   **25.** $-\dfrac{5}{8}$ **26.** 3.75

Subtract.

27. 4 − 10   **28.** 7 − 15   **29.** −6 − 1   **30.** −12 − 5

31. 8 − (−3)   **32.** 2 − (−9)   **33.** −1 − (−14)   **34.** −10 − (−4)

35. −40 − 40   **36.** −15 − (−15)   **37.** $\dfrac{1}{3} - \dfrac{5}{6}$ **38.** 2.8 − (−6.2)

[3] *Multiply or divide.*

39. −4 • 6   **40.** 5 • (−4)   **41.** −3 • (−5)   **42.** −8 • (−8)

43. $\dfrac{80}{-10}$ **44.** $\dfrac{-9}{3}$ **45.** $\dfrac{-25}{-5}$ **46.** $\dfrac{-120}{-6}$

47. (−37)(0)   **48.** (−1)(81)   **49.** $\dfrac{0}{-10}$ **50.** $\dfrac{-20}{0}$

51. $\dfrac{2}{3} \cdot \left(-\dfrac{6}{7}\right)$ **52.** $-\dfrac{4}{5} \div \left(-\dfrac{2}{15}\right)$ **53.** −0.5 • (−2.8)   **54.** $\dfrac{-5.28}{0.8}$

Name _____

[4] *Use the order of operations to simplify each of the following.*

55. $2 - 11 \cdot (-5)$

56. $(-4) \cdot (-8) - 9$

57. $48 \div (-2)^3 - (-5)$

58. $-36 \div (-3)^2 - (-2)$

59. $5 \cdot 4 - 7 \cdot 6 + 3 \cdot (-4)$

60. $2 \cdot 8 - 4 \cdot 9 + 2 \cdot (-6)$

61. $-4 \cdot 3^3 - 2 \cdot (5 - 9)$

62. $6 \cdot (-4)^2 - 3 \cdot (7 - 14)$

63. $\dfrac{3 - (5^2 - 4^2)}{14 + 24 \div (-3)}$

64. $(-0.8)^2 \cdot (0.2) - (-1.2)$

65. $\left(-\dfrac{1}{3}\right)^2 + \dfrac{1}{4} \cdot \left(-\dfrac{4}{9}\right)$

66. $\dfrac{12 \div (2 - 5) + 12 \cdot (-1)}{2^3 - (-4)^2}$

[5] *Find the value of each expression using the given values of the variables.*

67. $3k + 5m$
$k = 4, \quad m = 3$

68. $3k + 5m$
$k = -6, \quad m = 2$

69. $2p - q$
$p = -5, \quad q = -10$

70. $2p - q$
$p = 6, \quad q = -7$

71. $\dfrac{5a - 7y}{2 + m}$
$a = 1, \quad y = 4, \quad m = -3$

72. $\dfrac{5a - 7y}{2 + m}$
$a = 2, \quad y = -2, \quad m = -26$

In each of the following, use the formula and the values of the variables to find the value of the remaining variable.

73. $P = a + b + c; \quad a = 9, \quad b = 12, \quad c = 14$

74. $A = \dfrac{1}{2}bh; \quad b = 6, \quad h = 9$

[6–7] *Solve each equation. Check each solution.*

75. $y + 3 = 0$

76. $a - 8 = 8$

77. $-5 = z - 6$

78. $-8 = -9 + r$

79. $-\dfrac{3}{4} + x = -2$

80. $12.92 + k = 4.87$

81. $-8r = 56$

82. $3p = 24$

83. $\dfrac{z}{4} = 5$

84. $\dfrac{a}{5} = -11$

85. $20 = 3y - 7$

86. $-5 = 2b + 3$

Use the distributive property to simplify.

87. $6(r - 5)$

88. $11(p + 7)$

89. $-9(z - 3)$

90. $-8(x + 4)$

Combine like terms.

91. $3r + 8r$

92. $10z - 15z$

93. $3p - 12p + p$

94. $-6x - x + 9x$

Solve each equation. Check each solution.

95. $-4z + 2z = 18$

96. $-35 = 9k - 2k$

97. $4y - 3 = 7y + 12$

98. $b + 6 = 3b - 8$

99. $-14 = 2(a - 3)$

100. $42 = 7(t + 6)$

Name _____

[8] *Write in symbols by using x to represent the variable.*

101. 18 plus a number

102. half a number

103. the sum of four times a number and 6

104. five times a number decreased by 10

Solve each application problem. Show your equation and the steps you use to solve it.

105. If eight times a number is subtracted from eleven times the number, the result is −9. Find the number.

106. In Cicely, Alaska, Ruth Anne rents snowmobiles for $45 for the first day and $35 for each additional day. The bill for Joel's rental was $255. For how many days did he rent a snowmobile?

107. The perimeter of a rectangle is 124 cm. The width is 25 cm. Find the length. (Use the formula for the perimeter of a rectangle, $P = 2l + 2w$.)

108. My sister is 9 years older than I am. The sum of our ages is 51. Find our ages.

MIXED REVIEW EXERCISES

Add, subtract, multiply, or divide as indicated.

109. $-6 - (-9)$

110. $-8 \cdot (-5)$

111. $-12 + 11$

112. $\dfrac{-70}{10}$

113. $-4 \cdot 4$

114. $5 - 14$

115. $\dfrac{-42}{-7}$

116. $16 + (-11)$

117. $-10 - 10$

118. $\dfrac{-5}{0}$

119. $-\dfrac{2}{3} + \dfrac{1}{9}$

120. $0.7(-0.5)$

121. $|-6| + 2 - 3 \cdot (-8) - 5^2$

122. $9 \div |-3| + 6 \cdot (-5) + 2^3$

Solve each equation.

123. $-45 = -5y$

124. $b - 8 = -12$

125. $6z - 3 = 3z + 9$

126. $-5 = r + 5$

127. $-3x = 33$

128. $2z - 7z = -15$

129. $3(k - 6) = 6 - 12$

130. $6(t + 3) = -2 + 20$

131. $-10 = \dfrac{a}{5} - 2$

132. $4 + 8p = 4p + 16$

Solve each application problem. Show your equation and the steps you use to solve it.

133. When twice a number is decreased by 8, the result is the number increased by 7. Find the number.

134. The length of a rectangle is 3 inches more than twice the width. The perimeter is 36 inches. Find the length and the width. (Use $P = 2l + 2w$.)

135. A cheetah's sprinting speed is 25 miles per hour faster than a zebra can run. The sum of their running speeds is 111 miles per hour. How fast can each animal run?

136. A 90-centimeter pipe is cut into two pieces so that one piece is 6 centimeters shorter than the other. Find the length of each piece.

61. $-|-7.6| = -7.6$ First, $|-7.6|$ is 7.6 but the negative sign *outside* the absolute value bars is not affected, so the final answer is negative.

65. The opposite of positive 2 is -2.

69. The opposite of -11 is 11 (positive 11).

73. The opposite of 0 is 0. Zero is neither positive nor negative.

77. The opposite of positive 5.2 is -5.2.

81. Answers will vary. A sample answer follows:
Opposite numbers are the same distance from 0 but on opposite sides of it.

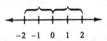

-2 and $+2$ are opposites.

85. True. $|-5| = 5$, therefore $|-5| > 0$.

89. False. $-|-4| = -4$ and $-|-7| = -7$; -4 is to the right of -7 on the number line, therefore, $-4 > -7$ and $-|-4| < -|-7|$ is false.

93. $\dfrac{5}{6} - \dfrac{1}{4} = \dfrac{10}{12} - \dfrac{3}{12} = \dfrac{7}{12}$

SECTION 9.2

1. $-2 + 5 = 3$
See graph in the answer section.

5. $3 + (-4) = -1$
See graph in the answer section.

9. $|-1| = 1$ $|8| = 8$ $8 - 1 = 7$
The positive number 8 has the larger absolute value, so the answer is positive.

$$-1 + 8 = 7$$

13. $|6| = 6$ $|-5| = 5$ $6 - 5 = 1$
The positive number 6 has the larger absolute value, so the answer is positive.

$$6 + (-5) = 1$$

17. $|-10| = 10$ $|-10| = 10$
Add the absolute values.

$$10 + 10 = 20$$

Write a negative sign in front of the sum because both numbers are negative.

$$-10 + (-10) = -20$$

21. The overdrawn amount is negative ($-\$52.50$) and the deposit is positive.

$$-\$52.50 + \$50 = -\$2.50$$

25. $\left|-\dfrac{1}{2}\right| = \dfrac{1}{2}$ $\left|\dfrac{3}{4}\right| = \dfrac{3}{4}$ $\dfrac{3}{4} - \dfrac{1}{2} = \dfrac{3}{4} - \dfrac{2}{4} = \dfrac{1}{4}$
The positive number $\frac{3}{4}$ has the larger absolute value, so the answer is positive.

$$-\dfrac{1}{2} + \dfrac{3}{4} = \dfrac{1}{4}$$

CHAPTER 9

SECTION 9.1

1. $+32$ Above zero is positive.

5. $+20$ Above flood stage is positive.

9. negative because of the "$-$" sign in front of the fraction.

13. negative because of the "$-$" sign in front of 6.3.

17.   **21.**

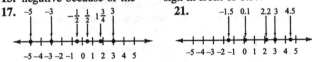

25. Since 9 is to the left of 14 on a number line, 9 is less than 14. Write it as $9 < 14$.

29. Since -6 is to the left of 3 on a number line, -6 is less than 3. Write it as $-6 < 3$.

33. Since -11 is to the left of -2 on a number line, -11 is less than -2. Write it as $-11 < -2$.

37. Since 2 is to the right of -1 on a number line, 2 is greater than -1. Write it as $2 > -1$.

41. $|5| = 5$ **45.** $|-1| = 1$

49. $|0| = 0$ **53.** $|-9.5| = 9.5$

57. $-|-10| = -10$ First, $|-10|$ is 10 but the negative sign *outside* the absolute value bars is not affected, so the final answer is negative.

29. $\left|-\dfrac{7}{3}\right| = \dfrac{7}{3}$ $\left|-\dfrac{5}{9}\right| = \dfrac{5}{9}$ $\dfrac{7}{3} + \dfrac{5}{9} = \dfrac{21}{9} + \dfrac{5}{9} = \dfrac{26}{9}$

Write a negative sign in front of the sum, since both numbers are negative.

$$-\dfrac{7}{3} + \left(-\dfrac{5}{9}\right) = -\dfrac{26}{9}$$

33. The additive inverse of positive 3 is -3 (change sign).

37. The additive inverse of positive $\frac{1}{2}$ is $-\frac{1}{2}$ (change sign).

41. $19 - 5 = 19 + (-5)$ Change 5 to its opposite (-5) and add.

$\qquad = 14$

45. $7 - 19 = 7 + (-19)$ Change 19 to its opposite (-19) and add.

$\qquad = -12$

49. $-9 - 14 = -9 + (-14)$ Change 14 to its opposite (-14) and add.

$\qquad = -23$

53. $6 - (-14) = 6 + (+14)$ Change (-14) to its opposite $(+14)$ and add.

$\qquad = 20$

57. $-30 - 30 = -30 + (-30)$ Change 30 to its opposite (-30) and add.

$\qquad = -60$

61. $-\dfrac{7}{10} - \dfrac{4}{5} = -\dfrac{7}{10} + \left(-\dfrac{4}{5}\right)$ Change $\dfrac{4}{5}$ to its opposite $\left(-\dfrac{4}{5}\right)$ and add.

$\qquad = -\dfrac{7}{10} + \left(-\dfrac{8}{10}\right)$

$\qquad = -\dfrac{15}{10} = -\dfrac{3}{2}$

65. $-8.3 - (-9) = -8.3 + (+9)$ Change (-9) to its opposite $(+9)$ and add.

$\qquad = 0.7$

69. $-2 + (-11) - (-3) = -13 - (-3)$

$\qquad = -13 + 3$

$\qquad = -10$

73. $-12 - (-3) - (-2) = -12 + 3 - (-2)$

$\qquad = -9 - (-2)$

$\qquad = -9 + 2$

$\qquad = -7$

77. $\dfrac{1}{2} - \dfrac{2}{3} + \left(-\dfrac{5}{6}\right) = \dfrac{1}{2} + \left(-\dfrac{2}{3}\right) + \left(-\dfrac{5}{6}\right)$

$\qquad = \dfrac{3}{6} + \left(-\dfrac{4}{6}\right) + \left(-\dfrac{5}{6}\right)$

$\qquad = -\dfrac{1}{6} + \left(-\dfrac{5}{6}\right)$

$\qquad = -\dfrac{6}{6} = -1$

81. $-2 + (-11) + |-2| = -13 + |-2|$

$\qquad = -13 + 2$

$\qquad = -11$

85. $2\dfrac{1}{2} + 3\dfrac{1}{4} - \left(-1\dfrac{3}{8}\right) - 2\dfrac{3}{8}$ Write mixed numbers as improper fractions.

$\dfrac{5}{2} + \dfrac{13}{4} - \left(-\dfrac{11}{8}\right) - \dfrac{19}{8}$ Rewrite all fractions with lowest common denominator (8).

$\underbrace{\dfrac{20}{8} + \dfrac{26}{8}} - \left(-\dfrac{11}{8}\right) - \dfrac{19}{8}$ Add and subtract from left to right.

$\underbrace{\dfrac{46}{8} - \left(-\dfrac{11}{8}\right)} - \dfrac{19}{8}$ Change subtraction to addition.

$\underbrace{\dfrac{46}{8} + \left(+\dfrac{11}{8}\right)} - \dfrac{19}{8}$

$\underbrace{\dfrac{57}{8} + \left(-\dfrac{19}{8}\right)}$

$\dfrac{38}{8} = \dfrac{19}{4}$ or $4\dfrac{3}{4}$

89.

$\quad 71.20 \leftarrow$ 2 decimal places
$\underline{\times\ 21.25} \leftarrow$ 2 decimal places
$\quad 35600$
$\quad 14240$
$\quad\ 7120$
$\underline{14240\quad}$
$1513.0000 \leftarrow$ 4 decimal places in answer
$\qquad\qquad$ 1513.0000 or 1513

93. $\dfrac{7}{9} \div \dfrac{14}{27} = \dfrac{7}{\underset{1}{\cancel{9}}} \cdot \dfrac{\overset{3}{\cancel{27}}}{\underset{2}{\cancel{14}}} = \dfrac{3}{2}$ or $1\dfrac{1}{2}$

SECTION 9.3

1. $-5 \cdot 7 = -35$ (different signs, product is negative)

5. $3 \cdot (-6) = -18$ (different signs, product is negative)

9. $(-1)(40) = -40$ (different signs, product is negative)

13. $11 \cdot 7 = 77$ (same signs, product is positive)

17. $-13 \cdot (-1) = 13$ (same signs, product is positive)

21. $-\dfrac{1}{2} \cdot (-8) = -\dfrac{1}{\underset{1}{\cancel{2}}} \cdot \left(\dfrac{\overset{4}{\cancel{-8}}}{1}\right) = \dfrac{4}{1} = 4$ (same signs, product is positive)

25. $\left(\dfrac{\overset{1}{\cancel{3}}}{5}\right)\left(-\dfrac{1}{\underset{2}{\cancel{6}}}\right) = -\dfrac{1}{10}$ (different signs, product is negative)

29. $-\dfrac{\overset{1}{\cancel{7}}}{\underset{3}{\cancel{15}}} \cdot \dfrac{\overset{5}{\cancel{25}}}{\underset{2}{\cancel{14}}} = -\dfrac{5}{6}$ (different signs, product is negative)

33. $9 \cdot (-4.7) = -42.3$ (different signs, product is negative)

37. $-6.2 \cdot (5.1) = -31.62$ (different signs, product is negative)

41. $(-8.23)(-1) = 8.23$ (same signs, product is positive)

45. $\dfrac{-14}{7} = -2$ (different signs, quotient is negative)

49. $\dfrac{-28}{0}$ Division by 0 is undefined.

53. $\dfrac{-20}{-2} = 10$ (same signs, quotient is positive)

57. $\dfrac{-18}{18} = -1$ (different signs, quotient is negative)

61. $\dfrac{0}{-9} = 0$ (zero is neither positive nor negative)

65. $\dfrac{-\frac{5}{7}}{-\frac{15}{14}} = -\dfrac{\overset{1}{\cancel{5}}}{7} \cdot \left(-\dfrac{\overset{2}{\cancel{14}}}{\underset{3}{\cancel{15}}}\right) = \dfrac{2}{3}$ (same signs, quotient is positive)

69. $5 \div \left(-\dfrac{5}{8}\right) = \dfrac{\overset{1}{\cancel{5}}}{1} \cdot \left(-\dfrac{8}{\underset{1}{\cancel{5}}}\right) = -8$ (different signs, quotient is negative)

73. $\dfrac{-18.92}{-4} = 4.73$ (same signs, quotient is positive)

77. $\dfrac{45.58}{-8.6} = -5.3$ (different signs, quotient is negative)

81. $(-0.6)(-0.2)(-3) = (0.12)(-3) = -0.36$

85. Answers will vary. A sample answer follows:
 (a) $6 \cdot (-1) = -6$; $2 \cdot (-1) = -2$;
  $15 \cdot (-1) = -15$
 (b) $-6 \cdot (-1) = 6$; $-2 \cdot (-1) = 2$;
  $-15 \cdot (-1) = 15$
 The result of multiplying any nonzero number times -1 is the number with the opposite sign.

89. $-36 \div (-2) \div (-3) \div (-3) \div (-1)$ Divide from left to right.
$\quad\quad 18 \quad\quad \div (-3) \div (-3) \div (-1)$
$\quad\quad\quad\quad -6 \quad\quad \div (-3) \div (-1)$
$\quad\quad\quad\quad\quad\quad 2 \quad\quad\quad\quad \div (-1) = -2$

93. $8 + 4 \cdot 2 \div 8$ Multiply first.
$\quad 8 + \quad 8 \div 8$ Divide next.
$\quad 8 + \quad\quad 1 \ = 9$ Add.

SECTION 9.4

1. $6 + \underbrace{3 \cdot (-4)}$ Multiply first.
$\quad \underbrace{6 + (-12)}$ Add.
$\quad\quad\quad -6$

5. $\underbrace{6^2} + \underbrace{4^2}$ Exponents first
$\quad \underbrace{36 + 16}$ Add.
$\quad\quad\quad 52$

9. $\underbrace{(-2)^5} + 2$ Exponents first
$\quad \underbrace{-32 \ + 2}$ Add.
$\quad\quad\quad -30$

13. $2 - (-5) + \underbrace{3^2}$ Exponents first
$\quad 2 - (-5) + 9$ Add and subtract from left to right.
$\quad \underbrace{2 + (+5)} + 9$
$\quad\quad \underbrace{7 \ + 9}$
$\quad\quad\quad 16$

17. $3 + 5 \cdot \underbrace{(6 - 2)}$ Parentheses first
$\quad 3 + 5 \cdot \underbrace{4}$ Multiply next
$\quad \underbrace{3 + \quad 20}$ Add.
$\quad\quad\quad 23$

21. $-6 + (-5) \cdot \underbrace{(9 - 14)}$ Parentheses first
$\quad -6 + \underbrace{(-5) \cdot \ (-5)}$ Multiply next.
$\quad \underbrace{-6 + \quad 25}$ Add.
$\quad\quad\quad 19$

25. $9 \div \underbrace{(-3)^2} + (-1)$ Exponents first
$\quad \underbrace{9 \div \quad 9} + (-1)$ Division next.
$\quad \underbrace{1 \quad + (-1)}$ Add.
$\quad\quad\quad 0$

29. $\underbrace{(-2) \cdot (-7)} + \underbrace{3 \cdot 9}$ Multiply from left to right.
$\quad \underbrace{14 \quad + \quad 27}$ Add.
$\quad\quad\quad 41$

33. $\underbrace{2 \cdot 5} - \underbrace{3 \cdot 4} + \underbrace{5 \cdot 3}$ Multiply from left to right.
$\quad \underbrace{10 \ - \ 12} + 15$ Add and subtract from left to right.
$\quad\quad \underbrace{-2 \quad + 15}$
$\quad\quad\quad 13$

37. First do the work in the numerator.

$\quad -1 + \underbrace{5^2} - (-3)$ Exponents first
$\quad \underbrace{-1 + 25} - (-3)$ Add and subtract from left to right.
$\quad\quad 24 \quad - (-3)$
$\quad\quad 24 \quad + \ 3$

Numerator $\rightarrow 27$

Now do the work in the denominator.

$\quad -6 - \quad 9 \ + 12$ Add and subtract from left to right.
$\quad \underbrace{-6 + (-9)} + 12$
$\quad\quad \underbrace{-15 \quad + 12}$

Denominator $\rightarrow -3$

The last step is the division.

$\quad \dfrac{\text{Numerator} \rightarrow 27}{\text{Denominator} \rightarrow -3} = -9$

41. First do the work in the numerator.

$2^3 \cdot \underbrace{(-2 - 5)} + 4 \cdot (-1)$ Parentheses first

$2^3 \cdot \quad (-7) \quad + 4 \cdot (-1)$ Exponents next

$\underbrace{8 \cdot \quad (-7)} + \underbrace{4 \cdot (-1)}$ Multiply from left to right.

$\underbrace{-56 \quad\quad + \quad (-4)}$ Add.

Numerator $\rightarrow \; -60$

Now do the work in the denominator.

$4 + 5 \cdot \underbrace{(-6 \cdot 2)} + \underbrace{(5 \cdot 11)}$ Parentheses first

$4 + \underbrace{5 \cdot \quad (-12)} + \quad 55$ Multiply next.

$\underbrace{4 + \quad (-60)} \quad + \quad 55$ Add from left to right.

$\underbrace{-56 \quad\quad + \quad 55}$

Denominator $\rightarrow \quad -1$

The last step is the division.

$$\begin{array}{l}\text{Numerator} \;\rightarrow \\ \text{Denominator} \rightarrow\end{array} \frac{-60}{-1} = 60$$

45. $\underbrace{(-0.3)^2} + \underbrace{(-0.5)^2} + 0.9$ Exponents first

$\underbrace{0.09 \quad + \quad 0.25} + 0.9$ Add from left to right.

$\underbrace{0.34 \quad\quad + 0.9}$

1.24

49. $\underbrace{(0.5)^2} \cdot (-8) - (0.31)$ Exponents first

$\underbrace{0.25 \cdot (-8)} - (0.31)$ Multiply next.

$-2 \quad + (-0.31)$ Change subtraction to addition.

$\underbrace{\quad -2.31 \quad}$

53. $\left(-\dfrac{1}{2}\right)^2 - \underbrace{\left(\dfrac{3}{4} - \dfrac{7}{4}\right)}$ Parentheses first

$\left(-\dfrac{1}{2}\right)^2 - \left(-\dfrac{4}{4}\right)$ Exponents next

$\dfrac{1}{4} \quad + \left(+\dfrac{4}{4}\right)$ Change subtraction to addition.

$\dfrac{5}{4}$

57. $5^2 \cdot \underbrace{(9 - 11)} \cdot (-3) \cdot (-2)^3$ Parentheses first

$5^2 \cdot \quad (-2) \quad \cdot (-3) \cdot (-2)^3$ Exponents next

$\underbrace{25 \cdot \quad (-2)} \cdot (-3) \cdot (-8)$ Multiply from left to right.

$\underbrace{-50 \quad\quad \cdot (-3)} \cdot (-8)$

$\underbrace{150 \quad\quad\quad \cdot (-8)}$

-1200

61. $(-2)^2 = 4 \qquad (-2)^6 = 64$

$(-2)^3 = -8 \qquad (-2)^7 = -128$

$(-2)^4 = 16 \qquad (-2)^8 = 256$

$(-2)^5 = -32 \qquad (-2)^9 = -512$

There is a pattern. When a negative number is raised to an even power, the answer is positive. When a negative number is raised to an odd power, the answer is negative.

65. $-7 \cdot \left(6 - \dfrac{5}{\overset{1}{\cancel{8}}} \cdot \overset{3}{\cancel{24}} + \dfrac{1}{\overset{1}{\cancel{3}}} \cdot \dfrac{8}{\overset{1}{\cancel{3}}}\right)$ Work inside parentheses; do multiplications first.

$-7 \cdot (6 - \quad 15 \quad + \quad 8 \;)$ Add and subtract inside parentheses, from left to right.

$-7 \cdot \quad (-9 \quad + 8)$

$-7 \cdot \quad\quad (-1)$ Multiply.

7

69. $\dfrac{\overset{2}{\cancel{6}}}{\underset{1}{7}} \cdot \dfrac{\overset{2}{\cancel{14}}}{\underset{3}{\cancel{9}}} = \dfrac{4}{3}$ or $1\dfrac{1}{3}$

SECTION 9.5

1. $\underset{\downarrow\;\downarrow}{2 \; r} + \underset{\downarrow\;\downarrow}{4 \; s}$

$\underbrace{2(2)} + \underbrace{4(6)}$ Multiply from left to right.

$\underbrace{4 \quad + \quad 24}$ Add.

28

5. $\underset{\downarrow\;\downarrow}{2 \; r} + \underset{\downarrow\;\downarrow}{4 \; s}$

$2(-4) + 4(4)$ Multiply from left to right.

$\underbrace{-8 \quad + \quad 16}$ Add.

8

9. $\underset{\downarrow\;\downarrow}{2 \; r} + \underset{\downarrow\;\downarrow}{4 \; s}$

$2(0) + 4(-2)$ Multiply from left to right.

$\underbrace{0 \quad + \quad (-8)}$ Add.

-8

13. $\underset{\downarrow\;\downarrow}{6 \; k} + \underset{\downarrow\;\downarrow}{2 \; s}$

$6(1) + 2(-2)$ Multiply from left to right.

$\underbrace{6 \quad + \quad (-4)}$ Add.

2

17. $\underset{\downarrow}{-m} - \underset{\downarrow\;\downarrow}{3 \; n}$

$-\left(\dfrac{1}{2}\right) - 3\left(\dfrac{3}{8}\right)$ Multiply first.

$-\dfrac{1}{2} - \dfrac{9}{8}$ Find common denominator.

$-\dfrac{4}{8} + \left(-\dfrac{9}{8}\right)$ Change subtraction to addition.

$-\dfrac{13}{8}$

21.

$-4x \;-\; y$

$\downarrow \qquad \downarrow$

$\underbrace{-4(5)} \;-\; (-15)$ Multiply first.

$-20 \;-\; (-15)$

    $\downarrow$ $\downarrow$

$\underbrace{-20 \;+\; (+15)}$ Change subtraction to addition.

$\qquad -5$

25. $\dfrac{-3s - t - 4}{-s + 6 + t} = \dfrac{-3(-1) - (-13) - 4}{-(-1) + 6 + (-13)}$

$\qquad\qquad = \dfrac{3 + (+13) - 4}{1 + 6 + (-13)}$

$\qquad\qquad = \dfrac{16 - 4}{7 + (-13)}$

$\qquad\qquad = \dfrac{12}{-6}$

$\qquad\qquad = -2$

29. $P = 2l + 2w$

$P = \underbrace{2(9)} + \underbrace{2(5)}$

$P = \;\; 18 \;\; + \;\; 10$

$P = \qquad 28$

33. $A = \dfrac{1}{2}bh$

$\quad = \dfrac{1}{2}(15)(3)$

$\quad = \dfrac{1}{2}(45)$

$\quad = \dfrac{45}{2}$ or $22\dfrac{1}{2}$

37. $d = rt$

$\quad = (53)(6)$

$\quad = 318$

41. The error was made when replacing x with -3; should be $-(-3)$, not -3.

$-x - 4y$ Replace x with (-3) and y with (-1).

$-(-3) - 4(-1)$

$(+3) - (-4)$ Opposite of (-3) is $+3$.

$3 + (+4)$ Change subtraction to addition.

7 Add.

45. $V = \dfrac{4\pi r^3}{3}$

$\approx \dfrac{4(3.14)(3)^3}{3}$

$\approx \dfrac{4(3.14)(27)}{3}$

$\approx \dfrac{12.56(27)}{3}$

$\approx \dfrac{339.12}{3} \approx 113.04$

Use this formula to find the volume of a sphere.

49. $-\dfrac{1}{9} \cdot 9 = -\dfrac{1}{\overset{1}{\cancel{9}}} \cdot \dfrac{\overset{1}{\cancel{9}}}{1} = \dfrac{-1}{1} = -1$

SECTION 9.6

1. $x + 7 = 11$

$4 + 7 = 11$

$11 = 11$ True

Yes, 4 is a solution of the equation.

5. $2z - 1 = -15$

$2(-8) - 1 = -15$

$-16 - 1 = -15$

$-17 = -15$ False

No, -8 is not a solution of the equation.

9. $k + 15 = 0$ Check:

$k + 15 - 15 = 0 - 15 \qquad -15 + 15 = 0$

$k = -15 \qquad\qquad\qquad 0 = 0$ True

The solution is -15.

13. $8 = r - 2$ Check:

$8 + 2 = r - 2 + 2 \qquad 8 = 10 - 2$

$10 = r \qquad\qquad\qquad 8 = 8$ True

The solution is 10.

17. $7 = r + 13$ Check:

$7 - 13 = r + 13 - 13 \qquad 7 = -6 + 13$

$-6 = r \qquad\qquad\qquad 7 = 7$ True

The solution is -6.

21. $-12 + x = -1$ Check:

$-12 + 12 + x = -1 + 12 \qquad -12 + 11 = -1$

$x = 11 \qquad\qquad\qquad -1 = -1$ True

The solution is 11.

25. $d + \dfrac{2}{3} = 3$ Check:

$d + \dfrac{2}{3} - \dfrac{2}{3} = 3 - \dfrac{2}{3} \qquad \dfrac{7}{3} + \dfrac{2}{3} = 3$

$d = \dfrac{7}{3}$ or $2\dfrac{1}{3} \qquad\qquad \dfrac{9}{3} = 3$

$\qquad\qquad\qquad\qquad\qquad 3 = 3$ True

The solution is $\frac{7}{3}$ or $2\frac{1}{3}$.

29. $\dfrac{1}{2} = k - 2$ Check:

$\dfrac{1}{2} + 2 = k - 2 + 2 \qquad \dfrac{1}{2} = \dfrac{5}{2} - 2$

$\dfrac{5}{2} = k \qquad\qquad\qquad \dfrac{1}{2} = \dfrac{1}{2}$ True

The solution is $\frac{5}{2}$ or $2\frac{1}{2}$.

33. $x - 0.8 = 5.07$ Check:

$x - 0.8 + 0.8 = 5.07 + 0.8 \qquad 5.87 - 0.8 = 5.07$

$x = 5.87 \qquad\qquad\qquad 5.07 = 5.07$

$\qquad\qquad\qquad\qquad\qquad\qquad\qquad$ True

The solution is 5.87.

37. $6z = 12$ Check:

$$\frac{\overset{1}{\cancel{6}} \cdot z}{\underset{1}{\cancel{6}}} = \frac{12}{6} \qquad \begin{array}{c} 6(2) = 12 \\ 12 = 12 \quad \text{True} \end{array}$$

$$z = 2$$

The solution is 2.

41. $3y = 0$ Check:

$$\frac{\overset{1}{\cancel{3}} \cdot y}{\underset{1}{\cancel{3}}} = \frac{0}{3} \qquad \begin{array}{c} 3(0) = 0 \\ 0 = 0 \quad \text{True} \end{array}$$

$$y = 0$$

The solution is 0.

45. $-36 = -4p$ Check:

$$\frac{-36}{-4} = \frac{\overset{1}{-\cancel{4}} \cdot p}{\underset{1}{-\cancel{4}}} \qquad \begin{array}{c} -36 = -4(9) \\ -36 = -36 \quad \text{True} \end{array}$$

$$9 = p$$

The solution is 9.

49. $-8.4p = -9.24$ Check:

$$\frac{\overset{1}{-\cancel{8.4}} \cdot p}{\underset{1}{-\cancel{8.4}}} = \frac{-9.24}{-8.4} \qquad \begin{array}{c} -8.4(1.1) = -9.24 \\ -9.24 = -9.24 \quad \text{True} \end{array}$$

$$p = 1.1$$

The solution is 1.1

53. $11 = \dfrac{a}{6}$ Replace $\frac{a}{6}$ with $\frac{1}{6}a$ and multiply both sides by 6.

Check:

$$6 \cdot 11 = \frac{\overset{1}{\cancel{6}}}{1} \cdot \frac{1}{\underset{1}{\cancel{6}}} a \qquad 11 = \frac{66}{6}$$

$$66 = a \qquad\qquad 11 = 11 \quad \text{True}$$

The solution is 66.

57. $-\dfrac{2}{5}p = 8$

Check:

$$-\frac{\overset{1}{\cancel{5}}}{\underset{1}{\cancel{2}}} \cdot -\frac{\overset{1}{\cancel{2}}}{\underset{1}{\cancel{5}}}p = -\frac{5}{\underset{1}{\cancel{2}}} \cdot \frac{\overset{4}{\cancel{8}}}{1} \qquad -\frac{2}{5}(-20) = 8$$

$$p = -20 \qquad\qquad\qquad 8 = 8 \quad \text{True}$$

The solution is -20.

61. $6 = \dfrac{3}{8}x$ Check:

$$\frac{8}{\underset{1}{\cancel{3}}} \cdot \overset{2}{\cancel{6}} = \frac{\overset{1}{\cancel{8}}}{\underset{1}{\cancel{3}}} \cdot \frac{\overset{1}{\cancel{3}}}{\underset{1}{\cancel{8}}}x \qquad \begin{array}{c} 6 = \dfrac{3}{8}(16) \\ 6 = 6 \quad \text{True} \end{array}$$

$$16 = x$$

The solution is 16.

65. $\dfrac{z}{-3.8} = 1.3$

Check:

$$\frac{-\overset{1}{\cancel{3.8}}}{1} \cdot \frac{1}{-\underset{1}{\cancel{3.8}}} z = (-3.8)(1.3) \qquad \frac{-4.94}{-3.8} = 1.3$$

$$z = -4.94. \qquad\qquad\qquad 1.3 = 1.3 \quad \text{True}$$

The solution is -4.94.

69. $x - 17 = 5 - 3$

$$x - 17 = 2$$

$$x - 17 + 17 = 2 + 17$$

$$x = 19 \qquad \text{The solution is 19.}$$

73. $\dfrac{7}{2}x = \dfrac{4}{3}$

$$\frac{\overset{1}{\cancel{2}}}{\underset{1}{\cancel{7}}} \cdot \frac{\overset{1}{\cancel{7}}}{\underset{1}{\cancel{2}}}x = \frac{2}{7} \cdot \frac{4}{3}$$

$$x = \frac{8}{21} \qquad \text{The solution is } \frac{8}{21}.$$

77. $\dfrac{1}{2} + \overbrace{\dfrac{\overset{1}{\cancel{3}}}{\underset{4}{\cancel{4}}} \cdot \dfrac{\overset{2}{\cancel{8}}}{\underset{3}{\cancel{9}}}}^{} - \dfrac{1}{6}$ Multiply first.

$$\underbrace{\frac{1}{2} + \frac{2}{3}}_{} - \frac{1}{6}$$ Add and subtract from left to right.

$$\underbrace{\frac{7}{6} - \frac{1}{6}}_{}$$

$$\frac{6}{6} = 1$$

Section 9.7

1. $7p + 5 = 12$

$$7p + 5 - 5 = 12 - 5 \qquad \text{Subtract 5 from both sides.}$$

$$7p = 7$$

$$\frac{\overset{1}{\cancel{7}} \cdot p}{\underset{1}{\cancel{7}}} = \frac{7}{7} \qquad \text{Divide both sides by 7.}$$

$$p = 1$$

Check:

$$7(1) + 5 = 12$$

$$7 + 5 = 12$$

$$12 = 12 \quad \text{True}$$

The solution is 1.

5. $-3m + 1 = 1$

$-3m + 1 - 1 = 1 - 1$ Subtract 1 from both sides.

$-3m = 0$

$\dfrac{\overset{1}{\cancel{-3}} \cdot m}{\underset{1}{\cancel{-3}}} = \dfrac{0}{-3}$ Divide both sides by -3.

$m = 0$

Check:

$-3(0) + 1 = 1$

$0 + 1 = 1$

$1 = 1$ True

The solution is 0.

9. $-5x - 4 = 16$

$-5x - 4 + 4 = 16 + 4$ Add 4 to both sides.

$-5x = 20$

$\dfrac{\overset{1}{\cancel{-5}} \cdot x}{\underset{1}{\cancel{-5}}} = \dfrac{20}{-5}$ Divide both sides by -5.

$x = -4$

Check:

$-5(-4) - 4 = 16$

$20 - 4 = 16$

$16 = 16$ True

The solution is -4.

13. $6(x + 4) = 6 \cdot x + 6 \cdot 4 = 6x + 24$

17. $-3(m + 6) = -3 \cdot m + (-3) \cdot 6 = -3m - 18$

21. $-5(z - 9) = -5 \cdot z - (-5) \cdot 9 = -5z - (-45)$
$\qquad\qquad\qquad = -5z + 45$

25. $10x - 2x = (10 - 2)x = 8x$

29. $3y - y - 4y = (3 - 1 - 4)y = -2y$

33. $54 = 10m - m$ Combine like terms.

$54 = 9m$

$\dfrac{54}{9} = \dfrac{\overset{1}{\cancel{9}} \cdot m}{\underset{1}{\cancel{9}}}$ Divide both sides by 9.

$6 = m$

Check:

$54 = 10(6) - 6$

$54 = 60 - 6$

$54 = 54$ True

The solution is 6.

37. $-12 = 6y - 18y$ Combine like terms.

$-12 = -12y$

$\dfrac{-12}{-12} = \dfrac{\overset{1}{\cancel{-12}} \cdot y}{\underset{1}{\cancel{-12}}}$ Divide both sides by -12.

$1 = y$

Check:

$-12 = 6(1) - 18(1)$

$-12 = 6 - 18$

$-12 = -12$ True

The solution is 1.

41. $9 + 7z = 9z + 13$

$9 + 7z - 9z = 9z + 13 - 9z$ Subtract $9z$ from both sides.

$9 - 2z = 13$

$9 - 2z - 9 = 13 - 9$ Subtract 9 from both sides.

$-2z = 4$

$\dfrac{\overset{1}{\cancel{-2}} \cdot z}{\underset{1}{\cancel{-2}}} = \dfrac{4}{-2}$ Divide both sides by -2.

$z = -2$

Check:

$9 + 7(-2) = 9(-2) + 13$

$9 + (-14) = -18 + 13$

$-5 = -5$ True

The solution is -2.

45. $b + 3.05 = 2$

$b + 3.05 - 3.05 = 2 - 3.05$ Subtract 3.05 from both sides.

$b = -1.05$

Check:

$-1.05 + 3.05 = 2$

$2 = 2$ True

The solution is -1.05.

49. $-10 = 2(y + 4)$ Use distributive property.

$-10 = 2y + 8$

$-10 - 8 = 2y + 8 - 8$ Subtract 8 from both sides.

$-18 = 2y$

$\dfrac{-18}{2} = \dfrac{\overset{1}{\cancel{2}} \cdot y}{\underset{1}{\cancel{2}}}$ Divide both sides by 2.

$-9 = y$

Check:

$-10 = 2(-9 + 4)$

$-10 = 2(-5)$

$-10 = -10$ True

The solution is -9.

53. $6(x - 5) = -30$ Use distributive property

$6x - 30 = -30$

$6x - 30 + 30 = -30 + 30$ Add 30 to both sides.

$6x = 0$

$\dfrac{\overset{1}{\cancel{6}} \cdot x}{\underset{1}{\cancel{6}}} = \dfrac{0}{6}$ Divide both sides by 6.

$x = 0$

Check:
$$6(0 - 5) = -30$$
$$6(-5) = -30$$
$$-30 = -30 \quad \text{True}$$

The solution is 0.

57. $30 - 40 = -2x + 7x - 4x$ Combine like terms.
$$-10 = (-2 + 7 - 4)x$$
$$-10 = 1x$$
$$-10 = x$$

The solution is -10.

61. $\dfrac{y}{2} - 2 = \dfrac{y}{4} + 3$

$\dfrac{y}{2} - 2 + 2 = \dfrac{y}{4} + 3 + 2$ Add 2 to both sides.

$\dfrac{y}{2} = \dfrac{y}{4} + 5$ Write $\dfrac{y}{2}$ as $\dfrac{1}{2}y$ and $\dfrac{y}{4}$

$\dfrac{1}{2}y = \dfrac{1}{4}y + 5$ as $\dfrac{1}{4}y.$

$\dfrac{1}{2}y - \dfrac{1}{4}y = \dfrac{1}{4}y - \dfrac{1}{4}y + 5$ Subtract $\dfrac{1}{4}y$ from both

sides.

$\dfrac{1}{4}y = 5$

$\dfrac{\cancel{4}^{\,1}}{1} \cdot \dfrac{1}{\cancel{4}_{\,1}}y = \dfrac{4}{1} \cdot 5$ Multiply both sides by $\dfrac{4}{1}$.

$y = 20$ The solution is 20.

65. Sales tax $= (0.06)(\$420) = \$25.20$

Section 9.8

1. $14 + x$ or $x + 14$ **5.** $20 - x$
9. $x - 4$ **13.** $2x$
17. $8 + 2x$ or $2x + 8$
21. $2x + x$ or $x + 2x$
25. Let n represent the unknown number.

$\underbrace{\text{four times a number}}_{4n} \ \underbrace{\text{decreased by 2}}_{-2} \ \underbrace{\text{result is}}_{=} \ \underbrace{26}_{26}$

$$4n - 2 = 26$$
$$4n - 2 + 2 = 26 + 2$$
$$4n = 28$$
$$\dfrac{\cancel{4}^{\,1} \cdot n}{\cancel{4}_{\,1}} = \dfrac{28}{4}$$
$$n = 7$$

The number is 7.
Check: 4 times 7 is 28
         28 decreased by 2 is 26   True

29. Let n represent the unknown number.

$\underbrace{\text{half a number}}_{\frac{1}{2}n} \ \underbrace{\text{is added to}}_{+} \ \underbrace{\text{twice the number}}_{2n} \ \underbrace{\text{answer is 50}}_{= \quad 50}$

$$2\dfrac{1}{2}n = 50$$
$$\dfrac{5}{2}n = 50$$
$$\dfrac{\cancel{2}^{\,1}}{\cancel{5}_{\,1}} \cdot \dfrac{\cancel{5}^{\,1}}{\cancel{2}_{\,1}}n = \dfrac{2}{\cancel{5}_{\,1}} \cdot \cancel{50}^{\,10}$$
$$n = 20$$

The number is 20.
Check: half of 20 is 10
        twice 20 is 40
        10 added to 40 is 50   True

33. Let d represent the number of days Kerwin rented the saw.

$\underbrace{\text{one-time \$9 fee}}_{9} \ \underbrace{\text{added to}}_{+} \ \underbrace{\text{\$16 per day}}_{16 \cdot d} \ \underbrace{\text{total is}}_{=} \ \underbrace{\$89}_{89}$

$$9 + 16d = 89$$
$$9 + 16d - 9 = 89 - 9$$
$$16d = 80$$
$$\dfrac{\cancel{16}^{\,1} \cdot d}{\cancel{16}_{\,1}} = \dfrac{80}{16}$$
$$d = 5$$

Kerwin rented the saw for 5 days.
Check: \$16 per day for 5 days is \$80
        \$80 plus \$9 one-time fee is \$89   True

37. Let w represent the width of the rectangle.
The length will be twice w, which is $2w$.

$$P = 2 \cdot \text{length} + 2 \cdot \text{width}$$
$$36 = 2 \cdot 2w + 2 \cdot w$$
$$36 = 4w + 2w$$
$$36 = 6w$$
$$\dfrac{36}{6} = \dfrac{\cancel{6}^{\,1} \cdot w}{\cancel{6}_{\,1}}$$
$$6 = w$$

Width $= w$ so width is 6 ft.
Length $= 2w$ so length is $2(6)$ or 12 ft.
Check: $36 = 2(12) + 2(6)$
        $36 = 24 + 12$
        $36 = 36$ True

41. Let x represent the length of each equal part.
The length of the third part is $x + 25$

Total length is 706

$$x + x + x + 25 = 706$$
$$3x + 25 = 706$$
$$3x + 25 - 25 = 706 - 25$$
$$3x = 681$$
$$\frac{\overset{1}{\cancel{3}} \cdot x}{\underset{1}{\cancel{3}}} = \frac{681}{3}$$
$$x = 227$$

Two parts are each 227 m long.
The third part is $227 + 25$ or 252 m long.
Check: $227 + 227 + 252 = 706$ True

45. amount $=$ percent $\cdot$ base

$$a = 0.80 \cdot 2900$$
$$a = 2320$$

80% of $2900 is $2320.

Appendix A

Fractions

Proper and Improper Fractions

A fraction in the form $\frac{a}{b}$ is called **proper** if a and b are counting numbers and a is less than b ($a < b$). If a is greater than or equal to b ($a \geq b$) then $\frac{a}{b}$ is called **improper**.

NOTE: a can be zero but b cannot, since you may not divide *by* zero.

Example 1: $\frac{2}{3}$ is proper since $2 < 3$.   **Example 2:** $\frac{7}{5}$ is improper since $7 > 5$.

Example 3: $\frac{0}{4} = 0$.   **Example 4:** $\frac{8}{0}$ has no numerical value and, therefore, is said to be **undefined.**

Reducing a Fraction

A fraction, $\frac{a}{b}$, is in **lowest terms** if a and b have no common divisor (other than 1).

Example 1: $\frac{3}{4}$ is in lowest terms. The only common divisor is 1.

Example 2: $\frac{9}{15}$ is not in lowest terms. 3 is a common divisor of 9 and 15.

To **reduce a fraction $\frac{a}{b}$ to lowest terms,** divide both a and b by a common divisor until the numerator and denominator no longer have any common divisors.

Example 1: Reduce $\frac{4}{8}$ to lowest terms.

Solution: $\dfrac{4}{8} = \dfrac{4 \div 4}{8 \div 4} = \dfrac{1}{2}$

Example 2: Reduce $\frac{18}{14}$ to lowest terms.

Solution: $\dfrac{18}{14} = \dfrac{18 \div 2}{14 \div 2} = \dfrac{9}{7}$

Mixed Numbers

> A **mixed number** is the sum of a whole number plus a proper fraction.

Example: $3\frac{2}{5} = 3 + \frac{2}{5}$

Changing an Improper Fraction, $\frac{a}{b}$, to a Mixed Number

1. Divide the numerator, a, by the denominator, b.
2. The quotient becomes the whole number part of the mixed number.
3. The remainder becomes the numerator, and b remains the denominator, of the fractional part of the mixed number.

Example 1: Change $\frac{7}{5}$ to a mixed number.

Solution: $7 \div 5 = 1$ with a remainder of 2.

          So $\frac{7}{5} = 1 + \frac{2}{5} = 1\frac{2}{5}$

Example 2: Change $\frac{22}{6}$ to a mixed number.

Solution: First reduce $\frac{22}{6}$ to lowest terms.

$$\frac{22}{6} = \frac{22 \div 2}{6 \div 2} = \frac{11}{3}.$$

          $11 \div 3 = 3$ with a remainder of 2.

          So $\frac{11}{3} = 3 + \frac{2}{3} = 3\frac{2}{3}$

Changing a Mixed Number to an Improper Fraction

1. To obtain the numerator of the improper fraction, multiply the denominator by the whole number and add the original numerator to this product.
2. Place this sum over the original denominator.

Example: Change $4\frac{5}{6}$ to an improper fraction.

Solution: $6 \cdot 4 + 5 = 29$

          So $4\frac{5}{6} = \frac{29}{6}$

EXERCISES

1. Reduce these fractions, if possible.

   a. $\frac{12}{16}$ **b.** $\frac{33}{11}$ **c.** $\frac{21}{49}$ **d.** $\frac{13}{31}$

2. Change each improper fraction to a mixed number. Reduce if possible.

   a. $\frac{20}{16}$ **b.** $\frac{34}{8}$ **c.** $\frac{48}{12}$ **d.** $\frac{33}{5}$

3. Change each mixed number to an improper fraction.

   a. $7\frac{2}{5}$ **b.** $8\frac{6}{10}$ **c.** $9\frac{6}{7}$ **d.** $11\frac{3}{4}$

Finding a Common Denominator of Two Fractions

> A **common denominator** is a number that is divisible by each of the original denominators.
>
> The **least common denominator** is the smallest possible common denominator.

A common denominator can be obtained by multiplying the original denominators. Note that this product may not necessarily be the least common denominator.

Example: Find a common denominator of $\frac{5}{6}$ and $\frac{7}{9}$.

Solution: $6 \cdot 9 = 54$, so 54 is a common denominator.
However, 18 is the least common denominator.

Equivalent Fractions

> Equivalent fractions are fractions with the same numerical value.

To obtain an equivalent fraction, multiply or divide both numerator and denominator by the same nonzero number.

NOTE: Adding or subtracting the same number to the original numerator and denominator does *not* yield an equivalent fraction.

Example: Find a fraction that is equivalent to $\frac{3}{5}$ whose denominator is 20.

Solution: $\dfrac{3}{5} = \dfrac{3 \cdot 4}{5 \cdot 4} = \dfrac{12}{20}$

NOTE: $\dfrac{3 + 15}{5 + 15} = \dfrac{18}{20} = \dfrac{9}{10} \neq \dfrac{3}{5}$

Comparing Fractions: Determining Which is Larger. Is $\frac{a}{b} < \frac{c}{d}$ or is $\frac{a}{b} > \frac{c}{d}$?

1. Obtain a common denominator by multiplying b and d.
2. Write $\frac{a}{b}$ and $\frac{c}{d}$ as equivalent fractions, each with denominator $b \cdot d$.
3. Compare numerators. The fraction with the larger (smaller) numerator is the larger (smaller) fraction.

Example: Determine whether $\frac{3}{5}$ is less than or greater than $\frac{7}{12}$.

Solution: A common denominator is $5 \cdot 12 = 60$.

$$\frac{3}{5} = \frac{3 \cdot 12}{5 \cdot 12} = \frac{36}{60}, \qquad \frac{7}{12} = \frac{7 \cdot 5}{12 \cdot 5} = \frac{35}{60}$$

Since $36 > 35$, $\qquad \frac{3}{5} > \frac{7}{12}$

EXERCISES

Compare the two fractions and indicate which one is larger.

1. $\frac{4}{7}$ and $\frac{5}{8}$ **2.** $\frac{11}{13}$ and $\frac{22}{39}$ **3.** $\frac{5}{12}$ and $\frac{7}{16}$ **4.** $\frac{3}{5}$ and $\frac{14}{20}$

Addition and Subtraction of Fractions with the Same Denominators

To add (or subtract) $\frac{a}{c}$ and $\frac{b}{c}$:

1. Add (or subtract) the numerators, a and b.
2. Place the sum (or difference) over the common denominator, c.
3. Reduce to lowest terms.

Example 1: Add $\frac{5}{16} + \frac{7}{16}$

Solution: $\dfrac{5}{16} + \dfrac{7}{16} = \dfrac{5+7}{16} = \dfrac{12}{16}$ $\dfrac{12}{16} = \dfrac{12 \div 4}{16 \div 4} = \dfrac{3}{4}$

Example 2: Subtract $\frac{19}{24} - \frac{7}{24}$

Solution: $\dfrac{19}{24} - \dfrac{7}{24} = \dfrac{19-7}{24} = \dfrac{12}{24}$ $\dfrac{12}{24} = \dfrac{12 \div 12}{24 \div 12} = \dfrac{1}{2}$

Addition and Subtraction of Fractions with Different Denominators

To add (or subtract) $\frac{a}{b}$ and $\frac{c}{d}$, where $b \neq d$:

1. Obtain a common denominator by multiplying b and d.
2. Write $\frac{a}{b}$ and $\frac{c}{d}$ as equivalent fractions with denominator $b \cdot d$.
3. Add (or subtract) the numerators of the equivalent fractions and place the sum (or difference) over the common denominator, $b \cdot d$.
4. Reduce to lowest terms.

Example 1: Add $\frac{3}{5} + \frac{2}{7}$

Solution: A common denominator is, $5 \cdot 7 = 35$

$$\dfrac{3}{5} = \dfrac{3 \cdot 7}{5 \cdot 7} = \dfrac{21}{35}, \qquad \dfrac{2}{7} = \dfrac{2 \cdot 5}{7 \cdot 5} = \dfrac{10}{35}$$

$$\dfrac{3}{5} + \dfrac{2}{7} = \dfrac{21}{35} + \dfrac{10}{35} = \dfrac{31}{35}$$

$\frac{31}{35}$ is already in lowest terms.

Example 2: Subtract $\frac{5}{12} - \frac{2}{9}$

Solution: Using common denominator, $12 \cdot 9 = 108$:

$$\dfrac{5}{12} = \dfrac{5 \cdot 9}{12 \cdot 9} = \dfrac{45}{108},$$

$$\dfrac{2}{9} = \dfrac{2 \cdot 12}{9 \cdot 12} = \dfrac{24}{108}$$

Using least common denominator, 36:

$$\dfrac{5}{12} = \dfrac{5 \cdot 3}{12 \cdot 3} = \dfrac{15}{36},$$

$$\dfrac{2}{9} = \dfrac{2 \cdot 4}{9 \cdot 4} = \dfrac{8}{36}$$

$$\frac{5}{12} - \frac{2}{9} = \frac{45}{108} - \frac{24}{108} = \frac{21}{108} \qquad \frac{5}{12} - \frac{2}{9} = \frac{15}{36} - \frac{8}{36} = \frac{7}{36}$$

$$\frac{21}{108} = \frac{21 \div 3}{108 \div 3} = \frac{7}{36}$$

Addition and Subtraction of Mixed Numbers

To add (or subtract) mixed numbers:

1. Add (or subtract) the whole number parts.
2. Add (or subtract) the fractional parts. In subtraction, this may require borrowing.
3. Add the resulting whole number and fractional parts to form the mixed number sum (or difference).

Example 1: Add $3\frac{2}{5} + 5\frac{3}{4}$

Solution: Whole number sum: $3 + 5 = 8$

Fractional sum:

$$\frac{2}{3} + \frac{3}{4} = \frac{2 \cdot 4}{3 \cdot 4} + \frac{3 \cdot 3}{4 \cdot 3} = \frac{8}{12} + \frac{9}{12} = \frac{17}{12} = 1\frac{5}{12}$$

Final result: $8 + 1\frac{5}{12} = 8 + 1 + \frac{5}{12} = 9\frac{5}{12}$

Example 2: Subtract $4\frac{1}{3} - 1\frac{7}{8}$

Solution: Because $\frac{1}{3}$ is smaller than $\frac{7}{8}$, you must borrow as follows:

$$4\frac{1}{3} = 3 + 1 + \frac{1}{3} = 3 + 1\frac{1}{3} = 3\frac{4}{3}$$

The original subtraction now becomes $3\frac{4}{3} - 1\frac{7}{8}$

Subtracting the whole number parts: $3 - 1 = 2$

Subtracting the fractional parts:

$$\frac{4}{3} - \frac{7}{8} = \frac{4 \cdot 8}{3 \cdot 8} - \frac{7 \cdot 3}{8 \cdot 3} = \frac{32}{24} - \frac{21}{24} = \frac{11}{24}$$

Final result is $2 + \frac{11}{24} = 2\frac{11}{24}$

EXERCISES

Add or subtract as indicated.

1. $1\frac{3}{4} + 3\frac{1}{8}$ 2. $8\frac{2}{3} - 7\frac{1}{4}$ 3. $6\frac{5}{6} + 3\frac{11}{18}$ 4. $2\frac{1}{3} - \frac{4}{5}$

5. $4\frac{3}{5} + 2\frac{3}{8}$ 6. $12\frac{1}{3} + 8\frac{7}{10}$ 7. $14\frac{3}{4} - 5\frac{7}{8}$ 8. $6\frac{5}{8} + 9\frac{7}{12}$

Multiplying Fractions

To multiply fractions, $\frac{a}{b} \cdot \frac{c}{d}$:

1. Multiply the numerators, $a \cdot c$, to form the numerator of the product fraction.
2. Multiply the denominators, $b \cdot d$, to form the denominator of the product fraction.
3. Write the product fraction by placing $a \cdot c$ over $b \cdot d$.
4. Reduce to lowest terms.

Example: Multiply $\frac{3}{4} \cdot \frac{8}{15}$.

Solution: $\dfrac{3}{4} \cdot \dfrac{8}{15} = \dfrac{3 \cdot 8}{4 \cdot 15} = \dfrac{24}{60} \qquad \dfrac{24}{60} = \dfrac{24 \div 12}{60 \div 12} = \dfrac{2}{5}$

NOTE: It is often simpler and more efficient to cancel any common factors of the numerators and denominators *before* multiplying.

Dividing by a Fraction

Dividing *by* a fraction, $\frac{c}{d}$, is equivalent to multiplying by its reciprocal, $\frac{d}{c}$.

To divide fraction $\frac{a}{b}$ by $\frac{c}{d}$, written $\frac{a}{b} \div \frac{c}{d}$:

1. Rewrite the division as an equivalent multiplication, $\frac{a}{b} \cdot \frac{d}{c}$:
2. Proceed by multiplying as described above.

Example: Divide $\frac{2}{3}$ by $\frac{1}{2}$.

Solution: $\dfrac{2}{3} \div \dfrac{1}{2} = \dfrac{2}{3} \cdot \dfrac{2}{1} = \dfrac{2 \cdot 2}{3 \cdot 1} = \dfrac{4}{3}$

NOTE: $\frac{4}{3}$ is already in lowest terms.

EXERCISES

Multiply or divide as indicated.

1. $\frac{11}{14} \cdot \frac{4}{5}$ **2.** $\frac{3}{7} \div \frac{3}{5}$ **3.** $\frac{8}{15} \cdot \frac{3}{4}$ **4.** $6 \div \frac{2}{5}$

Multiplying or Dividing Mixed Numbers

To multiply (or divide) mixed numbers:

1. Change the mixed numbers to improper fractions.
2. Multiply (or divide) the fractions as described earlier.
3. If the result is an improper fraction, change to a mixed number.

Example: Divide $8\frac{2}{5}$ by 3.

Solution: $8\frac{2}{5} = \frac{42}{5}, \quad 3 = \frac{3}{1}$

$\dfrac{42}{5} \div \dfrac{3}{1} = \dfrac{42}{5} \cdot \dfrac{1}{3} = \dfrac{42}{15}$

$\dfrac{42}{15} = \dfrac{42 \div 3}{15 \div 3} = \dfrac{14}{5}$

$\frac{14}{5} = 2\frac{4}{5}$

EXERCISES

Multiply or divide as indicated.

1. $3\frac{1}{2} \cdot 4\frac{3}{4}$ **2.** $10\frac{3}{5} \div 4\frac{2}{3}$ **3.** $5\frac{4}{5} \cdot 6$ **4.** $4\frac{3}{10} \div \frac{2}{5}$

Name _____

43. $5 \cdot \sqrt{100} - 7 \cdot 2$

44. $7 \cdot \sqrt{81} - 4 \cdot 5$

45. $6 \cdot 4 + 5 \cdot 7 - 10$

46. $9 \cdot 2 + 8 \cdot 3 + 15$

47. $2^3 \cdot 3^2 + (14 - 4) \cdot 3$

48. $3^2 \cdot 4^2 + (15 - 6) \cdot 2$

49. $8 + 10 \div 5 + \dfrac{0}{3}$

50. $6 + 8 \div 2 + \dfrac{0}{8}$ $= 6 + 4 + 0 = 10$
4

51. $3^2 + 6^2 + (30 - 21) \cdot 2$

$9 + 36 + (9) \cdot 2$
$9 + 36 + 18 = \boxed{63}$

52. $4^2 + 5^2 + (25 - 9) \cdot 3$

53. $7 \cdot \sqrt{81} - 5 \cdot 6$

54. $5 \cdot \sqrt{144} - 5 \cdot 7$

55. $7 \cdot 2 + 8(2 \cdot 3) - 4$

56. $5 \cdot 2 + 3(5 + 3) - 6$

57. $4 \cdot \sqrt{49} - 7(5 - 2)$

58. $3 \cdot \sqrt{25} - 6(3 - 1)$

59. $6 \cdot (5 - 1) + \sqrt{4}$

60. $5 \cdot (4 - 3) + \sqrt{9}$

61. $6^2 + 2^2 - 6 + 2$

62. $3^2 - 2^2 + 3 - 2$

63. $5^2 \cdot 2^2 + (8 - 4) \cdot 2$

64. $5^2 \cdot 3^2 + (30 - 20) \cdot 2$

65. $7 + 6 \div 3 + 5 \cdot 2$

66. $8 + 3 \div 3 + 6 \cdot 3$

67. $5 \cdot \sqrt{36} - 7(7 - 4)$

68. $9 \cdot \sqrt{64} - 5(4 + 2)$

69. $4^2 - 2^3 + 5 \cdot 3$

70. $5^2 + 6^2 - 9 \cdot 4$

71. $8 + 5 \div 5 + 7 + \dfrac{0}{3}$

72. $2 + 12 \div 6 + 5 + \dfrac{0}{5}$

73. $4 \cdot \sqrt{25} - 6 \cdot 2$

74. $8 \cdot \sqrt{36} - 4 \cdot 6$

75. $3 \cdot \sqrt{25} - 4 \cdot \sqrt{9}$

76. $8 \cdot \sqrt{100} - 6 \cdot \sqrt{36}$

77. $7 \div 1 \cdot 8 \cdot 2 \div (21 - 5)$

78. $12 \div 4 \cdot 5 \cdot 4 \div (15 - 13)$

79. $15 \div 3 \cdot 2 \cdot 6 \div (14 - 11)$

80. $9 \div 1 \cdot 4 \cdot 2 \div (11 - 5)$

81. $4 \cdot \sqrt{16} - 3 \cdot \sqrt{9}$

82. $10 \cdot \sqrt{49} - 4 \cdot \sqrt{64}$

83. $5 \div 1 \cdot 10 \cdot 4 \div (17 - 9)$

84. $15 \div 3 \cdot 8 \cdot 9 \div (12 - 8)$

85. $8 \cdot 9 \div \sqrt{36} - 4 \div 2 + (14 - 8)$

86. $3 - 2 + 5 \cdot 4 \cdot \sqrt{144} \div \sqrt{36}$

87. $1 + 3 - 2 \cdot \sqrt{1} + 3 \cdot \sqrt{121} - 5 \cdot 3$

88. $6 - 4 + 2 \cdot 9 - 3 \cdot \sqrt{225} \div \sqrt{25}$

89. $6 \cdot \sqrt{25} \cdot \sqrt{100} \div 3 \cdot \sqrt{4} + 9$

90. $9 \cdot \sqrt{36} \cdot \sqrt{81} \div 2 + 6 - 3 - 5$

5   *Exercises*

Multiply. Write all answers in lowest terms.

Example: $\dfrac{9}{16} \cdot \dfrac{8}{27} \cdot \dfrac{9}{10}$

Solution: $\dfrac{\overset{1}{\cancel{9}}}{\underset{2}{\cancel{16}}} \cdot \dfrac{\overset{1}{\cancel{8}}}{\underset{3}{\cancel{27}}} \cdot \dfrac{\overset{3}{\cancel{9}}}{10} = \dfrac{1 \cdot 1 \cdot 3}{2 \cdot 1 \cdot 10} = \dfrac{3}{20}$

1. $\dfrac{3}{8} \times \dfrac{1}{2}$

2. $\dfrac{2}{3} \times \dfrac{5}{8}$

3. $\dfrac{2}{5} \times \dfrac{2}{3}$

4. $\dfrac{1}{3} \times \dfrac{2}{5}$

5. $\dfrac{3}{8} \cdot \dfrac{12}{5}$

6. $\dfrac{4}{9} \cdot \dfrac{12}{7}$

7. $\dfrac{5}{6} \cdot \dfrac{12}{25} \cdot \dfrac{3}{4}$

8. $\dfrac{7}{8} \cdot \dfrac{16}{21} \cdot \dfrac{1}{2}$

9. $\dfrac{3}{4} \cdot \dfrac{5}{6} \cdot \dfrac{2}{3}$

10. $\dfrac{2}{5} \cdot \dfrac{3}{8} \cdot \dfrac{2}{3}$

11. $\dfrac{9}{22} \cdot \dfrac{11}{16}$

12. $\dfrac{5}{12} \cdot \dfrac{7}{10}$

13. $\dfrac{21}{30} \cdot \dfrac{5}{7}$

14. $\dfrac{6}{11} \cdot \dfrac{22}{15}$

15. $\dfrac{14}{25} \cdot \dfrac{65}{48} \cdot \dfrac{15}{28}$

16. $\dfrac{35}{64} \cdot \dfrac{32}{15} \cdot \dfrac{27}{72}$

17. $\dfrac{16}{25} \cdot \dfrac{35}{32} \cdot \dfrac{15}{64}$

18. $\dfrac{39}{42} \cdot \dfrac{7}{13} \cdot \dfrac{7}{24}$

Multiply. Write all answers in lowest terms; change answers to whole or mixed numbers where possible.

Example: $27 \cdot \dfrac{5}{9}$ **Solution:** $27 \cdot \dfrac{5}{9} = \dfrac{\overset{3}{\cancel{27}}}{1} \cdot \dfrac{5}{\underset{1}{\cancel{9}}} = \dfrac{3 \cdot 5}{1 \cdot 1} = \dfrac{15}{1} = 15$

19. $5 \cdot \dfrac{3}{5}$

20. $20 \cdot \dfrac{3}{4}$

21. $\dfrac{4}{9} \cdot 81$

22. $\dfrac{2}{3} \cdot 48$

23. $32 \cdot \dfrac{3}{8}$

24. $30 \cdot \dfrac{3}{10}$

25. $42 \cdot \dfrac{7}{10} \cdot \dfrac{5}{7}$

26. $35 \cdot \dfrac{3}{5} \cdot \dfrac{1}{2}$

27. $100 \cdot \dfrac{21}{50} \cdot \dfrac{3}{4}$

28. $300 \cdot \dfrac{5}{6}$

29. $\dfrac{3}{5} \cdot 400$

30. $\dfrac{5}{9} \cdot 360$

31. $\dfrac{3}{4} \cdot 363$

32. $\dfrac{12}{25} \cdot 430$

33. $\dfrac{28}{21} \cdot 640 \cdot \dfrac{15}{32}$

34. $\dfrac{21}{13} \cdot 520 \cdot \dfrac{7}{20}$

35. $\dfrac{54}{38} \cdot 684 \cdot \dfrac{5}{6}$

36. $\dfrac{76}{43} \cdot 473 \cdot \dfrac{5}{19}$

7   Exercises

Divide. Write all answers in lowest terms; change answers to whole or mixed numbers where possible.

Example: $\dfrac{3}{4} \div \dfrac{1}{2}$ **Solution:** $\dfrac{3}{\overset{4}{\underset{2}{4}}} \cdot \dfrac{\overset{1}{2}}{1} = \dfrac{3}{2} = 1\dfrac{1}{2}$

1. $\dfrac{1}{6} \div \dfrac{1}{3}$

2. $\dfrac{1}{2} \div \dfrac{2}{3}$

3. $\dfrac{7}{8} \div \dfrac{1}{3}$

4. $\dfrac{3}{4} \div \dfrac{5}{8}$

5. $\dfrac{3}{4} \div \dfrac{5}{3}$

6. $\dfrac{4}{5} \div \dfrac{9}{4}$

7. $\dfrac{7}{12} \div \dfrac{14}{15}$

8. $\dfrac{13}{20} \div \dfrac{4}{5}$

9. $\dfrac{\dfrac{7}{9}}{\dfrac{7}{36}}$

10. $\dfrac{\dfrac{15}{32}}{\dfrac{5}{64}}$

11. $\dfrac{\dfrac{36}{35}}{\dfrac{15}{14}}$

12. $\dfrac{\dfrac{28}{15}}{\dfrac{21}{5}}$

13. $6 \div \dfrac{2}{3}$

14. $7 \div \dfrac{1}{4}$

15. $\dfrac{15}{\dfrac{2}{3}}$

16. $\dfrac{6}{\dfrac{5}{8}}$

17. $\dfrac{\dfrac{4}{7}}{8}$

18. $\dfrac{\dfrac{11}{5}}{3}$

3   Exercises

Add the following fractions. Write answers in lowest terms.

Example: $\dfrac{2}{3} + \dfrac{1}{6}$ **Solution:**

Step 1
Rewrite as
like fractions.

Step 2
Add
numerators.

Step 3
Lowest
terms

$$\frac{2}{3} + \frac{1}{6} = \frac{4}{6} + \frac{1}{6} = \frac{4+1}{6} = \frac{5}{6}$$

Least common
denominator is 6.

1. $\dfrac{3}{4} + \dfrac{1}{8}$

2. $\dfrac{1}{3} + \dfrac{1}{2}$

3. $\dfrac{1}{14} + \dfrac{3}{7}$

4. $\dfrac{2}{9} + \dfrac{2}{3}$

5. $\dfrac{9}{20} + \dfrac{3}{10}$

6. $\dfrac{5}{8} + \dfrac{1}{4}$

7. $\dfrac{3}{5} + \dfrac{3}{8}$

8. $\dfrac{5}{7} + \dfrac{3}{14}$

9. $\dfrac{2}{9} + \dfrac{5}{12}$

10. $\dfrac{5}{8} + \dfrac{1}{12}$

11. $\dfrac{1}{3} + \dfrac{3}{5}$

12. $\dfrac{2}{5} + \dfrac{3}{7}$

13. $\dfrac{1}{4} + \dfrac{2}{9} + \dfrac{1}{3}$

14. $\dfrac{3}{7} + \dfrac{2}{5} + \dfrac{1}{10}$

15. $\dfrac{3}{10} + \dfrac{2}{5} + \dfrac{3}{20}$

16. $\dfrac{1}{3} + \dfrac{3}{8} + \dfrac{1}{4}$

17. $\dfrac{4}{15} + \dfrac{1}{6} + \dfrac{1}{3}$

18. $\dfrac{5}{12} + \dfrac{2}{9} + \dfrac{1}{6}$

19. $\dfrac{1}{3}$
$+ \dfrac{1}{4}$

20. $\dfrac{1}{12}$
$+ \dfrac{5}{8}$

21. $\dfrac{5}{12}$
$+ \dfrac{1}{16}$

22. $\dfrac{3}{7}$
$+ \dfrac{1}{3}$

4 Exercises

≈ *First estimate the answer. Then add to find the exact answer. Write answers as mixed numbers.*

Example:

$$2\dfrac{3}{5}$$
$$+\ 9\dfrac{2}{3}$$
_____

Solution:

estimate		*exact*
3	$\xleftarrow{\text{Rounds to}}$	$2\dfrac{3}{5} =\ 2\dfrac{9}{15}$
$+\ 10$	$\longleftarrow$	$+\ 9\dfrac{2}{3} =\ 9\dfrac{10}{15}$
13		$11\dfrac{19}{15}$

$\dfrac{19}{15} = 1\dfrac{4}{15}$, so

$$11\dfrac{19}{15} = 11 + 1\dfrac{4}{15}$$

The exact answer is close to the estimate. $= 12\dfrac{4}{15}$

---

1. *estimate* *exact*

$\xleftarrow{\text{Rounds to}}$ $\quad 5\dfrac{1}{2}$

$+\ \longleftarrow\ +\ 3\dfrac{1}{3}$
___ ___

2. *estimate* *exact*

$\qquad 7\dfrac{1}{10}$

$+\qquad +\ 2\dfrac{3}{10}$
___ ___

3. *estimate* *exact*

$\qquad 10\dfrac{1}{6}$

$+\qquad +\ 5\dfrac{1}{3}$
___ ___

---

4. *estimate* *exact*

$\qquad 6\dfrac{3}{8}$

$+\qquad +\ 15\dfrac{1}{4}$
___ ___

5. *estimate* *exact*

$\qquad 26\dfrac{5}{8}$

$+\qquad +\ 9\dfrac{1}{12}$
___ ___

6. *estimate* *exact*

$\qquad 82\dfrac{3}{5}$

$+\qquad +\ 15\dfrac{4}{5}$
___ ___

---

7. *estimate* *exact*

$\qquad 24\dfrac{5}{6}$

$+\qquad +\ 18\dfrac{5}{6}$
___ ___

8. *estimate* *exact*

$\qquad 14\dfrac{6}{7}$

$+\qquad +\ 15\dfrac{1}{2}$
___ ___

9. *estimate* *exact*

$\qquad 33\dfrac{3}{5}$

$+\qquad +18\dfrac{1}{2}$
___ ___

---

10. *estimate* *exact*

$\qquad 68\dfrac{3}{5}$

$+\qquad +\ 25\dfrac{3}{8}$
___ ___

11. *estimate* *exact*

$\qquad 22\dfrac{3}{4}$

$+\qquad +\ 15\dfrac{3}{7}$
___ ___

12. *estimate* *exact*

$\qquad 7\dfrac{1}{4}$

$+\qquad +\ 25\dfrac{7}{8}$
___ ___

13. *estimate*   *exact*

$$18\frac{3}{5}$$

$$47\frac{7}{10}$$

$$+ \underline{\qquad} \qquad + \ 25\frac{8}{15}$$

14. *estimate*   *exact*

$$28\frac{1}{4}$$

$$23\frac{3}{5}$$

$$+ \underline{\qquad} \qquad + \ 19\frac{9}{10}$$

15. *estimate*   *exact*

$$32\frac{3}{4}$$

$$6\frac{1}{3}$$

$$+ \underline{\qquad} \qquad + \ 14\frac{5}{8}$$

≈*First estimate the answer. Then subtract to find the exact answer. Write answers as mixed numbers.*

Example:

$$6$$
$$- \ 4\frac{7}{8}$$

Solution:

estimate   *exact*

$$6 \xleftarrow{\text{Rounds to}} 6$$

$$- \ 5 \longleftarrow - \ 4\frac{7}{8}$$

$$\overline{\quad 1 \quad}$$

Borrow. $6 = 5 + 1$

$$= 5 + \frac{8}{8}$$

$$= 5\frac{8}{8}$$

Subtract. $6 = 5\frac{8}{8}$

$$- \ 4\frac{7}{8} = 4\frac{7}{8}$$

$$\mathbf{1\frac{1}{8}}$$

The exact answer is close to the estimate.

16. *estimate*   *exact*

$$\xleftarrow{\text{Rounds to}} 16\frac{3}{4}$$

$$- \underline{\qquad} \longleftarrow - \ 12\frac{3}{8}$$

17. *estimate*   *exact*

$$19\frac{3}{8}$$

$$- \underline{\qquad} \qquad - \ 16\frac{1}{4}$$

18. *estimate*   *exact*

$$12\frac{2}{3}$$

$$- \underline{\qquad} \qquad - \ 1\frac{1}{5}$$

19. *estimate*   *exact*

$$11\frac{9}{20}$$

$$- \underline{\qquad} \qquad - \ 4\frac{3}{5}$$

20. *estimate*   *exact*

$$28\frac{3}{10}$$

$$- \underline{\qquad} \qquad - \ 6\frac{1}{15}$$

21. *estimate*   *exact*

$$15\frac{7}{20}$$

$$- \underline{\qquad} \qquad - \ 6\frac{1}{8}$$

22. *estimate*   *exact*

$$19$$

$$- \underline{\qquad} \qquad - \ 8\frac{7}{8}$$

23. *estimate*   *exact*

$$35$$

$$- \underline{\qquad} \qquad - \ 17\frac{3}{8}$$

24. *estimate*   *exact*

$$68\frac{3}{8}$$

$$- \underline{\qquad} \qquad - \ 6\frac{4}{5}$$

Name _____

Use the order of operations to simplify each of the following.

Example: $\left(\dfrac{2}{3}\right)^2 \cdot \left(\dfrac{1}{2} + \dfrac{1}{4}\right)$　　　**Solution:** $= \left(\dfrac{2}{3}\right)^2 \cdot \left(\dfrac{3}{4}\right)$　　Work in parentheses first.

$$= \dfrac{\overset{1}{\cancel{4}}}{\underset{3}{\cancel{9}}} \cdot \dfrac{\overset{1}{\cancel{3}}}{\underset{1}{\cancel{4}}}$$　　Evaluate exponential expression.

$$= \dfrac{1}{3}$$　　Multiply.

---

39. $4 + 2 - 2^2$

40. $3^2 + 3 \cdot 2$

41. $5 \cdot 2^2 - \dfrac{12}{3}$

42. $4 \cdot 3^2 - \dfrac{8}{2}$

43. $\left(\dfrac{1}{2}\right)^2 \cdot 4$

44. $3 \cdot \left(\dfrac{1}{3}\right)^2$

45. $\left(\dfrac{3}{4}\right)^2 \cdot \left(\dfrac{1}{3}\right)$

46. $\left(\dfrac{2}{3}\right)^3 \cdot \left(\dfrac{1}{2}\right)$

47. $\left(\dfrac{3}{4}\right)^2 \cdot \left(\dfrac{2}{3}\right)^2$

48. $\left(\dfrac{5}{8}\right)^2 \cdot \left(\dfrac{4}{25}\right)^2$

49. $6 \cdot \left(\dfrac{2}{3}\right)^2 \cdot \left(\dfrac{1}{2}\right)^3$

50. $9 \cdot \left(\dfrac{1}{3}\right)^3 \cdot \left(\dfrac{4}{3}\right)^2$

51. $\dfrac{4}{3} \cdot \dfrac{3}{8} + \dfrac{3}{4} \cdot \dfrac{1}{4}$

52. $\dfrac{3}{4} \cdot \dfrac{2}{5} + \dfrac{1}{3} \cdot \dfrac{3}{5}$

53. $\dfrac{1}{2} + \left(\dfrac{1}{2}\right)^2 - \dfrac{3}{8}$

54. $\dfrac{2}{3} + \left(\dfrac{1}{3}\right)^2 - \dfrac{5}{9}$

55. $\left(\dfrac{1}{3} + \dfrac{1}{6}\right) \cdot \dfrac{1}{2}$

56. $\left(\dfrac{3}{5} - \dfrac{3}{20}\right) \cdot \dfrac{4}{3}$

57. $\dfrac{9}{8} \div \left(\dfrac{2}{3} + \dfrac{1}{12}\right)$

58. $\dfrac{6}{5} \div \left(\dfrac{3}{5} - \dfrac{3}{10}\right)$

59. $\left(\dfrac{3}{5} - \dfrac{1}{10}\right) \div \dfrac{5}{2}$

60. $\left(\dfrac{8}{5} - \dfrac{7}{10}\right) \div \dfrac{3}{5}$

61. $\dfrac{3}{8} \cdot \left(\dfrac{1}{4} + \dfrac{1}{2}\right) \cdot \dfrac{32}{3}$

62. $\dfrac{1}{3} \cdot \left(\dfrac{4}{5} - \dfrac{3}{10}\right) \cdot \dfrac{4}{2}$

[1] *Add or subtract. Write answers in lowest terms.*

1. $\dfrac{2}{8} + \dfrac{5}{8}$

2. $\dfrac{1}{5} + \dfrac{2}{5}$

3. $\dfrac{1}{8} + \dfrac{3}{8} + \dfrac{2}{8}$

4. $\dfrac{7}{12} - \dfrac{2}{12}$

5. $\dfrac{3}{10} - \dfrac{1}{10}$

6. $\dfrac{5}{16} - \dfrac{1}{16}$

7. $\dfrac{36}{62} - \dfrac{10}{62}$

8. $\dfrac{79}{108} - \dfrac{47}{108}$

Solve each application problem. Write answers in lowest terms.

9. Tyrone milled $\frac{3}{16}$ of the lumber on the first day and $\frac{5}{16}$ of the lumber on the second day. What fraction of the lumber did he mill on these two days?

10. Dominique Moceanu completed $\frac{7}{10}$ of her workout in the morning and $\frac{1}{10}$ of her workout in the afternoon. How much less of a workout did she have in the afternoon than in the morning?

[2] *Find the least common multiple of each set of numbers.*

11. 4, 3

12. 8, 5

13. 10, 12, 20

14. 9, 20, 15

15. 6, 8, 5, 15

16. 24, 5, 16

Rewrite each of the following fractions by using the indicated denominators.

17. $\dfrac{3}{4} = \dfrac{}{16}$

18. $\dfrac{2}{3} = \dfrac{}{15}$

19. $\dfrac{2}{5} = \dfrac{}{25}$

20. $\dfrac{5}{9} = \dfrac{}{81}$

21. $\dfrac{7}{16} = \dfrac{}{144}$

22. $\dfrac{3}{22} = \dfrac{}{88}$

[1–3] *Add or subtract. Write answers in lowest terms.*

23. $\dfrac{1}{4} + \dfrac{1}{3}$

24. $\dfrac{1}{5} + \dfrac{3}{10} + \dfrac{3}{8}$

25. $\begin{aligned} &\dfrac{9}{16} \\ +\,&\dfrac{1}{12} \\ \hline \end{aligned}$

26. $\dfrac{4}{5} - \dfrac{1}{4}$

27. $\begin{aligned} &\dfrac{3}{4} \\ -\,&\dfrac{1}{3} \\ \hline \end{aligned}$

28. $\begin{aligned} &\dfrac{11}{12} \\ -\,&\dfrac{4}{9} \\ \hline \end{aligned}$

Solve each of the following application problems.

29. A dump truck contains $\frac{1}{4}$ cubic yard of fine gravel, $\frac{1}{3}$ cubic yard of pea gravel, and $\frac{3}{8}$ cubic yard of coarse gravel. How many cubic yards of gravel are on the truck?

30. Rachel is saving money for a birthday bash for Ross. Monica has raised $\frac{2}{5}$ of the amount needed through a bake sale; Joey has earned $\frac{1}{3}$ of the amount needed from an acting gig, and Phoebe has raised another $\frac{1}{4}$ singing at the local coffee shop. Find the portion of the total that has been raised.

Name _____

$\approx$ *First estimate the answer. Then add or subtract to find the exact answer. Write answers as mixed numbers.*

31. estimate   exact

Rounds to ⟵ $25\frac{3}{4}$

+   ⟵ $+ 16\frac{3}{8}$

─────   ─────

32. estimate   exact

$78\frac{3}{7}$

+ $+ 17\frac{6}{7}$

─────   ─────

33. estimate   exact

$12\frac{3}{5}$

$8\frac{5}{8}$

+ $+ 10\frac{5}{16}$

─────   ─────

34. estimate   exact

$18\frac{1}{3}$

− $- 12\frac{3}{4}$

─────   ─────

35. estimate   exact

$73\frac{1}{2}$

− $- 55\frac{2}{3}$

─────   ─────

36. estimate   exact

$215\frac{7}{16}$

− $- 136$

─────   ─────

Add or subtract by changing mixed numbers to improper fractions. Write answers as mixed numbers in lowest terms.

37. $3\frac{1}{4}$

$+ 2\frac{1}{2}$

─────

38. $2\frac{1}{3}$

$+ 3\frac{3}{4}$

─────

39. $3\frac{3}{5}$

$+ 2\frac{2}{3}$

─────

40. $4\frac{1}{4}$

$- 1\frac{5}{12}$

─────

41. $8\frac{1}{3}$

$- 2\frac{5}{6}$

─────

42. $5\frac{5}{12}$

$- 2\frac{5}{8}$

─────

≈ *First estimate the answer. Then solve each application problem.*

43. The lab had $14\frac{2}{3}$ gallons of distilled water. If $5\frac{1}{2}$ gallons were used in the morning and $6\frac{3}{4}$ gallons were used in the afternoon, find the number of gallons remaining.

estimate:

exact:

44. The ecology club collected $14\frac{3}{4}$ tons of cardboard on Saturday and $18\frac{2}{3}$ tons on Sunday. Find the total amount of cardboard collected.

estimate:

exact:

45. At birth, the Bolton triplets weigh $5\frac{3}{4}$ pounds, $4\frac{7}{8}$ pounds, and $5\frac{1}{3}$ pounds. Find their total weight.

estimate:

exact:

46. A developer wants to build a shopping center. She bought two parcels of land, one, $1\frac{11}{16}$ acres, and the other, $2\frac{3}{4}$ acres. If she needs a total of $8\frac{1}{2}$ acres for the center, how much additional land does she need to buy?

estimate:

exact:

[5] *Locate each fraction on the number line.*

47. $\frac{3}{8}$ **48.** $\frac{7}{4}$ **49.** $\frac{8}{3}$ **50.** $2\frac{1}{5}$

Write < or > to make a true statement.

51. $\frac{3}{4}$ ____ $\frac{7}{8}$ **52.** $\frac{5}{8}$ ____ $\frac{2}{3}$ **53.** $\frac{2}{3}$ ____ $\frac{8}{15}$ **54.** $\frac{7}{10}$ ____ $\frac{8}{15}$

55. $\frac{5}{12}$ ____ $\frac{8}{18}$ **56.** $\frac{7}{20}$ ____ $\frac{8}{25}$ **57.** $\frac{19}{36}$ ____ $\frac{29}{54}$ **58.** $\frac{19}{132}$ ____ $\frac{7}{55}$

Simplify each of the following.

59. $\left(\frac{1}{3}\right)^2$ **60.** $\left(\frac{3}{4}\right)^2$ **61.** $\left(\frac{3}{5}\right)^3$ **62.** $\left(\frac{3}{8}\right)^4$

Name _____

Simplify by using the order of operations.

63. $5 \cdot \left(\frac{1}{4}\right)^2$

64. $\left(\frac{3}{4}\right)^2 \cdot 20$

65. $\left(\frac{3}{4}\right)^2 \cdot \left(\frac{8}{9}\right)^2$

66. $\frac{3}{5} \div \left(\frac{1}{10} + \frac{1}{5}\right)$

67. $\left(\frac{1}{2}\right)^2 \cdot \left(\frac{1}{4} + \frac{1}{2}\right)$

68. $\left(\frac{1}{4}\right)^3 + \left(\frac{5}{8} + \frac{3}{4}\right)$

MIXED REVIEW EXERCISES

Solve by using the order of operations as necessary. Write answers in lowest terms or as mixed numbers.

69. $\frac{7}{8} - \frac{3}{8}$

70. $\frac{2}{3} - \frac{1}{4}$

71. $\frac{75}{86} - \frac{4}{43}$

72. $\frac{1}{4} + \frac{1}{8} + \frac{5}{16}$

73. $\begin{array}{r} 5\frac{2}{3} \\ -\ 2\frac{1}{2} \\ \hline \end{array}$

74. $\begin{array}{r} 9\frac{1}{2} \\ +\ 16\frac{3}{4} \\ \hline \end{array}$

75. $\begin{array}{r} 7 \\ -\ 1\frac{5}{8} \\ \hline \end{array}$

76. $\begin{array}{r} 2\frac{3}{5} \\ 8\frac{5}{8} \\ +\ \frac{5}{16} \\ \hline \end{array}$

77. $\begin{array}{r} 92\frac{5}{16} \\ -\ 27 \\ \hline \end{array}$

78. $\frac{7}{22} + \frac{3}{22} + \frac{3}{11}$

79. $\left(\frac{1}{4}\right)^2 \cdot \left(\frac{2}{5}\right)^3$

80. $\frac{1}{4} \div \left(\frac{1}{3} + \frac{1}{6}\right)$

81. $\left(\frac{2}{3}\right)^2 \cdot \left(\frac{1}{3} + \frac{1}{6}\right)$

82. $\left(\frac{2}{3}\right)^3 + \left(\frac{2}{3} - \frac{5}{9}\right)$

Write < or > to make a true statement.

83. $\dfrac{7}{8}$ —— $\dfrac{13}{16}$

84. $\dfrac{7}{10}$ —— $\dfrac{13}{20}$

85. $\dfrac{19}{40}$ —— $\dfrac{29}{60}$

86. $\dfrac{5}{8}$ —— $\dfrac{17}{30}$

Find the least common multiple of each set of numbers.

87. 18, 24

88. 10, 15, 20, 25

89. 8, 9, 12, 18

Rewrite each of the following fractions by using the indicated denominators.

90. $\dfrac{3}{8} = \dfrac{}{48}$

91. $\dfrac{9}{12} = \dfrac{}{144}$

92. $\dfrac{3}{7} = \dfrac{}{420}$

$\approx$ *First estimate the answer. Then solve each application problem.*

93. A carpet layer needs $13\frac{1}{2}$ feet of carpet for a bedroom and $22\frac{3}{8}$ feet of carpet for a living room. If the roll from which the carpet layer is cutting is $92\frac{3}{4}$ feet long, find the number of feet remaining after the two rooms have been carpeted.

estimate:

exact:

94. Quark's Place sold $2\frac{3}{8}$ liters of Klingon blood-wine and $4\frac{1}{2}$ liters of Regalian Ale. If Quark had stocked a total of 10 liters, find the number of liters that remain.

estimate:

exact:

Appendix B

Decimals

Reading and Writing Decimal Numbers

Decimal numbers are written numerically according to a place value system.

The following table lists the place values of digits to the *left* of the decimal point.

hundred million	ten million	million,	hundred thousand	ten thousand	thousand,	hundred	ten	one	*decimal point*

The following table lists the place values of digits to the *right* of the decimal point.

decimal point	tenths	hundredths	thousandths	ten thousandths	hundred thousandths	millionths

To read or write a decimal number in words:

1. Use the first place value table to read the digits to left of the decimal point.
2. Insert the word "and."
3. Read the digits to the right of the decimal point as though they were not preceded by a decimal point, and then attach the place value of its rightmost digit:

Example 1: Read and write the number 37,568.0218 in words.

		3	7	5	6	8	•
hundred million	ten million	million,	hundred thousand	ten thousand	thousand,	hundred	ten	one	*decimal point*

and

•	0	2	1	8		
decimal point	tenths	hundredths	thousandths	ten thousandths	hundred thousandths	millionths

Therefore, 37,568.0218 is read "thirty-seven thousand five hundred sixty-eight" "and" "two hundred eighteen" "ten-thousandths."

Example 2: Write the number "seven hundred eighty two million ninety three thousand five hundred ninety four and two thousand four hundred three millionths" numerically in standard form.

7	8	2,	0	9	3,	5	9	4	•
hundred million	ten million	million,	hundred thousand	ten thousand	thousand,	hundred	ten	one	*decimal point*

"and"

•	0	0	2	4	0	3
decimal point	tenths	hundredths	thousandths	ten thousandths	hundred thousandths	millionths

That is, 782,093,594.002403

EXERCISES

1. Write the number 9,467.00624 in words.

2. Write the number 35,454,666.007 in words.

3. Write the number numerically in standard form: four million sixty-four and seventy two ten thousandths.

4. Write the number numerically in standard form: seven and forty three thousand fifty two millionths.

Rounding a Number to a Specified Place Value

1. Locate the digit with the specified place value.

2. If the digit directly to its right is less than 5, keep the digit in step 1 and delete all of the digits to its right.

3. If the digit directly to its right is 5 or above, increase the digit in step 1 by 1 and delete all of the digits to its right.

4. If the specified place value is greater than one (i.e, to the left of the decimal point) proceed as instructed in step 2 or 3, but insert trailing zeros to the right as placeholders, and then drop the decimal point.

Example 1: Round 35,178.2649 to the nearest hundredth.

The digit in the "hundredths" place is 6. The digit to its right is 4. Therefore, keep the 6 and delete the digits to its right. The rounded value is 35,178.26

Example 2: Round 35,178.2649 to the nearest tenth.

The digit in the "tenths" place is 2. The digit to its right is 6. Therefore, increase the 2 to 3 and delete the digits to its right. The rounded value is 35,178.3

Example 3: Round 35,178.2649 to the nearest ten thousand.

The digit in the "ten thousand" place is 3. The digit to its right is 5. Therefore, increase the 3 to 4 and insert trailing zeros to its right as placeholders. The rounded value is 40,000

Note that the decimal point is not written.

EXERCISES

1. Round 7,456.975 to the nearest hundredth.

2. Round 55,568.2 to the nearest hundred.

3. Round 34.6378 to the nearest tenth.

Converting a Fraction to a Decimal

To convert a fraction to a decimal, divide the numerator by the denominator.

Example 1: Convert $\frac{4}{5}$ to a decimal.

Solution:

On a calculator:

Key in ④ ÷ ⑤ = to obtain 0.8

Using long division:
$$\begin{array}{r} 0.8 \\ 5\overline{)4.0} \\ \underline{4.0} \\ 0 \end{array}$$

Example 2: Convert $\frac{1}{3}$ to a decimal.

Solution:

On a calculator:

Key in ① ÷ ③ =
to obtain 0.3333333

Using long division:
$$\begin{array}{r} 0.333 \\ 3\overline{)1.000} \\ \underline{-9} \\ 10 \\ \underline{-9} \\ 1 \end{array}$$

Since a calculator's display is limited to a specified number of digits, it will cut off the decimal's trailing right digits.

Since this long division process will continue indefinitely, the quotient is a repeating decimal, 0.33333 . . . and is instead denoted by 0.$\overline{3}$. The bar is placed above the repeating digit or above a repeating sequence of digits.

Convert the given fractions into decimals.

1. $\frac{3}{5}$ **2.** $\frac{2}{3}$ **3.** $\frac{7}{8}$ **4.** $\frac{1}{7}$ **5.** $\frac{4}{9}$

Converting a Terminating Decimal to a Fraction

1. Read the decimal.

2. The place value of the right-most nonzero digit becomes the denominator of the fraction.

3. The original numeral, with the decimal point removed, becomes the numerator. Drop all leading zeros.

Example 1: Convert 0.025 to a fraction.

Solution: The right-most digit, 5, is in the "thousandths" place.

So, as a fraction, $0.025 = \frac{25}{1000}$, which reduces to $\frac{1}{40}$

Example 2: Convert 0.0034 to a fraction.

Solution: The right-most digit, 4, is in the ten-thousandths place.

So, as a fraction, $0.034 = \frac{34}{10,000}$, which reduces to $\frac{17}{5000}$

Convert the given decimals to fractions.

1. 0.4   **2.** 0.125   **3.** 0.64   **4.** 0.05

Converting a Decimal to a Percent

Multiply the decimal by 100. That is, move the decimal point two places to the right and attach the percent symbol.

Example 1: 0.78 written as a percent is 78%.

Example 2: 3 written as a percent is 300%

Example 3: 0.045 written as a percent is 4.5%

Write the following decimals as percents.

1. 0.35   **2.** 0.076   **3.** 0.0089   **4.** 6.0

Converting a Percent to a Decimal

Divide the percent by 100. That is, move the decimal point two places to the left and drop the % symbol.

Example 1: 5% written as a decimal is 0.05

Example 2: 625% written as a decimal is 6.25

Example 3: 0.0005% written as a decimal is 0.000005

EXERCISES

Write the following percents as decimals.

1. 45%   **2.** 0.0987%   **3.** 3.45%   **4.** 2000%

Comparing Decimals

1. Write the decimals one below the next, lining up their respective decimal points.
2. Read the decimals from left to right, comparing corresponding place values. The decimal with the first and largest nonzero digit is the largest number.

Example 1: Order from largest to smallest: 0.097,   0.48,   0.0356

Solution: Align by decimal point:

0.097
0.48
0.0356

Since 4 (in the second decimal) is the first nonzero digit, 0.48 is the largest number. Next, since 9 is larger than 3, 0.097 is next largest; and finally, 0.0356 is the smallest number.

Example 2: Order from largest to smallest: 0.043, 0.0043, 0.43, 0.00043

Solution: Align by decimal point:

0.043
0.0043
0.43
0.00043

Since 4 (in the third decimal), is the first nonzero digit, then 0.43 is the largest number. Similarly, next is 0.043; followed by 0.0043; and finally, 0.00043 is the smallest number.

EXERCISES

Place each group of decimals in order, from largest to smallest.

1. 0.058, 0.0099, 0.105, 0.02999

2. 0.75, 1.23, 1.2323, 0.9, 0.999

3. 13.56, 13.568, 13.5068, 13.56666

Adding and Subtracting Decimals

1. Write the decimals one below the next, lining up their respective decimal points. If the decimals have differing numbers of digits to the right of the decimal point, place trailing zeros to the right in the shorter decimals.

2. Place the decimal point in the answer.

3. Add or subtract the numbers as usual.

Example 1: Add: 23.5 + 37.098 + 432.17

Solution:
```
    23.500
    37.098
 + 432.170
 ---------
   492.768
```

Example 2: Subtract 72.082 from 103.07

Solution:
```
   103.070
 -  72.082
 ---------
    30.988
```

E X E R C I S E S

1. Calculate 543.785 + 43.12 + 3200.0043

2. Calculate 679.05 − 54.9973

Multiplying Decimals

1. Multiply the numbers as usual, ignoring the decimal points.

2. Sum the number of decimal places in each number; your product will contain the sum of their decimal places.

Example 1: Multiply 32.89 by 0.021

Solution:
```
    32.89      →    2 decimal places
 ×  0.021      →    3 decimal places
 -------
    3289
    6578
 -------
 0.69069       →    5 decimal places
```

Example 2: Multiply 64.05 by 7.3

Solution:
```
    64.05      →    2 decimal places
 ×   7.3       →    1 decimal place
 -------
    19215
    44835
 -------
  467.565      →    3 decimal places
```

EXERCISES

Multiply the following decimals:

1. 12.53×8.2 **2.** 115.3×0.003 **3.** 14.62×0.75

Dividing Decimals

1. Write the division in long division format.
2. Move the decimal point the same number of places to the right in both divisor and dividend so that the divisor becomes a whole number.
3. Place the decimal point in the quotient directly above the decimal point in the dividend and divide as usual.

Example 1: Divide   92.4   by   0.25
                     (dividend)   *(divisor)*

$0.25\overline{)92.4}$ becomes $25\overline{)9240}$

$$
\begin{array}{r}
369.6 \\
25\overline{)9240.0} \\
-75 \\
\hline
174 \\
-150 \\
\hline
240 \\
-225 \\
\hline
150 \\
-150 \\
\hline
0
\end{array}
$$

Example 2: $0.0052 \div 0.004$
              (dividend) *(divisor)*

$0.004\overline{)0.00052}$ becomes $4\overline{)0.52}$

$$
\begin{array}{r}
.13 \\
4\overline{)0.52} \\
-4 \\
\hline
12 \\
-12 \\
\hline
0
\end{array}
$$

EXERCISES

1. Divide 12.05 by 2.5

2. Divide 18.9973 by 78

3. Divide 14.05 by 0.0002

4. Calculate 150 ÷ 0.03

5. Calculate 0.00442 ÷ 0.017

6. Calculate 69.115 ÷ 0.0023

7 Exercises

Round as shown.

Example: Round 4336 to the nearest ten.	**Solution:**
	Next digit is 5 or more.
	4336
	Tens place changes (3 + 1 = 4). All digits to the right of the underlined place change to 0.
	≈4340

1. 623 to the nearest ten

2. 206 to the nearest ten

3. 1085 to the nearest ten

4. 2439 to the nearest ten

5. 7862 to the nearest hundred

6. 6746 to the nearest hundred

7. 86,813 to the nearest hundred

8. 17,211 to the nearest hundred

9. 42,495 to the nearest hundred

10. 18,273 to the nearest hundred

11. 5996 to the nearest hundred

12. 8451 to the nearest hundred

13. 15,758 to the nearest hundred

14. 28,065 to the nearest hundred

15. 78,499 to the nearest thousand

16. 14,314 to the nearest thousand

17. 5847 to the nearest thousand

18. 49,706 to the nearest thousand

19. 53,182 to the nearest thousand

20. 13,124 to the nearest thousand

21. 595,008 to the nearest ten thousand

22. 725,182 to the nearest ten thousand

23. 8,906,422 to the nearest million

24. 13,713,409 to the nearest million

CHAPTER REVIEW EXERCISES

[1] *Name the digit that has the given place value.*

1. 243.059
   tenths
   hundredths

2. 0.6817
   ones
   tenths

3. $5824.39
   hundreds
   hundredths

4. 896.503
   tenths
   tens

5. 20.73861
   tenths
   ten-thousandths

Write each decimal as a fraction or mixed number in lowest terms.

6. 0.5

7. 0.75

8. 4.05

9. 0.875

10. 0.027

11. 27.8

Write each decimal in words.

12. 0.8

13. 400.29

14. 12.007

15. 0.0306

Write each decimal in numbers.

16. eight and three tenths

17. two hundred five thousandths

18. seventy and sixty-six ten-thousandths

19. thirty hundredths

[2] *Round to the place indicated. Write your answers using the "≈" sign.*

20. 275.635 to the nearest tenth

21. 72.789 to the nearest hundredth

22. 0.1604 to the nearest thousandth

23. 0.0905 to the nearest thousandth

24. 0.98 to the nearest tenth

Round to the nearest cent.

25. $15.8333

26. $0.698

27. $17,625.7906

Round each income or expense item to the nearest dollar.

28. Income from pancake breakfast was $350.48.

29. Members paid $129.50 in dues.

30. Refreshments cost $99.61.

31. Bank charges were $29.37.

[3] ≈*First round the numbers so there is only one non-zero digit and estimate the answer.*
Then add to find the exact answer.

32. estimate   exact

                5.81
             423.96
+ _____   + 15.09

33. estimate   exact

               75.6
                1.29
           122.045
               0.88
+ _____   + 33.7

[4] ≈*First round the numbers so there is only one non-zero digit and estimate the answer.*
Then subtract to find the exact answer.

34. estimate   exact

            308.5
− _____   − 17.8

35. estimate   exact

             9.2
− _____   − 7.9316

[3–4] ≈*First round the numbers so there is only one non-zero digit and estimate the*
answer. Then find the exact answer.

36. Tim agreed to donate 12.5 hours of work at his children's school. He has already worked 9.75 hours. How many more hours will he work?

   estimate:
   exact:

37. Today Jasmin wrote a check to the daycare center for $215.53 and a check for $44.47 at the grocery store. What was the total of the two checks?

   estimate:
   exact:

38. Joey spent $1.59 for toothpaste, $5.33 for a gift, and $18.94 for a toaster. He gave the clerk three $10 bills. How much change did he get?

   estimate:

   exact:

39. Roseanne is training for a wheelchair race. She raced 2.3 kilometers on Monday, 4 kilometers on Wednesday, and 5.25 kilometers on Friday. How far did she race altogether?

   estimate:
   exact:

[5] ≈*First round the numbers so there is only one non-zero digit and estimate an answer*
Then multiply to find the exact answer.

40. estimate   exact

            6.138
× _____   × 3.7

41. estimate   exact

            42.9
× _____   × 3.3

Name _____

Multiply.

42. $(5.6)(0.002)$

43. $(0.071)(0.005)$

[6] ≈*Decide if each answer is reasonable by rounding the numbers and estimating the answer. If the exact answer is not reasonable, find the correct answer.*

44. $706.2 \div 12 = 58.85$
    estimate:

45. $26.6 \div 2.8 = 0.95$
    estimate:

Divide. Round to the nearest thousandth, if necessary.

46. $3 \overline{)43.4}$

47. $\dfrac{72}{0.06}$

48. $0.00048 \div 0.0012$

[5−6] *Solve these application problems.*

49. Adrienne worked 36.5 hours this week. Her hourly wage is $9.59. Find her total earnings to the nearest dollar.

50. A book of 12 tickets costs $23.89 at the amusement park. What is the cost per ticket, to the nearest cent?

51. Stock in MathTronic sells for $3.75 per share. Kenneth is thinking of investing $500. How many whole shares could he buy?

52. Hamburger meat is on sale at $0.89 per pound. How much will Ms. Lee pay for 3.5 pounds of hamburger, to the nearest cent?

Simplify by using the order of operations.

53. $3.5^2 + 8.7 \cdot 1.95$

54. $11 - 3.06 \div (3.95 - 0.35)$

[7] *Write each fraction as a decimal. Round to the nearest thousandth, if necessary.*

55. $3\dfrac{4}{5}$

56. $\dfrac{16}{25}$

57. $1\dfrac{7}{8}$

58. $\dfrac{1}{9}$

Arrange in order from smallest to largest.

59. $3.68, 3.806, 3.6008$

60. $0.215, 0.22, 0.209, 0.2102$

61. $0.17, \dfrac{3}{20}, \dfrac{1}{8}, 0.159$

316

Solve each problem.

62. 89.19 + 0.075 + 310.6 + 5

63. 72.8 × 3.5

64. 1648.3 ÷ 0.46   Round to thousandths.

65. 30 − 0.9102

66. (4.38)(0.007)

67. 0.005 $\overline{)0.047}$

68. 72.105 + 8.2 + 95.37

69. 81.36 ÷ 9

70. (5.6 − 1.22) + 4.8 • 3.15

71. 0.455 × 18

72. 1.6 • 0.58

73. 0.218 $\overline{)7.63}$

74. 21.059 − 20.8

75. $18.3 - 3^2 \div 0.5$

Use the information in the ad to solve Exercises 76–80. Round money answers to the nearest cent. (Disregard any sales tax.)

76. How much would one pair of men's socks cost?

77. How much more would one pair of men's socks cost than one pair of children's socks?

78. How much would Fernando pay for a dozen pair of men's socks?

79. How much would Akiko pay for five pairs of teen jeans and four pairs of women's jeans?

80. What is the difference between the cheapest sale price for athletic shoes and the highest regular price?

Glossary

absolute value For a non-negative number, the absolute value is that number itself; for a negative number the absolute value is its opposite.

algebraic expression A mathematical set of instructions (containing constant numbers, variables, and the operations among them) that indicates the sequence in which to perform the computations.

angle The figure formed by two rays starting from the same end point.

area The number of square units contained in a region.

average The sum of a collection of numbers, divided by how many numbers are in the collection.

axis of symmetry A vertical line that separates the graph of a parabola into two mirror images.

bar graph A diagram of parallel bars depicting data.

break-even number The number for which the total revenue equals total cost.

Cartesian (rectangular) coordinate system in the plane A two-dimensional scaled grid of equally spaced horizontal and vertical lines.

circle A collection of points that are the same distance from some given point called its center.

circumference The distance around a circle.

coefficient A number written next to a variable that multiplies the variable.

common factor A factor contained in each term of an algebraic expression.

commutative operation An operation in which you can interchange the order of the two numbers and always produce identical results. The commutative operations of arithmetic are addition and multiplication.

cone A three-dimensional surface with one circular base.

constant term A term that consists of only a number.

cylinder A three-dimensional surface with two circular bases.

delta Δ = change.

dependent variable If the input/output situation is a function, then the output variable is called the dependent variable.

diameter A line segment that goes through the center of a circle and connects two points on the circle; it measures twice the radius.

distributive property A property involving addition and multiplication that states that $a \cdot (b + c) = a \cdot b + a \cdot c$.

domain The set (collection) of all possible input values for a function.

equivalent expressions Two algebraic expressions are equivalent if they always produce identical outputs when given the same input value(s).

expand An instruction to use the distributive property to transform an algebraic expression from factored form to expanded form.

expanded form An algebraic expression in which all parenthesis have been removed using multiplication.

exponential function A function in which the variable appears in the exponent. For example, $y = 4 \cdot 5^x$.

extrapolation The assignment of values to a sequence of numbers beyond those actually given.

factor, a When two or more algebraic expressions or numbers are multiplied together to form a product, those individual expressions or numbers are called the factors of that product. For example, the product $5 \cdot a \cdot (b + 2)$ contains the three factors 5, a, and $b + 2$.

factor, to An instruction to use the distributive property to transform an algebraic expression from expanded form to factored form.

factored form An algebraic expression that has been rewritten in terms of its own factors.

fixed costs Costs (such as rent, utilities, etc.) that must be paid no matter how many units are produced or sold.

formula An algebraic statement describing the relationship between the input variables and output variable.

function terminology and notation The name of a functional relationship between input x and output y, then you say that y is a function of x and you write $y = f(x)$.

function A rule (given by tabular, graphical, or symbolic form) that relates (assigns) to any permissible input value exactly one output value.

goodness-of-fit A measure of the difference between the actual data values and the values produced by the model.

greatest common factor The product of all the common factors in the expression.

histogram A bar graph with no spaces between the bars.

horizontal (*x*-) axis The horizontal line, described most commonly by $y = 0$ in the Cartesian coordinate system; used to represent the input axis.

horizontal intercept The point(s) where a line or curve crosses the input (*x*) axis.

independent variable If the input/output situation is a function, then the input variable is called the independent variable.

input Replacement values for the variable in an algebraic expression, table, equation or function. In a cause-effect relationship, the input usually represents the explanatory variable (cause).

interpolation The insertion of intermediate values in a sequence of numbers between those actually given.

inverse operation An operation that undoes another operation. Addition and subtraction are inverses of each other as are multiplication and division. The inverse of squaring is taking the square root. Negation is its own inverse, as is taking reciprocals.

like terms Terms that contain identical variable factors (including exponents) and differ only in their coefficients.

line of best fit Line that will have as many of the data points as close to the line as possible.

linear function A function that has the form $f(x) = mx + b$ and whose graph is a straight line.

maximum value The largest output of a function.

mean The arithmetic average of a set of data.

minimum value The smallest output of a function.

operation (arithmetic) Addition, subtraction, multiplication, and division are arithmetic operations between two numbers. Exponentiation (raising a number to a power, for example, 10^4), taking roots (for example, $\sqrt{8}$), and negation (changing the sign of a number) are examples of operations on a single number.

order of operations An agreement for how to evaluate an expression with multiple operations.

ordered pair Pair of values, separated by a comma, and enclosed in a set of parenthesis. The input is given first, and the corresponding output is listed second as follows. (Input, Output). These numbers serve as an address for each point in the coordinate plane, giving a point's location with respect to the origin.

origin The point at which the horizontal and vertical axes intersect.

output Values produced by evaluating an algebraic expression, table, equation or function. In a cause-effect relationship, the output usually represents response variable (effect) corresponding to a given input.

parabola The graph of a quadratic function (second-degree polynomial function). The graph is U-shaped, opening upward or downward.

parallelogram A four-sided figure for which each pair of opposite sides are parallel.

percent(age) Parts per hundred.

percentage error The difference between an actual data value and a predicted value, divided by the actual value and then converted to a percent.

perimeter A measure of the distance around a figure; for circles, perimeter is called *circumference*.

pie chart A diagram of sectors of a circle depicting data.

piecewise defined function A function defined differently for different parts of its domain.

polynomial An expression containing the sum of a finite number of terms of the form ax^n, generally written in descending powers of the variable from left to right.

proportion An equation stating that two ratios are equal.

Pythagorean theorem The relationship among the sides of a right triangle, namely that the sum of the squares of the lengths of the two perpendicular sides (legs) is equal to the square of the length of the side opposite the right angle, called the hypotenuse.

quadrants The four regions of the plane separated by the vertical and horizontal axes. The quadrants are numbered from 1 to 4. Quadrant 1 is located in the upper right with the numbering continuing counterclockwise. Therefore, quadrant 4 is located in the lower right.

quadratic formula The formula $x = \dfrac{-b \pm \sqrt{b^2 - 4ac}}{2a}$ that represents the solutions to the quadratic equation $ax^2 + bx + c = 0$.

quadratic function A function of the form $y = ax^2 + bx + c$.

radius The distance from the center point of the circle to the outer edge of the circle.

range The set (collection) of all possible output values for a function.

rate of change The amount of change divided by the length of the interval over which the change takes place.

ratio A fraction.

regression line A line resulting from a scatterplot of data for a line of best fit.

rounding A technique to approximate numbers according to certain rules.

scatterplot A graph of the values of two variables on the coordinate plane. The values of explanatory variable (input) are plotted on the x-axis, and the corresponding values of the response variables (output) are plotted on the y-axis.

scientific notation A device for expressing very large or very small numbers as a product—(a number between 1 and 10) · (the appropriate power of 10).

signed numbers Numbers accompanied by a positive or negative sign.

slope of a line A measure of the steepness of a line.

slope-intercept form The form, $y = mx + b$, of a linear equation. The slope is denoted by m and the vertical intercept by b.

solution of a system A point that is a solution to both equations in a system of two linear equations.

sphere A three-dimensional surface for which all points are equidistant from a given point, the center.

substitution method A method used to solve a system of two linear equations. Solve one equation for one variable, then substitute for this variable in the other equation and solve for the other variable.

system of equations Two linear equations considered together.

terms Parts of an algebraic expression separated by the addition, $+$, and subtraction, $-$, symbols.

variable A quantity that takes on specific numerical values and will often have a unit of measure (e.g., dollars, years, miles) associated with it.

vertex The turning point of a parabola having coordinates $\left(\frac{-b}{2a}, f\left(\frac{-b}{2a}\right)\right)$, where a and b are determined from the equation $f(x) = ax^2 + bx + c$. The vertex is the highest or lowest point of a parabola.

vertical (y-) axis The vertical line, described most commonly by $x = 0$, in the Cartesian coordinate system that is used to represent the output axis.

vertical intercept The point where a line or curve crosses the vertical axis.

vertical line test A graph represents a function if and only if any vertical line that is drawn intersects the graph of the function in exactly one point.

volume A measure of three-dimensional space occupied by a figure.

weighted average An average in which some numbers count more heavily than others.

x-coordinate The first number of an ordered pair that indicates the horizontal directed distance from the origin. A positive value indicates the point is located to the right of the origin, a negative value indicates a location to the left of the origin.

y-coordinate The second number of an ordered pair that indicates the vertical directed distance from the origin. A positive value indicates the point is located to the above the origin, a negative value indicates a location below the origin.

Zero Product Rule The algebraic principle that says if a and b are real numbers such that $a \cdot b = 0$, then either a or b, or both, must be equal to zero.